Guide to the Building Regulations 1991

Guide to the Building Regulations 1991

For England and Wales   Lawrence Davis

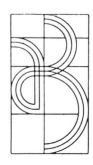

Butterworth Architecture
An imprint of Butterworth-Heinemann Ltd
Linacre House, Jordan Hill, Oxford OX2 8DP

 PART OF REED INTERNATIONAL BOOKS

OXFORD   LONDON   BOSTON
MUNICH   NEW DELHI   SINGAPORE   SYDNEY
TOKYO   TORONTO   WELLINGTON

First published 1992

© Butterworth-Heinemann Ltd 1992

British Library Cataloguing in Publication Data
Davis, Lawrence W.
    Guide to the Building Regulations, 1991
    I. Title
    344.2037869

ISBN 0 7506 1284 3

Library of Congress Cataloguing in Publication Data
Davis, Lawrence.
    Guide to the Building Regulations, 1991: for England and
    Wales/Lawrence Davis.
    p.   cm.
    Rev. ed. of: Guide to the Building Regulations, 1985/A.J. Elder.
    Includes index.
    ISBN 0 7506 1284 3
    1. Building laws – Great Britain.   2. Standards,
    Engineering – Great Britain.   I. Elder, Albert Joseph.
    Guide to the Building Regulations, 1985.   II. Title
    KD1140.Z9D38   1992
    346.42′07869–dc20
    [344.2067869]   92–5557
                                         CIP

Composition by Genesis Typesetting, Laser Quay, Rochester, Kent
Printed and bound in Great Britain by Thomson Litho, East Kilbride

Contents

Introduction

Some form of building control has been with us for a very long time. When man first started congregating in cities which grew up without any form of control other than that imposed by land ownership, the environment which developed must have been quite dreadful. In this country, the occurrence of events such as the Great Plague and the Great Fire of London led to efforts being made to prevent a recurrence, in other words to take positive steps to ensure the health and safety of the inhabitants. It is these two aspects which have dominated the provisions of building regulations ever since. More recently, the conservation of fuel and power and the prevention of waste or misuse of water have been added.

This history of modern building legislation goes back to 1845 when the first Public Health Act was passed. Housing was the primary concern and the defects to be cured were mainly damp, structural instability, poor sanitation, fire risk and lack of light and ventilation. In 1877, the first model by-laws were produced as a guide for local authorities, with whom lay the responsibility for setting and enforcing minimum standards. They applied only to 'new streets and buildings', but in 1936 new legislation was enacted covering all buildings and requiring all local authorities to make and enforce 'building by-laws'. At this time, although guidance from central government was given, local authorities still held direct responsibility for building standards and issued their own by-laws which, although generally similar, had individual differences which made it necessary for architects, designing buildings for the first time in a particular local authority area, to make sure of obtaining and studying a copy of the by-laws; undoubtedly a time-wasting routine! The breakthrough came with the issue of the 1952 Model By-laws, series IV (amended 1953), which saw two major advances. First, perhaps as a result of the development of a whole range of new materials, a different technique of control was used whereby standards of performance were stated, and these formed the mandatory part of the by-laws. Descriptions of actual structural minima, which previously had been mandatory, were now contained in the so-called 'deemed to satisfy provisions', leaving the way open for other newer methods and materials to be used, providing their performance could be established. This system has, of course, been effectively used ever since, and has enabled increasing reference to be made to advisory publications such as British Standard Specifications and Codes of Practice. Secondly, although the enforcement of the model by-laws was still a matter for local authorities, they were universally adopted throughout England and Wales (except by the LCC), and hence building control legislation became standard. They also contained major new controls introducing, for the first time, the concept of structural fire resistance periods in relation to building type and size.

This legislation really did cause all the building design offices to pause, think, and realise that, for the first time, they had a significant control system to satisfy, and one which was going to affect all fundamental design traditions. For example, prior to the 52 Model By-laws a decision as between structural steel or reinforced concrete for a frame would be made purely on such criteria as convenience, time for erection and cost. Subsequently the cost and time taken to fireproof the steel sections could, and often did, sway the decision in favour of reinforced concrete. With hindsight it can be seen that this was really the first, and probably still the most important step from ad-hoc by-laws (suitable only for use when buildings were a simple matter of bricks and mortar) towards a rationalised system under which the controls would gradually develop to embrace most parts of a building's skeleton, cladding and services.

In 1961, a new Public Health Act was introduced providing for the preparation of a national set of building regulations for England and Wales, but excluding Inner London which had a different system of administration from other local authorities, and was apparently able to persuade the Government that this system suited the special circumstances pertaining in a metropolitan area better than the proposed new standard regulations. After a lot of work by the Building Regulations Advisory Committee (BRAC), the Building Regulations 1965 were produced and came into operation on 1 February 1966. The inevitable drafting mistakes were made and, apart from these, the usual processes of development and invention called for alterations and, in all, a total of seven amendments were issued, the first coinciding with the issue of the Building Regulations themselves, and the seventh and last coming into operation on

1 November 1971. Most of these were a miscellaneous collection of amendments affecting several parts of the Building Regulations, but one at least, the famous fifth amendment, concerned only part D – *Structural stability* – and contained entirely new supplementary rules for controlling the design of buildings over five storeys to give protection against accidental loads, such as local explosions. It was issued as a direct result of the enquiry following the Ronan Point disaster.

2   The 1972 Regulations

The issue of successive amendments to the Building Regulations 1965 had made the keeping of an up-to-date complete copy virtually impractical, and a re-issue was overdue. Clearly, the question of metrication was affecting the date for complete revision. Finally, on 29 March 1972, the new metric Building Regulations were laid before Parliament and came into operation on 1 June 1972. These regulations incorporated all seven amendments to the 1965 issue and some additional miscellaneous alterations which might have become an eighth amendment had the revised issue not been made. The suggested metric values previously published were, in general, used without further alteration. In most cases, these are rounded off to the nearest appropriate metric unit, whether it be metres, millimetres, watts and so on. The millimetre is generally the smallest size dimension used. Thus an imperial half inch might become 12 mm or 13 mm, but there are a number of instances where 12.5 mm is used.

The issue of metric regulations does not give local authorities the right to demand drawings in metric but, to comply with the regulations, any imperial sizes or quantities used must be at least equal to the exact imperial equivalent of the metric standard specified. This is the reverse of the previous situation.

During the life of the 1972 Regulations three amendments were issued in 1973, 1974 and 1975 respectively. These all had considerable impact and were by no means concerned only with minor adjustments. Among the more major changes was a new part dealing with means of escape from fire and a completely revised part on the thermal insulation of dwellings including, for the first time, control on heat losses through windows as well as through solid construction.

3   The 1976 Regulations

These consolidated the three amendments mentioned above but also included a number of changes which had not been previously contained in an amendment. As a document it was a good deal larger than its predecessor (307 pages against 187). There were four amendments. The first of these extended the requirements for thermal insulation to embrace all buildings instead of only dwellings as before. The second included a completely revised Part F (Thermal insulation of dwellings) and introduced two new parts, Part Q (Heating controls) and Part R (Insulation of pipes etc.). The third amendment contained Part S which was concerned only with unvented hot water systems and the fourth Part T with access for disabled persons.

4   The 1985 Regulations

In the mid to late 1970s a good deal of critical comment started to appear in the technical press concerning the current state of Building Regulations. They were accused of being unwieldy, inflexible, unduly restrictive and confusing (some went so far as to say that they were written deliberately to confuse). In particular, the language in which they were written (parliamentary prose) was severely belaboured. The RIBA took the matter up and in 1978 *The Architects' Journal* ran an energetic campaign under the title 'Revise the Regs' with a view to stirring things up. Because of a coincidental change in government it did.

An attempt had been made to interest Reg Freeson, the Secretary of State at the DoE under the Labour government, in a complete revision of the Regulations and their enforcement system. He was not convinced. Following the Tory victory of 1979 a new Secretary of State in the shape of Michael Heseltine, seeking something to impress his personality on his newly acquired department, took on the job with considerable enthusiasm.

The AJ argument (supported by others) was concerned (*inter alia*) with the waste of time caused not only by the unwieldiness of the legislation itself, but also by Local Authorities having to deal with a multitude of small applications from unqualified persons. It proposed a separate simple set of Regulations for simple buildings and permission for architects to certify their own buildings as complying. It got neither.

On the procedural side, the first change was the imposition of fees to be paid to the Local Authority for checking plans and for inspections of work. The Building (Prescribed Fees) Regulations came into effect on 1 July 1982.

It was not until 1985 that the single set of Regulations appeared and these were a recast version of the 1976 Regulations. The Regulations themselves were twenty in number with three schedules.

The Regulations contained the procedural details and Schedule 1 contained the functional requirements. Schedule 2 has since been replaced by Part M – Access and facilities for disabled persons – and Schedule 3 set out those buildings which were exempt from the Regulations.

The requirements for Schedule 1 were supported by Approved Documents. These documents were considerably larger than the old Regulations but had the advantage of being written in normal, rather than Parliamentary, English. The self-certification hoped for by some members of the architectural profession did not materialise, but instead a system of private certification by Approved Inspectors came into operation at the same time as the 1985 Regulations.

Only one approved inspector has been appointed to date – the National House-Building Council's Building Control Services Ltd. No individual has yet been able to obtain insurance which meets the criteria set out by the Department of the Environment. In addition to approved inspectors, persons can be appointed as Approved Persons to certify structural stability and/or thermal insulation requirements, but as the insurance criteria set was very similar, no approved persons have yet appeared.

Apart from the certification question, the new Regulations introduce several changes from previous practice. The most important one is the 'building notice' procedure, whereby an applicant is no longer obliged to submit full plans, but may instead supply only a site plan and certain written details of the building. However, where means of escape regulations apply *and* the building is to be put to a designated use under the Fire Precautions Act 1971, full plans must be submitted. Under the 1991 Regulations, however, Part B 1 – Means of Escape – now applies to all building types.

5   This Guide

This Guide has a long history. It started as the *AJ Metric Guide to the Building Regulations 1965* running as a series in *The Architects' Journal* as a stop-gap to help architects through the change to metric. It was published in book form in 1969 and was succeeded by the *Guide to the Buildings Regulations 1972*, followed by a series of revised editions as amendments to the Regulations were published. The last was the seventh edition, and was followed by a supplement on the second amendment to the 1976 Regulations.

The original function disappeared long ago but there were several other objectives which remained valid.

In particular it was designed as a working tool, a single volume which designers could use without the need of constant reference to other publications. To this end, graphical or illustrated representations of the contents of tables in the schedules and summaries of the more important British Standards referred to in the Regulations were included. Today such references are far more numerous, so this aspect of the Guide has been much extended.

Some of the other objectives, such as the translation of parliamentary prose into plain English and the extensive use of diagrams, have been partially overtaken by the new system of Approved Documents, which purport to achieve the same purpose. However, the language of the Approved Documents remains firmly Whitehallese and the diagrams frequently lack realism. In this Guide some of the diagrams have been reproduced unchanged, but, where possible, they have been replaced by something which gives a more realistic interpretation, and in some cases avoids misinterpretation of the text. In addition, a good deal more of the information is presented in diagrammatic form than in the Approved Documents.

As regards the text, this has been restructured to avoid so far as possible repetition and pedantry (and there is a good deal of both) without omitting any essential content.

In addition, an attempt has been made to reduce the need for cross reference within the Approved Documents themselves. Civil Service draughtsmen always seem to prefer to give a cross reference in preference to saying what is in it (even if quite brief). In this Guide therefore instead of, for example, 'see G2 3.14,' a summary of the contents of that clause is given unless it is too lengthy. This can be quite a time saver.

6   Abbreviations and symbols

The following abbreviations and symbols are used in this Guide. The list is not necessarily comprehensive.

ADs	Approved Documents
BRs	Building Regulations
BBA	British Board of Agrément
BSI	British Standards Institution

BS	British Standard
CP	Code of Practice
CS	Civil Service
DoE	Department of the Environment
DES	Department of Education and Science
LA	Local Authority
SoS	Secretary of State
m, m^2, m^3	Metre, square metre, cubic metre
mm, mm^2	Millimetre, square millimetre
dB	Decibel
K	Kelvin ($=1°$C)
°C	Degree Celsius
N, kN	Newton, Kilonewton
W, kW	Watts, Kilowatts (note W also means width)
l	Litre ($100\,l = 1\,m^3$)
S	Second
>	more than
<	less than
$\not>$	not more than
$\not<$	not less than
$\geqslant$	equal to or more than
$\leqslant$	equal to or less than
=	equal
⌁	heat transfer
max	maximum
min	minimum
W or w	width (note W also means Watt)
H or h	height
L or l	length
B or b	breadth
₵	Centre line

ACTS, PRINCIPAL REGULATIONS AND RELATED MATTERS

7   The enabling legislation

The Building Act 1984 was purely a consolidating measure and so did not contain any new legislation. It contains items drawn from 46 other Acts or Instruments including

The Public Health Acts 1875–1961
The Water Acts 1945–1983
The Offices, Shops and Railway Premises Act 1963
The Fire Precautions Act 1971
The Housing and Building Control Act 1983.

Part 1 of the Act in Sections 1–46 deals with building regulations. Section 1 contains the power to make building regulations and Schedule 1 to the Act sets out the details for which building regulations may be made.

Section 2 extends this to continuing requirements which may be designated in Regulations to prevent their initial purpose being frustrated by subsequent negligence or misuse. So far, these powers have not been used. Sections 3, 4 and 5 relate to exemptions. These specifically exempt schools or other educational buildings controlled by regulations made under the Education Act 1980 or the Education Reform Act 1988; buildings of the UK Atomic Energy Authority, or Civil Aviation Authority, except for a house or a building used as offices or showrooms not being part of a railway station or, in the case of the CAA, part of an aerodrome owned by the authority. Under Section 5, bodies may also be made exempt from the procedural requirements while being required to comply with the substantive requirements. Those bodies include Local

Authorities, County Councils and any other bodies acting under an enactment for public purposes and not for profit. No regulations have yet been made under Section 5.

Sections 6 and 7 deal with Approved Documents and Section 7 makes clear their status. There have been many misconceptions regarding Approved Documents. They are *not* the regulations and, as the status implies, are purely for guidance and the relevant requirement may be met in other ways. Each Approved Document makes this clear with the following statement: 'The detailed provisions it [the AD] contains are intended to provide guidance for some of the more common building situations. Alternative ways of demonstrating compliance may be more appropriate in other circumstances. There is no obligation to adopt any particular solution in the document if you prefer to meet the relevant requirement in some other way.

When a contravention of a requirement is alleged, then if you have followed the guidance in the document that will be evidence tending to show that you have complied with the regulations. If you have not followed the guidance then that will be evidence tending to show that you have not complied. It will then be for you to demonstrate by other means that you have satisfied the requirement.'

Sections 8, 9 and 10 deal with relaxations on application to the Secretary of State and these powers may be (and have been) delegated to Local Authorities. Public bodies can have similar powers when regulations are specifically made.

Section 11 deals with the power of the Secretary of State to direct that a particular type of building matter may be eligible for relaxation generally instead of only in a specific case. Similarly, Section 12 allows regulations to be made for a particular type of building matter to be approved as complying and this power may be delegated. Section 12 has not yet been brought into force but some Local Authorities through LANTAC (Local Authority National Type Approval Consortium) have issued 'type approval' for certain house types being built within their areas.

Section 14 requires the Secretary of State to appoint a Building Regulations Advisory Committee and to consult before making building regulations containing substantive requirements. Section 15 requires consultation with the fire authority before a Local Authority grants a dispensation or relaxation of the requirements of Part B of the building regulations.

Section 16 requires Local Authorities to either pass plans or reject them if they are defective or show that the work would not comply within 5 weeks (or two months if the applicant agrees in writing). They may, however, pass the plans subject to conditions. The conditions are strictly limited and are:

(1)   that such modifications as the local authority may specify shall be made in the deposited plans and/or

(2)   that such further plans as may be specified shall be deposited.

If 'a question arises' between a Local Authority and the person who proposes to carry out work, that person may refer the question to the Secretary of State for a determination. It has been understood that 'a question arises' means that the plans have been rejected, and this tends to force Local Authorities to give a rejection in order that the application for a determination can go ahead. It would be more helpful if such an application could also be made on receipt of an approval which contained a condition under (1) above, with which the applicant disagreed.

This section also provides for the acceptance of certificates from 'approved persons' and Section 17 contains powers for approving such persons. The provisions of the Regulations prescribed for this purpose are Part A (structure) and L 1 (conservation of fuel and power).

Section 18 is one of the so-called 'linked powers' and relates to building over sewers. The Water Act 1989 has, however, clarified a point of issue concerning the interpretation of the word 'over' and, additionally, this section relates to drains, and disposal mains. It now requires a Local Authority to consider rejection of plans where it is shown that the proposed building will be either over a sewer or in such position as would interfere with the use of the sewer or obstruct access to it. Where the sewerage undertaker notifies the Local Authority how the Section 18 function is to be carried out, the Authority has a duty to do as it is instructed.

The drains, sewers and disposal mains affected by Section 18 must be shown on a map of sewers, and this includes any records kept by the sewerage undertaker under the Water Act 1989, or a map of pipes kept by an authority under the Control of Pollution Act 1974.

Section 19 relates to the use of short-lived materials specified in the Building Regulations as being unsuitable for use in the construction of permanent buildings. None have yet been specified and reference should be made to the Approved Document for Regulation 7. The Approved Document sets out criteria for some short-lived materials.

Section 20 is wider in scope than Section 19, which will be superseded on a day yet to be appointed.

Section 21 requires a Local Authority to reject plans deposited under Building Regulations unless satisfactory provision has been made for drainage. Part H of Schedule 1 to the Building Regulations contains the requirements for drainage, but operation of this section ensures that the drainage connects to a satisfactory outfall.

Section 22 allows the Local Authority to require buildings to be drained in combination.

Section 23 has been repealed and incorporated into Schedule 1 to the Building Regulations, Part H4.

Section 24 contains powers for a Local Authority to require certain buildings to have satisfactory arrangements for means of escape but does not apply to those buildings controlled through Part B1 (Means of Escape) of the Building Regulations. The extension of Part B1 to all new and altered buildings will curtail the operation of this section.

Section 25 requires plans of new houses to be rejected if there is an inadequate water supply.

Sections 26–29 – Provision of closets, bathrooms, food storage and sites containing offensive material – have been repealed as their content was included within the Building Regulations 1985. Since then, of course, the requirement to provide food storage accommodation has been abandoned.

Section 32 provides for the effect of the deposit of plans to lapse if work is not commenced within three years.

Section deals with tests for conformity.

Section 35 deals with penalties for a breach.

Section 36 contains the power to require work to be pulled down or altered if it does not comply (the issue of a Section 36 notice). If the owner fails to do so the Local Authority may execute the work itself and recover the cost from the owner. These powers lapse 12 months after completion of the work and do not apply if the work conforms to plans which the Local Authority has passed or not rejected within the time limit.

Section 37 allows a person receiving such a notice to have an independent report made, and if as a result the Local Authority withdraws its notice it must recompense the owner for the costs incurred.

Sections 39 to 43 deal with appeals:

○   To the Secretary of State against the refusal of a Local Authority to grant a dispensation or relaxation

○   To a Crown Court if aggrieved by the decision of a Magistrates' Court

○   In certain circumstances eventually to the High Court

○   Or the Secretary of State may arrange for the appellant and the Local Authority to appear before a person appointed by him for the purpose.

Section 44 makes work on buildings for Crown Authorities subject to the substantive requirements, but not to the procedural regulations. The National Health Service and Community Care Act 1990 removed Crown immunity for Building Regulation purposes from building work to be carried out on land held, used or occupied by health service bodies.

Section 45 deals with application to the UK Atomic Energy Authority.

Section 46 deals with the application of Part I to inner London by reference to Schedule 3.

Part II contains the legislation to allow the supervision of building work by private certifiers.

8   Other provisions of the Building Act 1984

Part III contains a lot of legislation which parallels that in Part I but consists of general powers not directly related to Building Regulations. It gives Local Authorities wide-ranging powers to ensure that all buildings have suitable arrangements to maintain public health and safety. Thus if it appears, for example, that a building has defective drainage or has inadequate closet accommodation, it must issue a notice to the owner to correct the defect or deficiency. In the event of the owner not complying, there is provision to allow the Local Authority to carry out the work and recover the costs (Section 99) and for appeal against the notice to a Magistrates' Court (Section 102). The substantive requirements are similar to those in Part I and concern (among other things) drainage, sanitary conveniences, entrances and exits, water supply, food storage, dangerous and dilapidated buildings or neglected sites.

Section 72 lays a duty on Local Authorities, after consultation with the Fire Authority in regard to certain buildings, to ensure that there are such means of escape from fire as they deem necessary, and if not to issue a notice requiring the necessary work to be done. The buildings to which this applies are over two storeys high with a floor more than 20 ft above ground and:

(*a*)   Let as flats or tenements.

(*b*) Used as an inn, hotel, boarding house, hospital, nursing home, boarding school, children's home or similar institution.

(*c*) Used as a restaurant, shop, store or warehouse having an upper floor containing sleeping accommodation for employees.

This does not apply if Regulation B 1 applies, a means of escape requirement or a fire certificate is in force.

Section 74 requires the consent of the Local Authority to be obtained for the construction of a cellar below the normal ground water level for a house, shop, inn, hotel or office, but not if it forms part of a premises where a Justices' licence has to be obtained.

Part IV contains the general sections on the forms of documents, powers of enforcement, appeals, compensation, prosecution etc, and interpretation.

Section 121 gives a very wide definition of 'building' which includes virtually every type of structure, including even a vehicle, vessel or aircraft if the circumstances suggest that it is being used in the manner of a building. In the Building Regulations however, a much more restricted definition is given.

Part V contains the transitional provisions, amendments, repeals etc. The Act in general came into effect on 1 December 1984, but certain sections were held back to come into force when the Secretary of State shall decide. The 'appointed day' provisions which are not yet in force or for which regulations have not been made are:

Section 12	Power of the Secretary of State to approve type of building matter
13	Delegation of power to approve
20	Use of materials unsuitable for permanent building
31	Proposed departure from plans
33	Tests for conformity with building regulations
38	Civil liability
42	Appeal and statement of case to the High Court in certain cases
43	Procedure on appeal to the Secretary of State on certain matters
44	Application to the Crown
45	Application to the United Kingdom Atomic Energy Authority
133(2)	Certain transitional provisions.

There are seven schedules.

Schedule 1 deals in detail with matters which may be the subject of Building Regulations and with the methods by which they may be prescribed (Section 1(3)). These are too well-established to require much comment here. They now include provisions for the acceptance of certificates of compliance, and so for the issue by Local Authorities of certificates that certain defined matters will comply with Building Regulations. Also included is the power to make prescribed persons responsible for performing the functions of Local Authorities (ie private certification).

Within the list of substantive requirements there are, in addition to those already included in Regulations, a number of items for which Regulations have never been made. These include telecommunications, lifts, escalators etc, standards of heating, artificial lighting, air-conditioning, electrical power outlets and means of access to and egress from buildings.

Building Regulations may also repeal or modify certain sections of the Act. These include the substantive requirements in both Parts I and III, and also most of Part IV. They may also repeal or modify any provisions of any Act passed before 20 September 1974 if it appears to the Secretary of State to be inconsistent with the Regulations.

Schedule 2 deals with applications for relaxation made after the work has been carried out (Section 9(4)) .

Schedule 3 deals with Inner London (Sections 46, 88 and 91(2)). It had five Parts, two of which have been repealed. The Parts still applicable are:

Part I   The application of Part I of the Act

Part II   The application of Part III of the Act

Part IV   By-laws relating to the demolition of buildings.

Schedule 4 deals with the provisions which apply when a Public Bodies Notice is issued (Section 54). These are parallel to those which apply when a private certifier is engaged.

Schedules 5, 6 and 7 deal with transitional provisions, consequential amendments and repeals.

9 Other legislation

The Building Regulations form only one part (although a very important one) of a miscellaneous and widely disseminated mass of legislation affecting buildings. The following is a list of other legislation affecting building, not necessarily comprehensive:

Cinematograph Acts 1909 and 1952
Water Acts 1945, 1973 and 1989
Clean Air Act 1956
Factories Act 1961
Offices, Shops and Railway Premises Act 1963
Fire Precautions Act 1971
Control of Pollution Act 1974
Education Act 1980
Local Government, Planning and Land Act 1980
Highways Act 1980
Housing Act 1985
Fire Safety and Safety of Places of Sport Act 1987
Town and Country Planning Act 1990

Various local acts
Some Local Authorities, mainly County Councils with large urban populations, have considered the provisions of the various Acts to be inadequate to meet their requirements. To remedy this they have obtained parliamentary consent to the making of local Acts. These remain in force. There are over 30 such Acts and they are each concerned with one or more of the following:
(*a*)   Requirements as to safety requirements for parking places.
(*b*)   Access for the fire brigade.
(*c*)   Fire precautions in certain large buildings.
(*d*)   Fire and safety precautions in public and other buildings.
(*e*)   Further precautions against fire in high buildings.
(*f*)   Provision of means of escape from fire in certain buildings.
(*g*)   Separate drainage systems.
(*h*)   Retaining walls.
(*i*)   Requirements as to paving of yards and passages (extended to buildings other than houses).

10 The 1991 Documents

In order to deal with an application under the Building Regulations a considerable quantity of paper is now essential (also available on microfiche). The relevant documents are:
The Building Regulations 1991 (SI 1991 No. 2768) known as the principal regulations.
The Building (Approved Inspectors etc) Regulations 1985 (SI 1985 No. 1066)
Approved Document to support Regulation 7 (Materials and workmanship)

Approved Document A	Structure
Approved Document B	Fire
Approved Document C	Site preparation and resistance to moisture
Approved Document D	Toxic substances
Approved Document E	Resistance to the passage of sound
Approved Document F	Ventilation
Approved Document G	Hygiene
Approved Document H	Drainage and waste disposal
Approved Document J	Heat producing appliances
Approved Document K	Stairs, ramps and guards
Approved Document L	Conservation of fuel and power
Approved Document M	Access and facilities for disabled people
Approved Document N	Glazing – materials and protection

The Building (Prescribed Fees) Regulations 1991
NOTE   The introduction of the Building Notice procedure and private certification (with reserve powers for the Local Authorities to take over should the certifier withdraw) have considerably complicated the fee structure. However, the fee payable for a Building Notice application is still the same as if full plans were submitted.

This was an excellent document because it contained what has never previously been available, a complete guide to the procedures required to obtain approval under the Building Regulations. There were three sections dealing with the following:

Section 1   The application of the Regulations.
Section 2   The procedures to be followed.
Section 3   The regulations and supporting documents.

Because of the many changes in the 1991 Regulations it has now been withdrawn but a revised version may be produced in 1992. In the meantime, the most important changes in application and procedures are set out on the following pages, following the pattern of the Manual.

THE APPLICATION OF THE BUILDING REGULATIONS

1   The Building Act 1984 and Regulations made under it apply in England and Wales to building work and certain changes of use of an existing building.

2   *Building work* is defined in Regulation 3(1) as

(*a*)   the erection or extension of a building, or

(*b*)   the provision or extension of a controlled service or fitting in or in connection with a building, or

(*c*)   the material alteration of a building, or a controlled service or fitting

(*d*)   work required by Regulation 6, ie on a material change of use

(*e*)   the insertion of insulating material into the cavity wall of a building

(*f*)   work involving the underpinning of a building

Certain small buildings and extensions as well as buildings used for certain special purposes are entirely exempt from the Regulations. You can find them listed in Schedule 2 to the Regulations.

3   The Regulations say nothing about the point at which repair which is not subject to control becomes work which has to be controlled. That is a judgement which often has to be made and depends on circumstances. Repair is basically replacement or making good, and not new work or alteration.

But in the case, for example, of a whole building which has been seriously damaged, there comes a point when so much has to be done to repair or replace it that the Local Authority could reasonably require it to be treated as if a new building was being erected. In such a case the Regulations apply. If you are in doubt the Local Authority may be able to advise you.

4   The Regulations apply to a *change of use if* after the change:

(*a*)   the building is used for the purposes of a dwelling where previously it was not, or

(*b*)   the building contains a flat where previously it did not, or

(*c*)   the building is used as a hotel or boarding house where previously it was not, or

(*d*)   the building is used as an institution where previously it was not, or

(*e*)   the building is a public building (as defined in Regulation 2(2)) where previously it was not, or

(*f*)   the building is not a building described in Classes I to VI in Schedule 2 where previously it was.

THE TWO SYSTEMS OF BUILDING CONTROL

5   If the Regulations apply to your project you must notify the Local Authority. You must first decide whether you want the Local Authority to be responsible for supervising the work or whether you wish to employ a private approved inspector.

If you decide on the Local Authority you will usually have a further choice of depositing full plans or giving them a 'Building Notice' which contains much less information. To start work without doing either is a contravention of Regulation 11 for which the Local Authority can prosecute. In either case you will have to pay the fee prescribed under the Building (Fees) Regulations.

6   If you decide to engage a private approved inspector you and the inspector must jointly give the Local Authority an 'initial notice' in accordance with the Building (Approved Inspectors etc) Regulations 1985. You should not commence the work before the notice has been accepted by the Local Authority. There is no fee to the Local Authority. The inspector's fee is a matter you must negotiate with him yourself. The procedures for these two systems of control are described in paragraphs 7 to 32 which follow.

A   Local Authority control

7   Before deciding whether to deposit full plans or give a building notice you should consider the pros and cons of the two procedures which are explained in paragraphs 8 to 14 below. If you are proposing to erect a building where paragraphs B1 of Schedule 1 (Means of escape) applies and the use to which the building will be put is a designated use under the Fire Precautions Act (ie hotels, boarding houses, offices, shops and certain factories) you must deposit full plans – see paragraph 13.

Deposit of plans

8   If you deposit 'full plans' (defined in Regulation 13) the Local Authority must pass them or reject them within 5 weeks, or 2 months if you agree. They can reject the plans on any of the following grounds (which must be given in the notice of rejection):
(*a*)   the plans show a contravention of the Building Regulations,
(*b*)   the plans are defective (eg incomplete – they fail to show compliance with the Regulations),
(*c*)   they are unsatisfactory as regards one of the Local Authority's functions under Sections 18, 21, 24 or 25 of the Building Act.

9   The functions mentioned in paragraph 8(*c*) are usually referred to as 'linked powers' because their operation is linked to the deposit of plans. Two of them relate to drainage: Section 18 controls any new building over an existing sewer and enables the Local Authority to impose requirements as a condition of passing the plans. The usual requirement is that you enter into an agreement with the sewerage undertaker (or local authority acting as their agent) to provide access to the sewer for maintenance.

Under Section 21 the Local Authority can insist that the drainage system connects with an existing public sewer where one is accessible. Section 24 concerns the provision of means of ingress and egress and passages or gangways in certain public buildings, and Section 25 concerns the provision of water supply to houses. Local legislation exists in some areas enabling local authorities to reject plans on particular grounds.

Certificates of compliance

10   When you deposit full plans you may accompany them with a certificate that the plans show compliance with certain requirements of the Building Regulations, namely those relating to structural stability (Part A) and/or energy conservation (Part L). Such a certificate can only be given by a person approved for the purposes of Section 16(9) of the Building Act 1984.

When it is properly given by a duly approved person and is accompanied by a declaration that an approved insurance scheme applies the local authority cannot reject the plans on the grounds that they do not show compliance with a requirement to which the certificate relates.

Regulation 27 of the Approved Inspectors etc Regulations sets out the detailed requirements relating to this procedure.

Building in accordance with plans

11   You are not obliged under Building Regulations to build exactly in conformity with the plans which you deposited – your obligation is to see that the work complies with the Regulations. Nevertheless, where you have had your plans passed (or they were not rejected) and the work conforms with them, you gain useful protection because the Local Authority may not then serve a notice requiring you to take it down or alter it (see paragraph 16). If you are deviating very much from the original plans, it is therefore sensible to let the Local Authority know (and you may need to if you have got planning permission on that basis).

Completion certificates

12   The Local Authority has to issue a completion certificate when it receives a notice that work has been completed for –
(*a*)   buildings put to a designated use under the Fire Precautions Act
(*b*)   buildings where a request has been made for such certificate when plans were deposited.

The Building Notice

13   If you decide to give a Building Notice, you must include with it a site plan (in the case of a new building or extension) and the information specified in Regulation 12. This is to enable the Local Authority to identify the site or the property concerned, the nature of the work proposed, and also to consider any aspect of the work to which the linked powers or local legislation might relate.

The Local Authority may respond by commenting on these matters and in particular may require you to enter into the kind of agreement that would have been made (regarding any building over an existing sewer) if you had deposited plans. The Local Authority may ask you to provide certain other plans or information, but it is not required to pass or reject a building notice or any such plans which you provide. Consequently the protection of having had your plans passed is not available.

The Local Authority can require work to be altered if it is not satisfactory as regards the linked powers, just as it can if work contravenes the Building Regulations. On the other hand, the Building Notice enables you to start work without having to provide the Local Authority with plans. You must, however, inform them before you start the work (see paragraph 15).

Consulting the fire authority

14   If you are proposing to erect a building which will be put to a use designated under Section 1 of the Fire Precautions Act 1971 and you deposit plans, the Local Authoity will be required to consult the fire authority before passing the plans. (Currently designated are certain factories, offices, shops, railway premises, hotels and boarding houses.)

If the building is put or intended to be put to a designated use, you cannot give a Building Notice. You are obliged to deposit full plans so that the Local Authority can consult the fire authority (see Regulation 11(2)). Additional copies of plans will have to be submitted where Part B applies (see Regulation 13).

The adequacy of fire precautions may be relevant to the licensing of premises for other uses (eg places of entertainment) and before constructing such a building it would be in your interest to ensure that the fire authority had been consulted.

Stage or conditional passing of plans

15   There is a halfway house between giving a Building Notice and depositing full plans at the outset. Section 16(2) of the Building Act allows a Local Authority to pass plans subject to both of two conditions. These are:

(*a*)   That such modifications as the Local Authority may specify shall be made in the deposited plans. This means that where the plans show a contravention the Local Authority may pass them subject to the necessary correction being made;

(*b*)   That such further plans as they may specify shall be deposited. This means that if the plans are incomplete they may pass them subject to the remainder being deposited. This second condition enables plans to be dealt with in stages.

These procedures can often be useful, though local authorites are not obliged to use them and your written agreement is required.

Starting work

16   You may begin work at any time after you have given a building notice or deposited plans, provided you give the Local Authority two days' notice. If you proceed with work without having notified it at the stages specified in Regulation 14 the Local Authority may ask you to undo it as far as is necessary for it to check whether it complies with the Regulations. If it then requires the work to be altered to secure compliance, you must inform it in writing when you have done the alterations. It is a contravention of the procedural Regulations not to give these notifications.

Contraventions of the technical requirements

17   If the Local Authority considers that your work contravenes any requirement of the Regulations it may serve a notice (under Section 36 of the Building Act) requiring you to take it down or alter it within 28 days. If you disagree with its view you may notify the Local Authority that you propose to obtain an independent expert report under Section 37, in which case the period is extended to 70 days. The Local Authority may withdraw the notice in the light of the report, but if it does not you may appeal to the magistrate's court under Section 40.

B   Supervision by approved inspector

The initial notice

18   If you engage an Approved Inspector you and the inspector should jointly give to the Local Authority an 'initial notice' together with a declaration that an approved scheme of insurance applies to the work, which must be signed by the insurer.

There is a prescribed form for an initial notice. It must contain a description of the work and, in the case of a new building or extension, a site plan and the information which the Local Authority needs in connection with its powers under the Building Act. In particular it needs to know what drainage will be provided and where it will connect to an existing sewer (Section 21) and, if you are proposing to build over an existing sewer, what precautions will be taken to protect it (Section 18).

There may also be local legislation which has to be satisfied about which the Local Authority will also require information (but not detailed plans); for example, some Local Authorities require separate drainage for foul water and rainwater and some require access for the fire brigade. (In showing where it is proposed to connect to the existing sewer it will often be sufficient to indicate that it will be between points A and B shown on the plan.)

19   You should discuss these matters with the Local Authority before giving the initial notice because if it is not satisfied with your proposals or the notice does not contain sufficient information it may reject it. The Local Authority has 10 working days in which to consider the notice and may only reject it on prescribed grounds (in Schedule 3 to the Approved Inspectors etc Regulations).

In accepting an initial notice the Local Authority may impose conditions: in the case of building over a sewer it may require you to enter into an agreement giving it access for inspection and maintenance and to inform it when you carry out the work.

If the Local Authority does not reject the notice within 10 days it is presumed to have accepted it without conditions. (Broadly speaking, the 10 days run from the date on which the Local Authority receives the notice. If the notice is sent by post it will be presumed, in the absence of any evidence to the contrary, to have been received in the normal course of post. A person sending a notice by post would therefore be prudent to check the date of receipt.)

20   It is a contravention of the Regulations to start work before the notice has been accepted. Thereafter the approved inspector is responsible for supervising the work as regards both the Building Regulations and the provision of drainage. Where new sewers are the subject of an adoption agreement (under Section 104 of the Water Industry Act 1991) the approved inspector may wish to rely on the sewerage undertaker's inspection of that part of the work. The Local Authority remains responsible for inspecting any connection to, or building over, an existing sewer and work to which any local legislation applies.

Independence

21   As a general rule, the approved inspector must be independent of the designer or builder, but he need not be if the work consists of alteration or extension of a one- or two-storey house. The criteria for independence are in Regulation 9 of the Approved Inspectors etc Regulations.

Consulting the fire authority

22   If you are erecting a building which is to be put to a designated use (see paragraph 13) you would be well advised to ensure that consultation has taken place with the fire authority. If Regulation B1 applies the approved inspector *must* consult the fire authority by giving it relevant plans and allowing it 15 working days to comment before giving a certificate. (See Regulation 11 of the Approved Inspectors etc Regulations.)

Plans certificates

23   If you wish to have the detailed plans of the work (or a part of it) certified as complying with the Building Regulations, you should ask your approved inspector to supply a plans certificate, which he should give to you and the Local Authority. This can be done at the time the initial notice is given or later, provided that the work has not been carried out.

Final certificates

24   When the work is complete the approved inspector should give you and the Local Authority a final certificate, which the Local Authority may reject only on prescribed grounds. A final certificate (or, for that matter, a plans certificate) need not relate to all the work specified in an initial notice. For example, where a single initial notice covered a new housing estate separate certificates might be given for individual houses or groups of houses.

Occupation, etc

25   If a new building or extension which is the subject of an initial notice is occupied (or a material change of use takes place) and no final certificate is given the initial notice will cease to have effect.

For most buildings there is a period of grace of 6 weeks before the initial notice lapses, but in the case of a building to be put to a use designated under Section 1 of the Fire Precautions Act 1971 or a building to which Section 24 of the Building Act applies the period is 1 day.

Once the initial notice has ceased to have effect, the approved inspector will be unable to give a final certificate, and the Local Authority's powers to enforce the Building Regulations will revive. This has the consequences described in paragraph 27 below. Local Authorities can, however, extend either period, and may wish to if they are reasonably confident that a final certificate will be given soon.

Withdrawal of approved inspector

26   If an approved inspector for any reason cannot continue to supervise work for which he has given an initial notice he must inform you and the Local Authority by cancelling the initial notice. If you become aware that he is unable to continue supervising the work you must cancel the initial notice yourself. If you fail to do so without reasonable excuse you will be liable to a maximum fine of £2000.

27   Where an initial notice is cancelled you can engage another inspector to take over responsibility. You and the second inspector should give the Local Authority a second initial notice for any work which has not already been the subject of a final certificate.

If possible, the second notice should be given before the first is formally cancelled and should be accompanied by an undertaking by the first inspector to cancel the first notice as soon as the second is accepted. This will ensure that one or other of them is always responsible for supervising the work.

Where this arrangement is not possible and an initial notice has already been cancelled the Local Authority *may* accept a second initial notice provided that it has not taken any positive steps to supervise the work in the intervening period. For this to be possible, all work would have to stop during that period.

Local Authority's powers

28   When an initial notice has been cancelled and you do not engage a second Approved Inspector the Local Authority becomes responsible for supervising any work which has been carried out which has not had a final certificate.

In that event, you must provide the Local Authority on request with sufficient plans of any partially completed building work – including, if necessary, plans of work which has been certified – to show that the work can be completed without contravention of the Building Regulations. It is a contravention of Regulation 11 to continue work before this has been done. You must also pay the Local Authority the full prescribed fee appropriate to that work. You may also be required by the Local Authority to cut into, lay open or pull down work so that it may ascertain whether any uncertified work contravenes the Regulations.

If the initial notice covered any separate buildings which had not been started, you would either have to give a building notice or deposit plans in respect of each of those buildings (again paying the appropriate fee) or give another initial notice before proceeding with the work.

Contravention of Building Regulations

29   Unlike a Local Authority, an Approved Inspector has no direct power to enforce the Building Regulations. He is, however, required to inform you if he believes that any work being carried out under his supervision contravenes them. If you fail to remedy the alleged contravention within 3 months he is obliged to cancel the initial notice. He must inform the Local Authority of the contravention, unless a second Approved Inspector is taking over responsibility.

C   Other procedures

Dispensations and relaxations of the requirements

30   Relaxation is the process whereby a Local Authority accepts that, because of special circumstances, all the terms of a requirement need not be fully met. Dispensation is agreement by the Local Authority that you need not comply with a requirement at all. It is up to you to ask for a relaxation or dispensation if you believe that in the particular circumstances of your proposal a requirement of the Regulations is unreasonable. You must ask the Local Authority even if you are using an Approved Inspector, since he has no power to relax or dispense with any requirement.

31   The technical requirements in Schedule 1 to the Regulations are 'functional' – they ask for something to be provided at the level set out in Regulation 8, ie Parts A–K and N do not require anything to be done except for the purpose of securing reasonable standards of health and safety for persons in or about buildings, and any others who may be affected by buildings or matters connected with buildings.

You will notice that words such as 'adequate' and 'reasonable' no longer appear in the requirements for Parts A, B, C, E, G and K.

Such requirements cannot be relaxed, because to provide something less than at this level is to fail to comply with the requirement (though in such a case it might be reasonable to dispense with the requirement).

32   If you ask the Local Authority for a dispensation or relaxation you will have to tell it why you believe that the specified requirement is unreasonable in the circumstances.

If the Local Authority refuses your request, you may appeal against its decision to the Secretary of State for the Environment within one month of the date on which the Local Authority notifies you of its refusal. If the Local Authority does not notify you of its decision within 2 months (or a longer period if you have agreed) you may appeal to the Secretary of State as if the Local Authority had refused, and in such a case the one-month period for appeal runs from the end of the 2-month period.

The Local Authority cannot give you a relaxation or dispensation if, before you apply, it has given you a notice under Section 36 of the Building Act, requiring you to pull down, alter or remove work and you have not done so (see paragraph 16). On the other hand, it cannot issue a Section 36 notice if an application for relaxation or dispensation is still active.

Determinations

33   If the Local Authority rejects your plans or your Approved Inspector refuses to give you a plans certificate on the grounds that the plans show some contravention of the Regulations, you may ask the Secretary of State to determine the issue.

You should send the plans, the precise grounds on which they were rejected or not certified, a statement of your side of the case, with any information you consider relevant, and the appropriate fee (from the fees regulations). You do not need the agreement of the Local Authority or Approved Inspector in order to ask for a determination.

THE REGULATIONS AND SUPPORTING DOCUMENTS

34   The Building Regulations 1991 are explained later in this Guide. The technical requirements to the Regulations and the notes at this point refer to the relevant 'Approved Documents' explained below.

Approved Documents

35   Approved Documents give practical guidance about some of the ways of meeting the requirements of the Regulations. They are issued by the Secretary of State or on his authority under the powers in Section 6 of the Building Act. Approved Documents cover each of the requirements of Schedule 1 to the Regulations and there is also an Approved Document which gives guidance on meeting Regulation 7.

Using the Approved Documents

36   You can choose whether or not to use the Approved Documents or you can follow some of them or only parts of them. You are obliged only to meet the requirements of the Regulations. You may wish to devise your own solution or there may be circumstances in which it would be unnecessary and unreasonable to follow the guidance in the document in full, so long as what you do will still be adequate to meet the requirements of the Regulations in those circumstances.

37   If you follow the guidance in the documents and it is then alleged that you have contravened the Regulations you could use the fact that you have followed the guidance as evidence tending to show that you have complied with the Regulations.

If you choose not to follow the guidance you may have to demonstrate by other means that you have satisfied the requirements, bearing in mind that in relation to Parts A–K and N nothing needs to be done beyond what is necessary to secure reasonable standards of health and safety. If it is then alleged that you have contravened the Regulations, the fact that you have not followed the guidance could be used as evidence tending to show that you have not complied with the Regulations.

38   Approved Documents may give guidance in more than one form. They may describe particular methods of construction (Technical Solutions), give references to other publications (Alternative Approaches) or give Acceptable Levels of Performance.

Technical Solutions

39   Technical Solutions describe some of the more widely used forms of construction which achieve an Acceptable Level of Performance. Although they give detailed guidance, in some cases they are written to give you sufficient flexibility to adapt them to suit a method of construction which you prefer.

Alternative Approaches

40   If there is no Technical Solution that you wish to use or adapt, you should see if there is an Alternative Approach. This is usually based on the relevant recommendations of a British Standard and may give you an opportunity to use a more complex procedure to 'fine tune' your solution.

Performance

41   Some Approved Documents also contain a Level of Performance. This may be a useful guide if neither of the other two approaches is suitable for your proposals. The Level should not be seen as the minimum standard: there may be circumstances where something less may satisfy the requirements in Schedule 1.

Materials and Workmanship

42   An Approved Document on Regulation 7 – Materials and Workmanship – gives guidance on how you can show that you have complied with this requirement. You may show this in a number of ways, for example by following an appropriate British Standard or by using a product with a British Board of Agrément Certificate.

Products bearing a CE mark, and those which conform to an equivalent national technical specification of a member state of the European Community are also materials which will satisfy Regulation 7.

British Standards and British Board of Agrément

43   Some of the Approved Documents refer to specific British Standards. In each case the appropriate version of the Standard is listed at the back of the Approved Document. However, if there is a later version of the same standard which contains guidance which is relevant to a requirement, the new version may be used.

44   British Standards and British Board of Agrément Certificates sometimes cover aspects of performance which go beyond the requirements of the Building Regulations: they may cover serviceability or recommendations for good practice. The guidance in Standards and Certificates is relevant to compliance with the Regulations where it concerns health and safety (Parts A–K and N), conservation of energy (Part L) or access for disabled people (Part M).

45   The Secretary of State has agreed with the British Board of Agrément the aspects of performance which it needs to assess in preparing its Certificates in order that the Board may demonstrate the compliance of a product or system which has an Agrément Certificate with the requirements of the Regulations. An Agrément Certificate issued by the Board under these arrangements will give assurance that a product or system to which the Certificate relates, if properly used in accordance with terms of the Certificate, will meet the relevant requirements.

12   The principal Regulations

The 1991 Regulations are contained in Statutory Instrument 1991 No. 2768. There are 21 Regulations and three Schedules.

The 1985 Manual gave many explanatory notes and the following pages contain the author's interpretation and comments on the principal regulations together with some of the explanations which were in the Manual.

**PART I   General Title,
commencement and
application**

1   This is simply the citation saying that the Regulations came into force on 1 June 1992.

Interpretation

2   This is a list of definitions. Some of these are self-evident or are described elsewhere in the Regulations. Such cases are not included here.

(1) 'Building' means any permanent or temporary building, but not any other kind of structure or erection. *The term includes a part of a building.*

This is a much narrower definition than the one in Section 121 of the Building Act 1984.

'Controlled service of fitting' means those to which G 1/2/3, Parts H and J of Schedule 1 apply (bathrooms, unvented hot water storage systems, sanitary appliances, drains and waste disposal and heat producing appliances). Those services and fittings in Part L (eg boiler controls and insulation, are now excluded).

'Dwelling' includes a dwelling house and a flat.

'Dwelling house' does not include a flat or a building which contains a flat.

'Flat' means separate and self-contained premises constructed or adapted for use for residential purposes and forming part of a building from some other part of which it is divided horizontally. It includes maisonettes.

'Floor area': see diagram below.

'Height': see diagram below.

Height

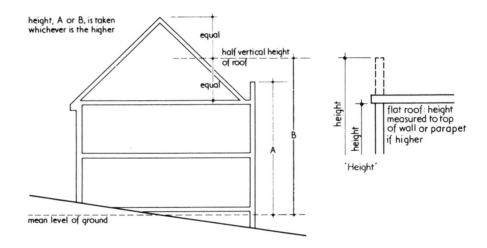

Floor area of storey of building or compartment

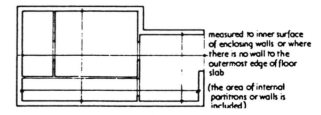

'Institution' means a hospital, home, school or the like used as living accommodation for, or for treatment care or maintenance of –

persons with disabilities due to illness, old age or physical or mental disability or,

under five years old,

where such persons sleep on the premises.

'Office': the definition of office has been deleted.

'Shop' includes premises used for the sale to members of the public of food or drink for consumption on or off the premises, retail sales by auction, the business of lending books or periodicals for the purpose of gain, the business of a barber or hairdresser and premises where the public may hire any item, or take goods for repair or other treatments.

A basement storey is a storey the floor of which is at any point more than 1.2 m below the finished level of the ground adjacent to the building. (This definition is in AD B. Appendix E).

(2) 'Public building' a building containing:

(*a*) A theatre, public library, hall or other place to which the public are admitted, or

(*b*) A school or other educational establishment not exempted by Section 4(1)(a) of the Act (these are schools etc controlled by the DES), or

(*c*) A place of public worship;

but not a building containing a shop, storehouse or warehouse or a dwelling to which members of the public are occasionally admitted.

Note: Regulation 2(4)(5) and (5) which laboriously expressed the 'adverse affect' rule is no longer included. A much more simple explanation of the application of the regulations to alterations and extensions is given in Regulation 3(2) – material alteration.

PART II Control of building work
Meaning of building work

3(1) 'Building work' means:

(*a*) the erection or extension of a building,

(*b*) the provision or extension of a controlled service or fitting in or in connection with a building,

(*c*) the material alteration of a building, or a controlled service or fitting as mentioned in paragraph 2,

(*d*) work required by Regulation 6 (material change of use),

(*e*) the insertion of insulation material into the cavity wall of a building,

(*f*) work involving the underpinning of a building.

(2) An alteration is 'material' if any work would at any stage result in a building or controlled service or fitting –

not complying with a relevant requirement, where previously it did, or

which before the work commenced did not comply with a relevant requirement, being more unsatisfactory in relation to such a requirement.

Relevant requirement means any of the following applicable requirements of Schedule 1, ie Part A (structure) paragraphs B 1 (means of escape) B 3 (internal fire spread – structure, B 4 (external fire spread, B 5 (access and facilities for the fire service) and Part M (access and facilities for disabled people).

This is the simplified version of the previous Regulation 2(4,5 and 6).

It will not usually be necessary to bring the building up to the standards of the Regulations but it should not be made worse.

NOTE This does not include B 2 (fire spread, internal surfaces).

Some examples of such alterations are

Removing part of a loadbearing wall, necessitating a beam.

Altering a three-storey house, requiring additional work to maintain the means of escape from the third storey.

Removing part of a non-loadbearing wall which is, however, required for fire resistance.

Removing a sanitary convenience suitable for disabled people if requirement M 3 is thereby no longer met.

O An alteration to a service or fitting would be unlikely to affect any of the requirements mentioned in (2) above except possibly B 3, if a service penetrates separating structure. Structural alterations are a different matter.

O 'Erection' is not defined in the regulations but Section 123 of the Act states that any reference to 'construction' or 'erection' includes the carrying out of such operations (whether for the reconstruction of a building, the roofing over of an open space between walls or otherwise) as may be designated in building regulations as operations to be treated as the construction or erection of a building for regulation purposes.

O The insertion of insulating material into a cavity must comply with C 4 (resistance to moisture) as well as with D 1 (toxic substances).

Requirements relating to building work

4(1) Building work must be carried out so that:

(*a*) It complies with the relevant requirements of Schedule 1 and

(*b*) The method of complying with a requirement does not result in the failure of the work to comply with any other requirement.

NOTE As mentioned above, some requirements only apply to certain types of building, or are limited in other ways (see Schedule 1).

(2) The work must be carried out so that any existing building (including any controlled service or fitting) which is extended or materially altered [see 3(2)] either complies with the requirements of Schedule 1 or where it did not comply is no less satisfactory than before the work was carried out.

Meaning of material change of use

5   The following circumstances constitute a material change of use – that the building:

(a)   Becomes a dwelling when previously it was not,

(b)   Contains a flat when previously it did not,

(c)   Is used as a hotel or a boarding house when previously it was not,

(d)   Is used as an institution when previously it was not,

(e)   Is a public building when previously it was not,

(f)   Was an exempted building (in classes I to VI of Schedule 2) and no longer is.

The Local Authority must always be informed of a change of use even if no work will be required. A change which does not concern the Regulations may still involve the Fire Authority (eg from domestic to office use).

Requirements relating to material change of use

6(1)   Where the change concerns a whole building the completed building must comply with the following parts of Schedule 1:

(a)   In all cases,

B 1   (means of escape).

B 2   (internal fire spread, linings).

B 3   (internal fire spread, structure).

B 4(2)   (external fire spread – roofs).

B 5   (access and facilities for the fire service)

F1 and F2 (ventilation)

G1   (sanitary conveniences and washing facilities)

G2   (bathrooms)

H4   (solid waste storage)

J1 to J3 (heat producing appliances)

(b)   In cases described in 5(c)–(f), A 1 to A 4 (structure).

NOTE (b is an extension to the requirements and where a material change of use occurs to a hotel, an institution, a public building or a previously exempt building, the building will have to be appraised to see whether it is structurally sound. This will not necessarily mean a complete structural survey but it will be necessary for the architect to provide some indication of the ability of the building to support the new loading which will be placed upon it.

(c)   If the building exceeds 15 m in height B 4(1) (external fire spread – walls).

(d)   In cases described in 5(a) or 5(b), C 4 (resistance to weather and ground moisture) and Part E (airborne and impact sound).

NOTE This further extension (c) and (d) to the requirements affects building which are converted to living accommodation. It was permissible previously to carry out conversion work without having to insert a damp proof course or indeed to make the building weathertight. This, of course, was not satisfactory, and the opportunity has also been taken to require sound insulation to be taken into account in such conversion work.

(2)   If the change applies only to part of a building, that part only need comply with the requirements in (1)(a) and (b) above. However if (1)(c) above applies (over 15 m high) then the whole building must comply with B 4(1).

NOTE Although the whole building, after the change of use, need only comply with the above requirements, any new work that is done in the process is 'building work' (see 3(1)(d)) and hence must comply with all relevant requirements.

Materials and workmanship

7   Building work must be carried out with proper materials and in a workmanlike manner.

Proper materials are now defined and are materials which are appropriate to the purpose for and conditions in which they are used and include materials which –

(a)   bear an EC mark, or

(b)   conform to an appropriate harmonised standard or European Technical Approval, or

(c)   conform to a BS or BBA Certificate or with an alternative technical specification of any member state of the EC which gives an equal level of protection or performance.

NOTE The mark of the EC (European Community) – confusingly written 'CE' – harmonised standards, and ETAs are provided for in the Construction Products Directive. (See Section 17 below.)

Limitation on requirements

8   To comply with the requirements set out in Schedule 1, Parts A–K and N, nothing more need be done than is necessary to ensure the health and safety of persons in or about the building and others who may be affected by a failure to comply.

NOTE In the 1985 Regulations, many of the functional requirements included the words 'adequate' or 'reasonable', and these have been deleted from the new requirements. Apparently the adequacy or reasonableness of a requirement is related to the limitations of Regulation 8 (ie the level of performance can only be that necessary to ensure the health and safety of persons in or about buildings). Persons also included are members of the fire service carrying out the task of rescuing persons from incidents which occur in buildings.

Exempt buildings and work

9 Schedule 2 contains details of seven classes of buildings or extensions which are exempt, both as to their erection, and also as to any work later carried out which does not result in them becoming non-exempt.

PART III Relaxation of requirements
Powers to dispense with or relax requirements

10(1) This Regulation delegates to Local Authorities powers of the Secretary of State under Section 8(1) of the Act to relax or dispense with any of the requirements.

(2) If the Local Authority refuses an application it must inform the applicant of the contents of Section 39(1) and (3) of the Act (appeals against refusals etc). If the Local Authority does not notify the applicant of its decision within two months, a refusal is assumed and an appeal can be made. Under the Act an appeal must be lodged within one month of the date of the notification of refusal. The notice of appeal must set out the grounds on which it is based. It is submitted to the Secretary of State with a copy to the Local Authority.

PART IV Notices and plans
Giving of a Building Notice or deposit of plans

11(1) A person intending to carry out building work or make a material change of use may either:

(a) Give a Building Notice (see Regulation 12), or

(b) Deposit full plans (see Regulation 13).

(2) If the building is to be put to a use which is designated under Section 1 of the Fire Precautions Act 1971 full plans must be deposited.

The uses which have been designated under the 1971 Act and for which full plans must be deposited are:

factories,

offices, shops and railway premises, and

hotels and boarding houses.

(3) If the work consists only of the installation of a gas heating appliance by or under the supervision of a person approved under the Gas Safety (Installation and Use) Regulations 1984 a Building Notice or full plans are not required.

(4) If Regulation 18 of the Building (Approved Inspectors) Regulations 1985 applies, it supplants this Regulation.

This is where work is being supervised by an approved inspector who withdraws before it is complete. The Local Authority can then require plans of the work to enable it to take over the inspector's duties.

(5) For the purposes of Sections 219 to 225 of the Highways Act (1980) which refer to advance payments, the giving of a Building Notice is treated as the deposit and passing of plans.

Particulars and plans where a Building Notice is given

12 This is a long regulation which lists the information which must be supplied with a Building Notice.

(1) The notice must state the name and address of the applicant, be signed by him or his agent and be accompanied by:

(a) A statement that it is given in accordance with regulation 11(1)(a).

(b) A description of the work or material change of use, and

(c) Details of location and intended use.

(2) In the case of the erection or extension of a building:

(a) A plan to a scale of not less than 1/1250 showing:

(i) Its size and position in relation to adjoining boundaries.

(ii) The boundaries of the curtilage and the size, position and use of every other building or proposed building within that curtilage.

(iii) The width and position of any street on or within the said boundaries.

(b) A statement of the number of storeys, (each basement level counts as one storey).

(c) Particulars of:

(i) The provision for drainage

(ii) If Section 18 applies (building over a sewer etc) the precautions to be taken.

(iii) Steps to comply with any local Act.

The item (c) above concerns the linked powers in the Building Act which have not been transferred to the regulations. For some reason Section 25 (water supply) is omitted. Where Section 18 is involved the Local Authority may require the owner to enter into an agreement (regarding future access).

(3)   Where the work involves the insertion of insulation into cavity walls details must be provided of:

(a)   The name and type of material.

(b)   Whether or not it is approved by the British Board of Agrément or conforms to a British Standard.

(c)   Whether or not the installer has a BSI certificate of registration or is approved by the BBA (see the Approved Document to C4).

(4)   Where the work involves a hot water storage system to which G3 relates (unvented hot water systems) the following details must be supplied:

(a)   The name, make, model and type of the system,

(b)   whether approved or certified in accordance with:

　　(i)   an ETA,

　　(ii) a National Technical Approval issued by BBA,

　　(iii) a certificate issued by a body accredited by the NACCB,

　　(iv) an approval by any other body in the EC which assesses the performance of hot water storage systems in a manner similar to those in (i–iii),

(c)   the name of the body giving approval or certifying,

(d)   whether or not the installer holds a current registered operative identity card for the installation of uvhwss and the name of the body.

(5)   When the building notice procedure is being used, the applicant must nevertheless give to the Local Authority such plans as are necessary for the discharge of its functions as are specified by it in writing. Plans in this context include drawings, specifications and any other information concerning the building (eg structural calculations).

NOTE   This power might be used in widely differing degrees by various Local Authorities and in some circumstances could result in the Local Authority requiring almost as much information as if full plans were being deposited.

(6)   Neither a Building Notice, nor any plans given under (5) above are treated as 'deposited' (but subject to Regulation 11(5): see above).

This is to say that the Local Authority has no duty to pass or reject them, and they do not confer on the applicant the protection afforded by Section 36(5) of the Act, ie that the Local Authority may not issue a Section 36 Notice (to pull work down) if the work is built in accordance with plans that it has passed.

(7)   If work to which a Building Notice relates has not been started or a material change of use described in the Notice has not been made, a Building Notice ceases to have effect three years from the date on which the Notice was given.

NOTE   This is a new provision and is similar to the 'lapse of deposit of plans' (full plans) in Section 32 of the Building Act 1984. However, unlike Section 32, the Local Authority does not have to serve notice declaring that the Building Notice is of no effect.

Full plans

13(1)   These must be accompanied by a statement that they are deposited in accordance with Regulation 11(1)(b).

(2)   They must be in duplicate and the Local Authority may keep one copy.

Where plans relate to Part B (fire safety) two extra copies of the plans must be deposited. These copies are necessary to enable consultation to take place with the fire authority and for the fire authority to retain a copy.

(3)   Full plans shall consist of:

(a)   A description of the building work or change of use and all the particulars required under 12(1) to (4) above.

(b)   Such other plans as are necessary to show compliance with the Regulations.

(4)   Full plans must state whether the building is to be put to a designated use under the Fire Precautions Act 1971.

(5)   Additionally, a request may be made for a completion certificate to be issued (see Regulation 15).

Local Authorities can reject plans on the grounds of incomplete information, and frequently do. Under Section 16 of the Act a notice of rejection must specify the defects, or the grounds on which they have been rejected. A notice that the plans have been passed may make this subject to conditions specified in that Section.

| **Notice of commencement and completion of certain stages** | **14**(1)   A person proposing to carry out building work must not commence the work until he has given notice and two clear days have elapsed since the notice was given. |

14(1)   A person proposing to carry out building work must not commence the work until he has given notice and two clear days have elapsed since the notice was given.

(2)   Notice of one clear day must be given before covering up

(*a*)   any foundation, excavation for a foundation, damp proof course, concrete or other material laid over the site,

(*b*)   any drain or sewer.

(3)   Notice within five clear days of the completion of drainage works must be given.

(4)   Five clear days notice must also be given that the erection of a building or part or of any stage of a building has been completed.

(5)   Where part of a building is occupied before completion, five clear days notice must be given before occupation.

(6)   If the above notices are not given the Local Authority may, by notice, require the person carrying out the work to 'cut into, lay open or pull down' as much of the work as is necessary to check compliance with the Regulations.

(7)   Where the Local Authority has issued a notice specifying the manner in which work contravenes the Regulations, and the person carrying out the work has carried out further work to correct this, he must inform the Local Authority of the completion of this work 'within reasonable time'.

(8)   A clear day means any period of 24 hours commencing at midnight and Saturdays, Sundays, Bank Holidays and public holidays are not counted.

Completion certificates

15(1)   A Local Authority must issue a completion certificate where –

(*a*) they receive under Regulation 14(4) or (5) a completion notice or a notice that the building has been partly occupied before completion if,

(*b*)   (i)   they were notified (Regulation 13(4)) when full plans were deposited that the building is put or is intended to be put to a designated use under the Fire Precautions Act, or

(ii)   they were requested to do so under Regulation 13(5).

(2)   The Local Authority must give a completion certificate if it has been able to ascertain, after taking all reasonable steps, that the relevant requirements of Schedule 1 have been satisfied.

(3)   Where the building is a 'designated use' building the relevant requirements which have to be certified are only those in Part B (Fire Safety) but where a completion certificate is specifically requested all applicable requirements have to be certified.

NOTE   Presumably it would be possible for a request to be made under 13(5) for a certificate for any type of building including one which was of designated use.

(4)   Completion certificates will be evidence (but not conclusive evidence) that the relevant requirements have been met.

NOTE   Many Local Authorities already give completion certificates in one form or another. There is no time limit within which such a certificate has to be issued and Regulation 21 (see below) states that Section 35 of the Building Act (penalty for contravening building regulations) does not apply.

PART V   Miscellaneous Testing of drains and private sewers

16   This gives Local Authorities powers to test drains for compliance with Part H.

Sampling of material

17   This gives Local Authorities power to take samples for testing as necessary to check compliance with any part of the Regulations.

Supervision of building work other than by Local Authorities

18(1)   This disapplies Regulations 11, 14, 15, 16 and 17 when an initial notice has been given under Section 47 of the Act, or a Public Body's Notice under Section 54.

(2)   Regulations 16 and 17 do not apply to any work for which a final certificate has been given under Section 51 of the Act or paragraph 3 of Schedule 4 of the Act (in the case of public bodies) and accepted by the Local Authority.

This means that the private certification procedure has been adopted and the Local Authority has no further duties other than checking certificates issued by the private certifier or public body. After completion the Local Authority's powers to test drains and take samples remain disapplied.

Revocations	**19**	The regulations revoked and the extent of revocation are in Schedule 3.

Transitional provisions

20(1)   This is the usual arrangement to cover cases in the pipeline. Thus the new regulations do not apply to:

(a)   Building Notices given, plans deposited or initial notice given before 1 June 1992,

(b)   Work carried out after that date in accordance with such plans, whether or not any departure or deviation is made

(c)   Before 1st June 1992 anything referred to in regulation 4 of the Building (Inner London) Regulations (1985 and 1987) has occurred, and in such cases the 1985 Building Regulations and the Inner London Regulations continue to apply.

Section 35 of the Building Act 1984 (Penalty for contravening building regulations) does not apply to Regulation 15 (completion certificates).

**Schedule 1
Requirements**

This contains the substantive requirements and has 13 parts. They are set out in the form of functional requirements. These may clearly be subject to widely differing interpretations and hence it is necessary to refer to the Approved Documents, one or more of which are provided for use with each part (see later). The actual requirement of each part of Schedule 1 is restated at the beginning of each Approved Document.

**Schedule 2   Exempt
buildings and work**

Schedule 2 sets out six classes of buildings which are exempt from the requirements of the Regulations. Class 7 refers to small extensions. A brief summary follows, and for more detail refer to Schedule 2.

Class I   Buildings controlled under other legislation
1   The Explosives Acts 1875 and 1923.
2   The Nuclear Installations Act 1965 (except if used as a dwelling office or canteen).
3   The Ancient Monuments Act 1979.

Class II   Buildings not frequented by people
These include detached buildings not normally used by people, or visited only for the inspection or maintenance of fixed plant or machinery unless any part of the building is less than 1½ times its height from the boundary or from a building normally frequented by people, whichever is nearer.

Class III   Greenhouses and agricultural buildings
1(a)   A greenhouse or
(b)   A building used for agriculture or principally for the keeping of animals sited not less than 1½ times its height from any building containing sleeping accommodation, and with a fire exit not more than 30 m from any point within the building, unless the purpose is retailing, packing or exhibiting.
2   A wide definition of agriculture is given which includes not only growing things, but also fish farming.

Class IV   Temporary buildings
1   A building which does not remain for more than 28 days.

Class V   Ancillary buildings
1   An estate office.
2   Builders' site huts containing no sleeping accommodation.
3   A building used in connection with a mine or quarry, not containing a dwelling or used as an office or showroom.

Class VI   Small detached buildings
1   A detached single storey building not exceeding 30 m^2 floor area containing no sleeping accommodation and either:
(a)   more than 1 m from the boundary, or
(b)   of substantially non-combustible material.
2   A detached shelter against any form of attack if:
(a)   The floor area does not exceed 30 m^2, and
(b)   The excavation is sited at a distance at least equal to its depth plus 1 m from any other building.

3   A detached building having a floor area which does not exceed 15 m² and containing no sleeping accommodation.

Class VII   Extensions
The addition at ground level of:
(*a*)   A conservatory, porch, covered way or covered yard, or
(*b*)   a carport, open on at least two sides,
having in either case a floor area not exceeding 30 m² provided that a wholly glazed conservatory or porch has glazing which satisfies Part N Requirements.
NOTE   There are quite a few changes from the 1985 regulations.
A detached building not normally used by people should be at least 1½ times its height from the boundary and builders' site huts are no longer exempt if they contain sleeping accommodation. Small detached single storey buildings with no sleeping accommodation can be of substantially non-combustible material and there is total exemption for a detached building with a floor area of not more than 15 m².
Conservatories and porches are exempt only if the glazing satisfies the requirement of Part N (safety glazing).

Schedule 3   Revocations   The 1985 Regulations are wholly revoked together with Regulation 19 of the Fees Regulations. In the Building (Disabled People) Regulations 1987 and the Building Regulations (Amendment) Regulations 1989 Regulation 2 and the Schedule in each are revoked.
Paragraph 1 of Schedule 2 to the Inner London Regulations of 1985 and 1987 is revoked in each case.

13   The Approved Documents

These are issued by the Secretary of State under the powers in Section 6 of the Act. Under this section they may also be issued by a body designated for that purpose by the Secretary of State, such designation to be in the form of a Statutory Instrument, but this power has not been exercised to date.
They give guidance on ways of meeting the requirements, but they are not now part of the law and do not need parliamentary approval for their issue or amendment. Hence they no longer need to be couched in the language of parliament or the law and can contain diagrams.
They are not mandatory and a designer can choose to use other solutions, providing these meet the requirements.
Since these are based on the limits set out in Regulation 8, ie the limitation is that which is necessary for securing reasonable standards of health and safety for persons in or about the building, it may well be difficult to decide when another solution does satisfy the requirements.
It would seem that a designer would be well advised to deposit full plans if he is not using an Approved Document as the basis for any part of his design.
Although they are not the law it is stated that following the guidance in the Approved Documents will, in the event of any dispute, tend to show compliance with the Regulations. If the guidance is not followed it may be necessary to demonstrate this by other means, bearing in mind that it is only necessary to secure reasonable standards of health and safety. However, not following the guidance may be used as evidence tending to show non-compliance with the Regulations.
Approved Documents basically give three kinds of guidance:

1   Performance
These are criteria amplifying the requirements themselves and are sometimes helpful, but sometimes only say the same thing as the requirement in different words. Not all Approved Documents have them.

2   Technical solutions
These give detailed guidance on widely used construction methods and details.

3   Alternative approaches
These are virtually all based on British Standards. In any case much of the material in the technical solutions has clearly been drawn from BSS, so that the alternative is not all that different. However, BSS do generally give a lot more guidance which may often be helpful to a designer, regardless of Regulations.
In this Guide comments are included on changes from the 1985 Regulations where these appear significant.

14 Approved Inspectors

As stated earlier, the powers necessary to establish the proposed system of private certification are contained in Part II of the Act (Sections 47 to 58). In addition to private certification it also provides for self-certification by specified public bodies. These are the national corporations which are run on a profit-making basis (or theoretically should be) such as, for example, British Gas, British Rail, British Coal etc. There are about 20 of them.

The system is controlled by the Building (Approved Inspectors etc) Regulations 1985, but apart from public bodies, and a corporate scheme set up by the NHBC, is so far not operational. This is because a basic and clearly essential component is the existence of a scheme of liability insurance required in each case to protect the employer of the approved inspector against damages arising from inadequate inspection. Unlike Local Authorities, Approved Inspectors are not permanent continuing establishments. They will in due course pass on, and even whilst still here are unlikely to have the sort of resources needed to meet a hefty claim for damages. The insurance industry is known to be sceptical about the number of unknown factors and lack of experience in dealing with liability of this type although it is possible that changes may be made in the insurance requirements to enable more persons to act as Approved Inspectors. It is thought that there will be more chance for a professional body to secure adequate insurance for its members than for a private individual.

Details of how the system operates are set out in paragraph 11B of this Introduction.

There are provisions for the designation of bodies to approve inspectors and such approvals may specify a limitation on the extent of their field of operation (there may be more than one class of inspector).

Adequate insurance and total independence of inspectors are essential parts of the system.

15 Inner London

The Building (Application to Inner London) Regulations came into force in January 1986 and applied the Building Regulations 1985, the Building (Approved Inspectors, etc) Regulations 1985 and the Building (Prescribed Fees) Regulations to the Inner London Boroughs, the Temples and the City.

In the past control was exercised by means of the London Building Acts and by-laws made under them administered by the GLC and District Surveyors. However, matters concerning sanitary conveniences, drainage and waste disposal were administered by the inner London Boroughs under local by-laws.

With the abolition of the GLC, the whole of the national Regulations are now administered by the boroughs. However, some parts of the London Building Acts (Amendment) Act 1939 will remain in force in modified form, in particular, Section 20, which concerns special precautions against fire in large buildings, is modified. The section now applies only in special circumstances where precautions are needed beyond those imposed by building regulations. It applies to buildings over 28 m high and buildings of the warehouse class, or used for trade or manufacture, exceeding 7100 m^3 unless sub-divided in the manner required to form a 'separate part' in the Regulations. It allows for the provision of fire alarms, extinguishers, smoke control and access for the fire brigade. Special provisions may also be required when mechanical plant is installed or inflammable substances are stored.

For these buildings the builder will still have to supply full details of the scheme and the Council may impose conditions.

Similar powers have been taken by Councils in large conurbations by means of local Acts. In the future these powers may be transferred to the regulations as a functional requirement supported by an Approved Document.

Powers are also retained in respect of special and temporary structures and rights of adjoining owners (Sections 29 and 46).

Section 34 is retained to control means of escape from fire in buildings not covered by Part B 1 of the Regulations.

Part VII (dangerous and neglected structures) is also retained.

However, since virtually all the requirements of the Building Regulations now apply, this Guide should be equally useful in Inner London.

16 Fees

In practice, these are not too complicated as the fees for a Building Notice application are the same as those where full plans are submitted (one does not get any reduction because plans no longer have to be passed or rejected). As regards private certification, a fee known as a reversion fee becomes payable if the Local Authority has to take over due to the cancellation of an 'initial notice' (ie because the private certifier is for some reason unable to continue his supervision). In this case the fees chargeable by the Local Authority are the same as if a new application had been made.

No fees are payable where the work is solely for the benefit of disabled people.

There are four schedules giving the fee scales:

Schedule 1

(*a*)   For single small domestic buildings where there is a set fee for each dwelling in the building, plus an extra for dwellings over 64 m².

(*b*)   In a multiple scheme, which might comprise single dwellings or a group of buildings containing several dwellings, there is a formula which is an extrapolation of (*a*) above.

Schedule 2

This deals with small garages and carports and small domestic extensions or alterations for which fixed fees are set. The size limit here is 40 m² but note that carports up to 30 m² are exempt under Schedule 3 of the principal regulations.

Schedule 3

This deals with all other cases where the fee is based on 70 per cent of 'a reasonable written estimate' of the cost of the building, which has to be supplied with the deposited plans or Building Notice. As before, there are two scales, a plans fee and an inspection fee which is approximately three times the plans fee. A Building Notice fee is equal to the total of both.

The same anomaly as before persists; namely that at the lower end of the scale the total fee amounts to 1.2 per cent of the cost reducing as one might expect to 0.42 per cent.

Schedule 4

This amends fees for a determination of questions by the Secretary of State and in the latest amendment the amount of fee payable was doubled.

The most recent amendment is the Building (Amendment of Prescribed Fees) Regulations 1990 (SI 1990 No 2600) which merely raises fees for small domestic buildings in line with inflation. It is the intention that the building control service of Local Authorities should be self-financing and when a satisfactory conclusion has been reached with the Local Authority associations to restructure the pattern of fees, Local Authorities will be able to set their own charges for their building control service. These would inevitably vary from authority to authority, but it is understood that the fees which may be charged will be kept within certain limits which will be laid down by the Secretary of State.

17   Building Regulations and the Construction Products Directive

The work in the EC to eliminate technical barriers to trade, initiated by the Commission, has been going on for more than 20 years.

The existing national regulations – especially in the technical field – frequently have long traditions and diverge, not only in their principles and systems but also in their very fine technical detail. Where these divergences result in barriers to trade between Member States and where market access is made impossible, the EC is in danger and therefore a need for action by the Commission arises.

The Construction Products Directive (CPD) is one of the most important Directives announced in the Commission's White Paper *Completing the Internal Market* in June 1985, and its adoption represents a major step in the removal of technical barriers to trade by 31 December 1992. When fully implemented, the CPD will be the framework for, and the regulatory regime within which, trade in construction products will be conducted in the Community in the post-1992 period. It will replace National Regulations, and the Standards will replace equivalent National Standards both within the Community and in EFTA countries.

As its name implies, the Directive applies to construction products. However, a link is made between the products themselves and the construction works into which they will be incorporated.

Not only buildings but also civil engineering works are covered by the CPD, which means that the total range of products covered by the CPD is very large, even compared to other so-called 'new approach' Directives.

Contrary to all the other known new approach Directives, the compulsory Essential Requirements related to building works are spelled out in a very general way. These relate to – mechnical resistance and stability,

safety in the case of fire,

hygiene, health and environment,

safety in use,

protection against noise,

energy economy and heat retention.

These requirements have to be satisfied during an economically reasonable working life. The realisation of compliance with these objectives has to take into account the existing geographical and/or climatic conditions and ways of life. This may give rise to the establishment of quality classes for the products concerned.

The six Essential Requirements are of such a general formulation and nature that they are not all suitable as direct terms of reference for mandated European standardisation.

It is, therefore, necessary to provide so-called Interpretative or Intermediate Documents which detail the links between the Essential Requirements and the various products Standards. The publication of these documents will give them sufficient backing as terms of reference for the standardisation mandate and for the practical application of the Directive itself.

European Standards themselves are not compulsory, but are the preferable means of proof of conformity. In the transition period before the establishment of European Technical Specifications, National Technical Specifications complying with the Requirements may be accepted, where they are nominated by the Member States and accepted by the Commission.

In the first instance, the EC mark, applied on the product itself, on labelling, packaging or on the relevant accompanying commercial documents, constitutes a refutable presumption of conformity with the relevant Harmonised or nominated National Standards or with the European Technical Approval.

However, in the case where Harmonised Standards are not followed entirely or not at all, the Directive provides for some variations of third-party testing and certification, depending on the relevant product and the production control or quality assurance system practised by the manufacturer.

For products playing only a minor part with respect to health and safety, only declaration of conformity with the recognised state of the art is required and no EC marking is permitted. This solution gives the possibility, on grounds of common agreement within the Standing Committee to keep a wide range of products within the Directive and under the common ruling which would otherwise have to be excluded from it.

The free circulation of products satisfying the provisions of the Directive has to be assured by all Member States and should not be impeded by bodies acting in public on the basis of a monopoly position.

The attestation of conformity by applying the EC mark and issuing the relevant written declaration is the responsibility of the manufacturer or his agent established in the Community. The kind of procedure for the product as well as its characteristics and their importance will be specified by the Standing Committee assisting the Commission.

Where harmonised standards or specifications for European technical approval do not exist, Member States may maintain national provisions and allow products not bearing the EC mark to be placed on their market, when complying with their national specification.

The technical specifications which give concrete form to the Essential Requirements are either Harmonised Standards established by CEN (the European Centre for Standardisation) expressed in performance terms or technical assessments of fitness for use contained within European Technical Approvals (ETA).

An ETA has to be issued by one of the designated members of the European organisation for Technical Approvals and is immediately recognised by all other member bodies.

The ETA procedure is, in the first instance, conceived for new and innovative building products.

During the transition period, the CPD reserves a very important role for the approval bodies. As long as the ETA harmonised specifications are not existing, the relevant national approvals are still valid. However, the recognition of Technical Approvals given by a designated body in the Member States of production shall, according to the rules of the Member State of destination, be recognised as fully valid.

The regulations implementing the CPD in the UK came into force at the end of 1991. They established the procedures by which manufacturers may legally fix the EC mark to their products. Such products which carry this mark may be used anywhere within the European Community without having to make any technical or procedural requirements. In the meantime, however, as CE marking requires products to be produced in accordance with a national standard transposing a European standard or in accordance with an ETA, it will be some time before these standards and approvals are available, and manufacturers will continue to be able to market products within the UK that are 'fit' under current domestic regulatory requirements.

For the issue of ETAs in the UK, the body designated is the British Board of Agrément.

18 References and sources

Acts of Parliament
The Building Act, 1984.
The Fire Precautions Act, 1971.
Health and Safety at Work etc Act, 1974.
Housing Act, 1985.

Department of the Environment/Welsh Office
The Building Regulations, 1985 (SI 1985/1065).
The Building (Prescribed Fees etc.) Regulations, 1985 (SI 1985/1576).
The Building (Inner London) Regulations, 1985 (SI 1985/1936).
The Building (Inner London) Regulations, 1987 (SI 1987/798).
The Building (Disabled People) Regulations, 1987 (SI 1987/1445).
The Building Regulations (Amendment) Regulations, 1989 (SI 1989/1119).
The Building (Amendment of Prescribed Fees) Regulations, 1990 (SI 1990/2600).
Manual to the Building Regulations, 1985.
Mandatory Rules for Means of Escape, 1985.
The Building Regulations, 1991 (SI 1991/2768).
Approved Document to Part D, 1985 edition.
Approved Documents to Parts F, H, J, L, 1990 edition.
Approved Documents A, B, C, E, G, K, M, N, 1992 edition.
Approved Document to Regulation 7, 1992 edition.

Addresses of organisations whose publications are referred to in the Approved Documents:
Association of Builders Hardware Manufacturers, Heath Street, Tamworth, Staffordshire, B79 7JH (0827 52337).
Association of Structural Fire Protection Contractors and Manufacturers, PO Box 111, Aldershot, Hampshire, GU11 1YW (0252 21322).
British Board of Agrément, PO Box 195, Bucknalls Lane, Garston, Watford, Herts, WD2 7NG (0923 670844).
British Standards Institution, Sales Office, Linford Wood, Milton Keynes, MK14 6LE (0908 320066).
Building Research Establishment, Garston, Watford, WD2 7JR (09273 674040).
Chartered Institution of Building Services Engineers, 222, Balham High Road, London, SW12 9BS (081-675 5211).
Department of Transport, Disability Unit, 2 Marsham Street, London, SW1P 3EB
Directorate of Planning Services, Room C15/19, 2 Marsham Street, London, SW1P 3EB.
Fire Protection Association, 140 Aldersgate Street, London, EC1A 4HX (071-606 3757).
Fire Research Station, Melrose Avenue, Borehamwood, Herts, WD6 2BL (081-953 6177).
HMSO (for publications by all Government Departments), PO Box 276, London, SW8 5DT (071-873 9090).
Institution of Electrical Engineers, Savoy Place, London, WC2R 0BL (071-240 1871).
Institution of Structural Engineers, 11 Upper Belgrave Street, London, SW1X 8BH (071-235 4535).
Loss Prevention Council, Melrose Avenue, Borehamwood, Herts, WD6 2BJ (081-207 2345).
NATLAS Accreditation Scheme for Testing Laboratories, National Physical Laboratory, Teddington, Middlesex
Steel Construction Institute, Silwood Park, Ascot, Berks, SL5 7QN.

APPROVED DOCUMENT TO SUPPORT REGULATION 7
Materials and workmanship

Unlike the other ADs all of which relate to one of the 12 parts of Schedule 1, this relates directly to one of the principal Regulations.

Materials and workmanship

7(1)   So much of any building work as is required to comply with any relevant requirement of Schedule 1 shall be carried out:

(*a*)   with proper materials which are appropriate for the circumstances in which they are used; and

(*b*)   in a workmanlike manner.

(2)   Subject to paragraph (1), 'proper materials' shall include materials which:

(*a*)   bear an appropriate EC mark in accordance with the Construction Products Directive or

(*b*)   conform to an appropriate harmonised standard or European Technical Approval or

(*c*)   conform to an appropriate British Standard or British Board of Agrément Certificate; or

(*d*)   conform to some other national technical specification of any Member State which provides, in use, an equivalent level of protection and performance with respect to the relevant requirements of Schedule 1, as an appropriate British Standard or British Board of Agrément certificate.

NOTE   Attention is drawn to the requirements of Regulation 8 of the Building Regulations 1991:

'8. Parts A to K and N of Schedule 1 to these regulations shall not require anything to be done except for the purpose of securing reasonable standards of health and safety for persons in or about buildings (and others who may be affected by buildings or matters connected with buildings).'

The main changes in this Approved Document are in connection with the extension of Regulation 7 itself to incorporate reference to the status and meaning of the EC mark.

Other changes include specific reference to natural materials, the omission of sampling procedures, greater emphasis on quality assurance and the inclusion of a list of organisations and their abbreviations, mainly relative to Europe.

The role of technical specification is made clear in the first page of the Approved Document under the heading 'Use of the Guidance'. This states that standards and technical approvals are relevant guidance to the extent that they relate to the specific purposes for which Building Regulations are made.

They may (and quite often do) address other aspects of performance which, although concerned with health and safety are not covered in the Regulations.

The specific purposes for which Building Regulations are made are: health and safety – Schedule 1 Parts A–K and N, energy conservation – Part L and the welfare and convenience of disabled people – Part M. The Approved Document to Regulation 7 is applicable to all the requirements of Schedule 1 to the extent stated in Regulation 7.

There is a list of acceptable levels of performance which expand on the regulation itself as follows:

0.1   Materials should be:

(*a*)   Of a suitable nature and quality in relation to the purposes and conditions of their use, and

(*b*)   Adequately mixed or prepared, and

(*c*)   Applied, used or fixed so as to perform adequately the functions for which they are intended.

Materials include products, components, fittings, naturally occurring materials (eg stone, timber and thatch), items of equipment and backfilling for excavations in connection with building work.

0.2   For Parts A–K and N of Schedule 1 the standards of material and workmanship need to be no more than necessary to ensure adequate standards of health and safety of persons in or about the building.

NOTE It would seem that herein lies the safeguard against the possibility of too high a standard being demanded by the controlling authority.

0.3 For Part L they need to be no more than needed to restrict calculated heat losses to the levels set out in the Schedule.

For Part M they need be no more than necessary to serve their purpose.

0.4 The Regulations contain no provisions for continuing control over the use of materials following completion of the building.

The Approved Document is divided into two sections, Materials (1) and Workmanship (2). A number of aids to establishing the fitness of both are described.

NOTE The 1991 Regulations include references to many British Standards some of which are quite complex. The Designer (and even the Building Control Officer) may well have little knowledge of the contents of a particular standard even through it may be referred to on drawings. With the advent of the arrival of harmonised standards, European Technical Approvals and national technical specifications, the references needed by the specifier will become much more extensive. It is now quite a time-consuming operation to track down the relevant parts of a British Standard, and this will be exacerbated when the European scene expands. One of the objectives of this Guide is to make life easier by summarising the essential parts of the references.

Section 1 Materials

1.1 The Approved Documents contain references to materials and products likely to be suitable by reference to BSS or Agrément Certificates which cover them. Such references are not exclusive and other materials may be suitable in particular circumstances.

Ways of establishing fitness
1.2 The following aids may be useful:

(*a*) *EC marks*

A material has an EC mark (see earlier). This mark shows that the material complies with a harmonised standard, that is –

a CEN or CENELEC standard mandated by the European Commission,

a European Technical Approval, or

a national technical specification recognised at Community level.

Material bearing an authorised EC mark must be accepted as fit for its purpose by the inspectorate, ie Building Control Authority or Approved Inspector, if it is in a satisfactory condition and is being used appropriately.

Such marked material can only be rejected by the inspectorate if its performance does not accord with its technical specification. The inspectorate has the onus of proof and they must notify the Trading Standards Officer if they find this is the case. The TSO will then inform central government who may take up the matter with the Commission.

An EC marked material must not be rejected by the Inspectorate on grounds relating to the manufacturer or the organisation which tested or certified the material.

(*b*) *Standards*

The material is used and conforms to an appropriate British Standard (BS) or to an equivalent standard (which would be a national standard of a Member State of the EC) or any other equivalent national technical specification. The person carrying out the work has the onus to show equivalence.

NOTE Materials produced to BS 5750: *Quality systems* or the equivalent ISO or CEN standards can be expected to be of consistent quality but may not necessarily conform to a particular standard.

(*c*) *Technical approvals*

The material used in accordance with and covered by an Agrément Certificate or a technical approval issued by any other Member State. Again it is up to the person carrying out the work to show equivalence.

BS 000

BSI Kitemark

(*d*)   *Independent certification schemes*
The only one referred to is the BS Kitemark scheme (see diagram).

If so marked the material can be taken to conform to the relevant BS but unmarked materials may still conform. Accreditation of schemes is carried out by NACCB. If a product has been tested to a BS by an approved body in another Member State of the EC in accordance with the CPD (Article 16), the inspectorate must accept that the product complies with that standard.

(*e*)   *Tests and calculations*
It can be shown by test or calculation that the material can perform adequately. The NAMAS accreditation scheme for testing laboratories offers one way of ensuring that the tests are conducted to recognised standards.
Similar schemes run by other equivalent certification bodies (including those in the EC designated under the CPD) are also acceptable.

(*f*)   *Past experience*
The material may be considered suitable because it has behaved satisfactorily in a building in use.

(*g*)   *Sampling*
The Approved Document gives a reminder that local authorities under Regulation 17 have the power to take samples of material used in building work.

Short-lived materials
This section gives very little guidance on which material might be considered unsuitable and much will depend on the judgement or prejudices of the individual building control official, or Approved Inspector.
1.3   Some materials in the absence of special care may be unsuitable because of their rapid deterioration in relation to the life of the building. It is not possible to lay down specific criteria in relation to the Regulations. Often the choice is influenced by economic factors which are not proper considerations as matters affecting health and safety.
1.4   Short-lived materials which are readily accessible for maintenance or replacement may be acceptable if the consequences of failure are not likely to have a serious effect on health or safety.
1.5   Such materials, if not readily accessible and where failure is likely to have a serious effect on health or safety, are unlikely to be suitable. However, if failure is likely to have only a minor effect on health and safety the use of the materials may be admissible.
The last item seems to be a built-in source of controversy.
NOTE Section 19 of the Building Act 1984 allows Local Authorities to reject plans where it is proposed to construct a building of materials to which Section 19 applies.
Section 19(7) states that building regulations may provide that Section 19 applies to any materials specified in regulations as being short-lived because of their liability to rapid deterioration or are otherwise unsuitable for use in permanent buildings. Regulation 7 does not include any reference to Section 19 neither is there any mention in the Approved Document. It is doubtful if Section 19 has any effect in relation to construction materials, and this is probably why Section 20 (Use of materials unsuitable for permanent building) was included. Section 20 is wider ranging and may ultimately replace Section 19 by order of the Secretary of State. In the meantime the only control on short-lived materials is the guidance in paragraphs 1.3, 1.4 and 1.5.

Resistance to moisture
Here we are on firmer ground.
1.6   Any material which may be adversely affected by condensation, ground moisture, rain or snow will meet the requirements if:
(*a*)   The construction will resist the passage of moisture to the material, or
(*b*)   The material is treated or protected from moisture
1.7   Any material in contact with the ground should be able to resist attacks by deleterious substances in the subsoil such as sulphates (see Approved Document C1/2/3 Section 2).

High alumina cement (HAC)
1.8   Any material containing high alumina cement should only be used as a heat-resisting material and never in structural work or foundations.

House longhorn beetle
1.9   In the areas specified softwood used for roof construction, or within the roof space (including ceiling joists), should be treated with a suitable preservative to prevent infestation by the house longhorn beetle (*Hylotrupes bajulus L.*).

Geographical area

The District of Bracknell
The Borough of Elmbridge
The Borough of Guildford (other than the area of the former borough of Guildford)
The District of Hart (other than the area of the former urban district of Fleet)
The District of Runnymede
The Borough of Spelthorne
The Borough of Surrey Heath
In the Borough of Rushmore, the area of the former district of Farnborough
The District of Waverley (other than the parishes of Godalming and Haslemere)
In the Royal Borough of Windsor and Maidenhead, the parishes of Old Windsor, Sunningdale and Sunninghill
The Borough of Woking

Section 2   Workmanship

This is really just a repeat of 1.2 above.
2.1   The following aids may be useful in establishing the adequacy of workmanship:

(*a*)   *Standards*
The method of carrying out the work is covered by a British Standard Code of Practice: BS 8000 *Workmanship on building sites* which gathers together guidance from the other BS Codes and Standards.

(*b*)   *Technical approvals*
The workmanship is specified for a material having an Agrément Certificate issued by BBA or covered in an equivalent technical approval (including an approval by EOTA). As with materials, it is up to the person carrying out the work to show equivalence.

(*c*)   *Management systems*
The workmanship is covered by a scheme complying with ISO 9000/EN 29000/BS 5750: *Quality systems*. These schemes may relate to products which are also covered by a BS.

(*d*)   *Past experience*
A method of workmanship may be shown to be adequate because of its performance in use.

(*e*)   *Tests*
Regulation 16 enables Local Authorities to make tests for compliance with Part H of Schedule 1 for:
    (*i*)   Sanitary pipework and drainage
    (*ii*)   Cesspools, septic and settlement tanks
    (*iii*)   Rainwater drainage
Guidance on testing is contained in Approved Documents H 1 and H 3.

Appendix

Many abbreviations are used, particularly in connection with the move towards a common European market.

Those relating to Europe are set out first:

CEN

Comité Européean de Normalisation.

This is the European standards body recognised by the Commission to prepare harmonised standards to support the Construction Products Directive. There are 18 members comprising the standards bodies of all the members of the EC and EFTA.

The countries are:

Austria	Belgium	Denmark
Finland	France	Germany
Greece	Iceland	Ireland
Italy	Luxemburg	Netherlands
Norway	Portugal	Spain
Sweden	Switzerland	United Kingdom

CENELEC

The European standards body for electrical standards analogous to CEN.

Commission

The executive organisation of the EC based in Brussels.

CPD

Construction Products Directive.

The Council Directive reference 89/1106/EEC dated 21 December 1988 and published in the *Official Journal of the European Communities*, No. 140/12 dated 11 February 1989.

EC

European Community, includes the EEC or Common Market.

The twelve countries bound by the Treaty of Rome.

EC mark

The EC conformity mark.

It will be accompanied by a reference to the technical specification to which it conforms and, where appropriate, by indications to identify the characteristics of the product.

EEC

European Economic Community.

EN

The prefix followed by a number for standards issued through CEN.

EOTA

European Organisation for Testing and Certification.

Technical approvals will be issued through this body.

International
ISO

International Organisation for Standardisation.

This is the worldwide standards organisation, some of whose standards may be adopted for use with the CPD. Standards are identified by 'ISO' and a number.

British
BS

British standards issued by the British Standards Institution (BSI).

NACCB

The National Accreditation Council for Certification Bodies.

NAMAS

The National Measurement Accreditation Service.

BS 5750: *Quality systems:*

Part 1: 1987 *Specification for design/ development, production, installation and servicing.* This standard is the same as ISO 9001 and EN 29001.

Part 2: 1987 *Specification for production and installation.* This standard is the same as ISO 9002 and EN 29002.

BS 8000: *Workmanship on building sites:*

Part 1: 1989 *Code of Practice for excavation and filling*

Part 2: *Code of Practice for concrete work*

Section 2.1: 1990 *Mixing and transporting concrete*

Section 2.2: 1990 *Sitework with in situ and precast concrete*

Part 3: 1989 *Code of practice for masonry* Amendment slip 1: AMD 6195.

Part 4: 1989 *Code of practice for waterproofing*

Part 5: 1990 *Code of practice for carpentry, joinery and general fixings*

Part 6: 1990 *Code of practice for slating and tiling of roofs and claddings*

Part 7: 1990 *Code of practice for glazing*

Part 8: 1989 *Code of practice for plasterboard partitions and dry linings* Amendment slip 1: AMD 6475.

Part 9: 1989 *Code of practice for cement/sand floor screeds and concrete floor toppings*

Part 10: 1989 *Code of practice for plastering and rendering* Amendment slip 1: AMD 6476.

Part 11: *Code of practice for wall and floor tiling*

Section 11.1: 1989 *Ceramic tiles, terrazzo tiles and mosaics*

Section 11.2: 1990 *Natural stone tiles*

Part 12: 1989 *Code of practice for decorative wallcoverings and painting*

Part 13: 1989 *Code of practice for above ground drainage and sanitary appliances*

Part 14: 1989 *Code of practice for below ground drainage*

Part 15: 1990 *Code of practice for hot and cold water services (domestic scale)*

Chapter 1

Approved Document A: Structure

Part A now contains four requirements in two Approved Documents. The first and largest AD covers requirements A 1/2 – *Loading and ground movement*, the second, A 3/4, deals with *Disproportionate collapse*. AD 1/2 Section 1, as previously, gives sizes of structural elements for certain residential and other small buildings of traditional construction, and this Section and paragraph numbers are listed as 1 A–1 E.

The timber tables are now in Appendix A at the end of the document and these have been extended to cover the increased imposed snow loading in certain areas of the country, mainly North East England and sites between 100 and 200 m above ordnance datum. There is also a simplified procedure for design wind speed. Guidance regarding buttressing walls has been revised and extended and there are recommendations regarding timber strutting to floor joists. Section 2 gives new guidance on the support and fixing of external wall cladding and Section 3 deals with the measures which should be taken when re-covering existing roofs. It is now clear that re-roofing can be subject to Building Regulation control where there is a change in the type of covering with either heavier or lighter materials.

It is hoped that Local Authority building control staff will not take this to its ultimate and insist on a full structural survey in each instance.

Because of the amendments made to the main regulations, a building has to comply with Requirements A 1 to A 4 where there is a material change of use to an hotel, institution or a public building.

Section 4 makes reference to publications regarding appraisal of existing structures.

Section 4 also refers to a series of reports concerning sites where there may be ground instability.

Section 5 is relative to Requirement A 3 which has been amended to safeguard the 'building' from disproportionate collapse where previously the Requirement was concerned with the 'structure'.

Section 6 deals with reducing the sensitivity of a building to disproportionate collapse in the event of a local failure in the roof structure or its supports. Requirement A 4 is concerned with safety of roofs of certain public buildings, shops and shopping malls.

A 1/2   LOADING AND GROUND MOVEMENT

The new Requirements are:

Requirement	Limits on application
Loading A 1. – (1) The building shall be so constructed that the combined dead, imposed and wind loads are adequately sustained and transmitted to the ground – (*a*) safely, and (*b*) without causing such deflection or deformation of any part of the building, or such movement of the ground, as will impair the stability of any part of another building. (2) In assessing whether a building complies with sub-paragraph (1) regard shall be had to the imposed and wind loads to which it is likely to be subjected in the ordinary course of its use for the purpose for which it is intended.	

Ground movement

A 2. The building shall be adequately constructed so that ground movement caused by:

(*a*) Swelling, shrinkage or freezing of the subsoil; or
(*b*) Landslip or subsidence (other than subsidence arising from shrinkage) in so far as the risk can be reasonably foreseen will not impair the stability of any part of the building.

General

There are six sections each covering A 1 and A 2 jointly. Section 1, which contains five parts is concerned only with 'certain structural elements of residential buildings up to three storeys and other small buildings', and this occupies a large proportion of the document. However this class of building forms a very large part of the output of the building industry. Furthermore, it is a valuable guide for designers, who in this case do not need to be highly specialised structural engineers. For the purist this, no doubt, is giving too much specific guidance but it has the advantage of satisfying designers' requirements without the need to consult textbooks on structural matters. It should, however, be borne in mind that the guidance in Section 1 is limited to residential and other small buildings. For example, the timber sizes given should not be used when designing buildings which may have commercial use.

Introduction to the provisions

This outlines the general philosophy regarding structural safety.

0.1 The safety of the structure depends on the successful combination of design and construction, particularly:

(*a*) Loading, where dead and imposed loads should be in accordance with BS 6399: Parts 1 and 3 and wind loads in accordance with CP 3: Chapter V: Part 2.
(*b*) Properties of materials.
(*c*) Design analysis.
(*d*) Details of construction.
(*e*) Safety factors.
(*f*) Workmanship.

0.2 Defines three approaches to meeting the requirements by using:

(*a*) Section 1 Relevant to small buildings of traditional masonry construction. Section 1B (timber elements) and 1C (walls) are the important parts, and, strangely, there is a difference in the types of buildings to which each refers – single family houses for Section 1 B and residential buildings, annexes and small buildings for Section 1C (see later for fuller description).
(*b*) Section 2: External wall cladding and Section 3: Re-covering of roofs are relevant to all types of building.
Section 4 lists references for structural design and construction, but where precise guidance is not given, regard should be had to 0.1.
(*c*) Other approaches. If these are used, regard should be had to 0.1. Numerical values of safety factors, explicit or implicit, in equations or design values should be derived from the aspects of design and construction given in 0.1 *as a whole*. Any change in one aspect may affect safety. Loads used a.e to allow for possible dynamic, concentrated and peak effects.
(*d*) ENV Eurocodes. Pre-standard Structural Eurocodes will be issued by the BSI. They are provisional standards and will be available to designers for trial use. Feedback from experience gained in using these ENVs will help in the development of final EN standards. When the final approved standards are issued they will be referenced in future editions of the Approved Document.
ENV. EC2 Part 1 and ENV. EC3 Part 1 (General Rules and Rules for Buildings) have been carefully considered by UK structural engineers and give appropriate guidance for the design of concrete and steel buildings respectively.

Section 1 Sizes for certain structural elements for certain residential buildings and other small buildings of traditional construction

1.1   The section is arranged in five parts:

1 A   Basic requirements for stability.

1 B   Sizes of timber members in single family houses not over three storeys high – application and use.

1 C   Masonry walls in certain residential buildings not over three storeys and small single-storey buildings and annexes.

1 D   Masonry chimneys.

1 E   Strip foundations of plain concrete.

Comment

Why there is a difference in the designations of the building types to which 1B and 1C apply is not (and never has been) clear.

1.2   Sections 1B to 1E may be used independently of each other.

Definitions

The following are given (wording summarised):

Buttressing wall designed to afford lateral support to a wall at right angles, extending from base to top.

Compartment wall: constructed to meet requirements of Regulation B 3(2).

Dead load: due to weight of all walls, permanent partitions, floors, roofs, finishes, services and all permanent construction.

Imposed load assumed to be produced by occupancy or use including movable partitions, distributed, concentrated, impact, inertia and snow loads but excluding wind loads.

Pier: a thickened section at intervals along a wall.

Separating wall: common to adjoining buildings to satisfy Regulation B 3(2).

Spacing: least distance between centres of adjacent timber members of the same type (see diagram [1.3]).

Span: distance between centre of bearings, except in Section 1 B where spans for timber members are clear spans between faces of supports (see diagram [1.4]).

Supported wall: one to which lateral support is given by buttressing walls, piers or chimneys in conjunction with floors and roofs.

Wind load: due to effect of wind pressure or suction.

Section 1A   Basic Requirements for Stability

1A 1   This section should be used in conjunction with Sections 1B and 1C.

1A 2   Trussed rafter roofs should be braced as recommended in BS 5268: Part 3: 1985. Traditionally framed roofs without sufficient built-in stability (eg hips, rigid sarking, etc) should also be braced in a similar way.

1A 3   If the roof is braced as above, adequately anchored to the structure below and walls designed as in Section 1C, no special provisions should be needed against wind loads.

Section 1B   Sizes of certain timber floor, ceiling and roof members in single-family houses

1B 1/2   The section applies only to single-family houses not exceeding three storeys and should be used with Section 1A.

1B 3   The following assumptions are made:

(*a*)   Dead and imposed loads will not exceed the values given in the tables. (NOTE The imposed loads are the same as those given in BS 6399: Part 1 – see Section 2.)

(*b*)   Species and stress grades of timber to be used are stated in Table 1. There is a more comprehensive table in BS 5268: Part 2: 1988.

(*c*)   Floor boarding should comply with BS 1297: 1987.

1B 4   Strength classes, species, stress grades etc are as defined in BS 5268: Part 2: 1988.

1B 5   Cross-sectional dimensions in the tables are applicable to either basic sawn or regularised sizes as given in BS 4471: Part 1: 1987.

The tables should be referred to when determining whether sawn or regularised sizes apply and the tables cannot be used where sizes have been reduced by planing. North American sizes are surface sizes unless resawn to BS 4471.

NOTE   These occur mainly in the 38 mm width.

1B 6   Notches and holes – see diagram [1.5].

1B 7   Bearing areas and workmanship should comply with BS 5268: Part 2: 1984.

Spans and spacing

1B 8   In tables A1–A24 in the Appendix all spans, except floorboards, are clear spans between faces and spacings are between centres (see diagrams [1.3] and [1.4]).

1B 9   The imposed snow loading applicable to roofs at particular sites is given in the diagram.

NOTE   This paragraph introduces different loadings depending on the location of the site. Generally, as shown on the map sites in areas where imposed loading for rafters, purlins, flat roof joists and purlins supporting sheeted roofs of 1.00 kN/m^2 should be used are parts of North East England. Additionally, at those sites which are between 100 m and 200 m above ordnance datum snow loading of 1.00 kN/m^2 should similarly be used.

[1.1–1.6] *Illustration of terms and rules for timber construction.*

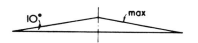

[1.1] *Flat roofs: includes all pitches up to 10°.*

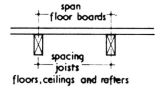

[1.3] *Span: floorboards.*

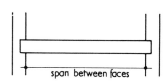

1B 8 **[1.3]** *Span: joists.*

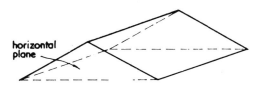

[1.2] *Measurements per m^2 are to be in horizontal plane.*

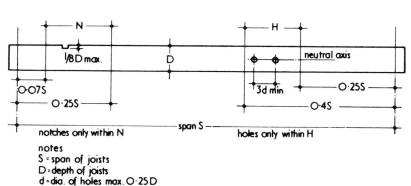

notes
S = span of joists
D = depth of joists
d = dia. of holes max. 0·25 D

1B 6 **[1.5]** *Notches and holes.*

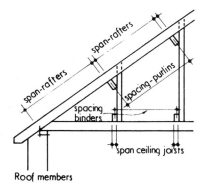

1B 8 [1.4] *Span: roof members.*

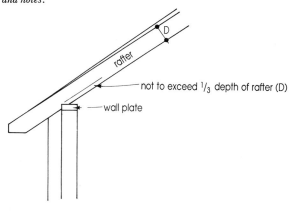

1B 6 **[1.6]** *Birdsmouthing.*

Table to 1 B3
For convenience, this is included below.

Table to 1B3 Common species/grade combinations, which satisfy the requirements for the strength classes to which Tables to A1–A24 in Appendix A relate

Species	Origin	Grading rules	SC3			SC4	
Redwood or whitewood	Imported	BS 4978	GS	MGS	M50	SS	MSS
Douglas fir Larch Scots pine Corsican pine European spruce Sitka spruce	UK	BS 4978	M50 GS G5	SS MGS MGS M50 M75 M75	MSS M50 M50	– SS SS SS	– MSS MSS MSS
Douglas fir-larch Hem-fir Spruce-pine-fir	Canada	BS 4978	GS	MGS	M50	SS	MSS
Douglas fir-larch Hem-fir Spruce-pine-fir	Canada	NLGA	Joist and plank Structural light framing	No. 1 and No. 2 No. 1 and No. 2	Joist and plank Structural light framing	Select Select
Douglas fir-larch Hem fir Spruce-pine-fir	Canada	MSR	Machine stress rated	1450f–1.3E	Machine stress rated	1650f–1.5E
Douglas fir-larch Hem fir Western whitewoods Southern pine	USA	BS 4978	GS GS SS GS	MGS MGS MSS MGS	M50	SS SS – SS	MSS MSS – MSS
Douglas fir-larch Hem-fir Western whitewoods Southern pine	USA	NGRDL	Joist and plank Structural light framing Jost and plank Structural light framing Joist and plank Stud grade	No 1 and No 2 No 1 and No 2 Sellect Select No. 3	Joist and plank Structural light framing – – Joist and plank	Select Select Select
Douglas fir-larch Hem-fir Southern pine	USA	MSR	Machine Stress rated	1450f–1.3E	Machine Stress rated	1650f–1.5E

Notes
The common species/grade combinations given in this table are for particular use with the other tables in this section and for the cross section sizes given in those tables.
Definitive and more comprehensive tables for assigning species/grade combinations to strength classes are given in BS 5268: Part 2: 1988.
The grading rules for American and Canadian Lumber are those approved by the American Lumber Standards (ALS) Board of Review and the Canadian Lumber Standards Accreditation Board respectively (see BS 5268: Part 2: 1988).

NLGA denotes the National Lumber Grading Association.
NGRDL denotes the National Grading Rules for Dimensional Lumber.
MSR denotes the North American Export Standard for Machine Stress Rated Lumber.

Notes on British Standards

Generally the recommendations given in Approved Documents such as the foregoing are drawn from British Standards (BSS). In addition, the reader is often referred to the standards themselves, which usually provide a great deal more useful information, although it may take some time and trouble to track down. To assist the reader, in accordance with the general policy of this Guide, a brief description of those used in this Section is given below.

BS 1297: 1987

This gives rules regarding the timber quality, defects and manufacture of floorboards.

BS 4471: 1987

This defines the rules as to sizing. Generally softwood for carcassing is sawn and any further treatment, planing, machining etc involves reduction of sizes by allowances which are specified. This means they are not acceptable as full sized structural sections. Some Canadian timber is, however, supplied surfaced (known as CLS) and is marked in the tables.

BS 4978: 1988

This deals with 'softwood grades for structural use' and specifies two methods of grading, visual stress grading and machine stress grading. Also specified are the permissible limits of characteristics for two visual stress grades General Structural Grade (GS) and Special Structural Grade (SS).

Machine stress grades also included are Machine General Structural (MGS), Machine Special Structural (MSS), M50 and M75.

Strength Class (SC) is also given.

The stresses appropriate to these grades are set out in BS 5268.

BS 5268: Part 2: 1988

Introduces the concept of 'strength classes' of which two (SC 3 and SC 4) are used in the tables to Section B and includes more comprehensive tables for assigning species and grades to strength classes than are given in Table to 1 B3 above. The grades are those defined ind BS 4978 and also those set by the Canadian and USA Lumber Standards Boards. In addition to allocating grades to strength classes, the BS also gives comprehensive tables showing the actual stresses (shear, bending, compression etc) which can be taken by the various species/grade combinations. In assigning these to strength classes account cannot be taken of compression stresses at bearing, which must be individually calculated. The BS also requires lateral stiffening of one or both flanges, or between, as the depth to width ratio increases. This is not required in the tables although it is common practice to use strutting between floor joists. It is also interesting to note that Section 1B defines spans as clear spans whereas the BS gives them as between centres of bearings. The BS assumes that its contents will be used by qualified designers, eg civil or structural engineers.

There is a comprehensive section on workmanship including moisture content, machining, joints, storage, assembly, inspection and maintenance.

BS 5268: Part 3: 1985

This is mentioned in Section 1A and covers trussed rafter construction. This includes recommendations for bracing which may also be applied to other roofs (see 1 A2). It also deals with potential condensation problems requiring ventilation.

The 1988 edition amends the 1984 edition to extend the range of timbers covered and includes the related stresses. There are new appendices on grade marks for plywood and factors for determining clear wood stresses have been added. An appendix lists acceptable agencies for grading in accordance with BS 4978.

Table to 1 B8

This is the key to the 24 tables which give sizes for all the normal timber members used in this type of building (A 1 to A 24). They are one of the most useful (as opposed to restricting) parts of the Approved Documents. They are not included in BS 5268 which merely gives the necessary data for designing them, and they represent a considerable body of work.

For quick reference the table is summarised below.

Members	Strength class	Table numbers
Floor joists	SC3	A1
	SC4	A2
Ceiling joists	SC3/4	A3
Binders for ceiling joists	SC3/4	A4
Rafters	SC3/4	A5, A9, A13 (A7, A11, A15)
Purlins supporting rafters	SC3/4	A6, A10, A14 (A8, A12, A16)
Flat roof joists	SC3	A17 (A19)
	SC4	A18 (A20)
Flat roof joists (full access)	SC3	A21
	SC4	A22
Purlins for sheeted roofs	SC3/4	A23 (A24)

(The table numbers in parentheses refer to design loading of 1.00 kN/m^2)

All categories include two separate strength classes, SC3 and SC4. The figures for rafter roofs include three different slopes. Figures for flat roofs include for those with maintenance access only and with full access. The strength classes are as determined in the Table to 1 B3. Each table has a diagram illustrating the meaning of the terms 'span' and 'spacing' in relation to the members involved. These are shown in the general illustration following A4.

Notes to tables
Each table has a note to the effect that the dead load is the load supported by the member excluding its selfweight and a note concerning the superimposed loads allowed. These are taken from BS 6399: Part 1: 1984 and Part 3: 1988.

The tables are generally very similar to those in the 1985 Regulations. The differences are:
1   The number of tables has been reduced from 26 to 24.
2   Some timber sizes have been altered and clear spans are given to 3 decimal places.
3   The tables for purlins for sheeted or decked roofs have been amended and one table is now used for any pitch between 10° and 35°.
4   Spans are given as clear spans, that is, spans between the faces of the supports.
5   Loadings used are those given in BS: 6399: Part 1, basically $1.5\,\text{kN/m}^2$ for floors. For roofs reference is now made to BS 6399: Part 3 and the tables have been extended to cover two loading figures.
$1.00\,\text{kN/m}^2$ should be used in the design of roofs –
(*a*)   within the hatched area of the map [1.7] at an altitude of less than 100 m above ordnance datum, and
(*b*)   outside the hatched area at an altitude between 100 m and 200 m above OD.
$0.75\,\text{kN/m}^2$ outside the hatched area at an altitude of less than 100 m above OD.
For sites at greater altitude imposed snow loading should be determined from BS 6399: Part 3.

1 B 9 **[1.7]** *Imposed snow roof loading.*

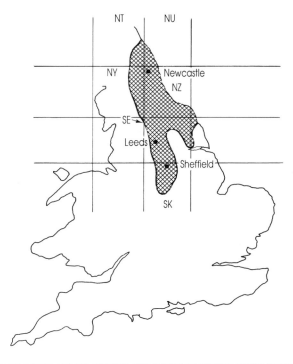

These areas with reference to the National Grid are
NT South East
NU South West
NY East
NZ All except North East
SE All except parts of the West and South East
SK North Central

Site location	Loading
WITHIN hatched area and at altitude of less than 100 m above OD	$1.00\,\text{kN/m}^2$
OUTSIDE hatched area:	
altitude of less than 100 m above OD	$0.75\,\text{kN/m}^2$
altitude between 100 m and 200 m	$1.00\,\text{kN/m}^2$
altitude above 200 m	Refer to BS 6399: Part 3

1 B 10 *Strutting to floor joists*

Joists spanning more than 2.5 m should be strutted with one or more rows of solid or herring bone strutting. Solid strutting should be ≮38 mm thickness extending to at least ¾ of the joist depth. Herring bone strutting should be <38 mm × 38 mm. Where the distance between the joists is greater than three times the depth of the joists herring bone strutting should not be used. (See Table to 1 B10.)

Comment

Clear spans are given to two places of decimals (ie metres and centimetres)

Table to 1 B 10   Strutting to joists

Joist span (m)	No. of rows of strutting
less than 2.5	none
2.5–4.5	1 at mid span
more than 4.5	2 at ⅓ span positions

Readers are referred to Tables A1 to A24 in the Approved Document for the selection of timber sizes (but see below).

Section 1C   Thickness of walls in certain small buildings

1C 1   The section applies to:

(*a*)   Residential buildings up to three storeys;

(*b*)   Small single-storey non-residential buildings;

(*c*)   Small annexes to residential buildings (including garages and outbuildings).

1C 2   Only the following wall types are considered:

1   External walls;

2   Internal loadbearing walls;

3   Compartment and separating walls.

Item (3) does not apply to categories (*b*) and (*c*) above.

1C 3   This section must be used in conjunction with Section 1 A

(*b*)   If the wall thickness is to be determined by using 1C 4 to 1C 13 'all appropriate design considerations given in this Section should be satisfied'. This is to say that these should not be used separately in conjunction with other data drawn from elsewhere.

(*c*)   Walls should comply with the relevant parts of BS 5628: Part 3 except as regards the conditions in 1C 14 to 1C 39. These are those relating to limiting dimensions, materials, supporting structure etc, which differ from similar recommendations in BS 5628. The essential difference is that the BS gives general recommendations to be used in conjunction with structural calculations, whereas this document supplies a convenient set of rules of thumb which should only be used within the strictly limited conditions set by 1C 1 and 1C 2 above. Here again we have an example of the AD providing a useful design tool.

(*d*)   To allow for the use of such simplified rules the worst combination of circumstances should be used. Some minor departures on the basis of experience or judgement, in respect of a particular aspect of a wall, may be permissible, especially if supported by calculation.

(*e*)   The guidance given in this part is based on the use of three compressive strengths for masonry units, ie bricks 5 N/mm^2; blocks 2.8 N/mm^2; bricks/blocks 7 N/mm^2 (in certain circumstances see Diagram to 1C 22).

Arrangement

In addition to the general clauses above, the Section is divided into the following main sections:

Thickness of walls 1C 4 to 1C 13.

Conditions relating to the building 1C 14 to 1C 17.

Conditions relating to the wall 1C 18 to 1C 38.

External walls of small single-storey buildings and annexes 1C 39.

Thickness of walls

Wall thicknesses

1C 4   May be as specified in 1C 6 to 1C 13 providing the conditions in the remaining paragraphs 1C 14 to 39 are met. This is laid out in a much lengthier and quite unnecessary way in Diagram 3, which is therefore not reproduced.

Bay windows

1C 5   The guidance does not apply to wall sections, including gables, forming parts of bay window structures above ground floor sill level.

Thickness

1C 6   For solid walls in coursed brickwork or blockwork the minima are illustrated in diagram [1.8].

1C 6 **[1.8]** *Thickness of external compartment and separating walls.*

key to min thickness

‖ 190 mm   also no wall to be less than ⅙ th storey height

▮ 290 mm

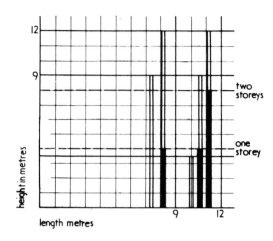

Solid external walls, compartment walls and separating walls, walls of uncoursed stone, flints etc

1C 7   These, including those formed of 'clunches or bricks or other burnt or vitrified material' should be at least 1.33 times the thickness specified in 1C 6.

Cavity walls

1C 8   For cavity external compartment or separating walls the rules illustrated in diagram [1.9] apply.

1C 8 **[1.9]** *Cavity walls.*

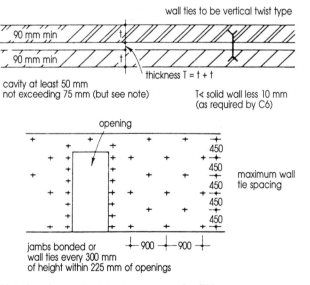

Note that if vertical twist-type ties are used at 750 mm horizontal spacing, the cavity may be up to 100 mm. Also, if courses do not permit, spacing may be varied if the number of ties per unit area is maintained.

Walls providing vertical support to other walls

1C 9   These should never be less in thickness than the supported wall.

Internal loadbearing walls of bricks or blocks

1C 10   These (excluding compartment or separating walls) should have a minimum thicknes of half the thickness specified in 1C 6 less 5 mm, but with a minimum of 140 mm for walls on the lower floor of a three-storey building which carry a load from both upper floors.

Parapet walls

1C 11　　The minimum thickness should be as shown in diagram [1.10].

1C 11　　*Parapet walls – thickness*

	Thickness	Parapet height H to be not more than (mm)
Type A	$t_1 + t_2$ equal to or less than 200	600
	$t_1 + t_2$ greater than 200 equal to or less than 250	860
Type B	$t = 150$	600
	$t = 190$	760
	$t = 215$	860

NOTE　　t should be less than or equal to T.

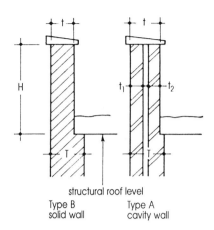

1C 11 **[1.10]** *Parapet walls: thickness.*

structural roof level

Type B
solid wall

Type A
cavity wall

Single leaves of certain external ealls

1C 12　　This says that 'the single leaves of external walls of small non-residential buildings, and of annexes, need only be 90 mm thick, notwithstanding para 1C 39. It has to be assumed that the buildings referred to are those described later under that heading in 1C 14, which defines certain limiting sizes. 1C 39 also deals with the same type of building and makes rules regarding the provision of buttressing walls and piers. This rule seems to be suggesting that these provisions are not needed, in which case why are they there? The only possible interpretation is that the rules are really unchanged but are now confusingly spread out among three separate items each of which has to be interrelated. In other words, such walls may be only 90 mm thick in buildings described in 1C 14(*b*) and (*c*) if limited or supported as described in 1C 39.

Modular bricks and blocks

1C 13　　Where modular units derived from BS 6750: 1986 are used prescribed wall thicknesses may be reduced by an amount not exceeding the deviation from work size allowed by a BS for units of the same material. It may be noted that the reduction of 10 mm in minimum thicknesses from round figures (300 to 290, 200 to 190 etc) made some time ago assisted in the use of modular systems.

Conditions relating to the building

Size

1C 14　　Limitations on the height and proportions of buildings are shown in diagram [1.11] subject to the limits of 1C 17.

Maximum floor areas

1C 15　　These are limited as shown in diagram [1.12].

Imposed loads

1C 16　　These must not exceed the following:

	Distributed		Concentrated
Floors above ground storey	$2.0 \, kN/m^2$		
Roofs – spans not exceeding 12 m	$1.00 \, kN/m^2$		
Ceilings – spans not exceeding 6 m	$0.25 \, kN/m^2$	plus	$0.9 \, kN$
	$1.5 \, kN/m^2$		

The guidance in Part C of Approved Document A is intended to be adequate where the design wind speed is no greater than 44 m/s determined in accordance with CP3 Chapter V: Part 2: 1972.

Design wind speed (V_s)

1C 14 **[1.11]** *Limits on size and proportion of buildings.*

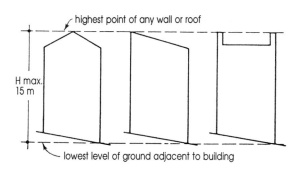

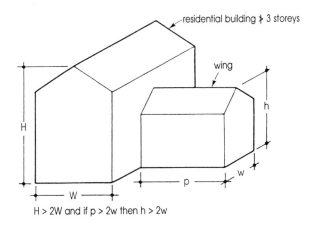

H > 2W and if p > 2w then h > 2w

(a) Residential buildings

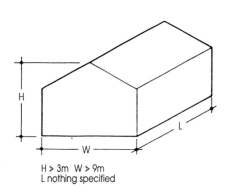

H > 3m W > 9m
L nothing specified

(b) Small single storey non residential buildings

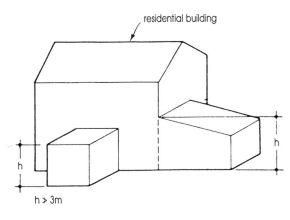

h > 3m

(c) Annexes

1C 15 **[1.12]** *Sizes of subdivisions.*

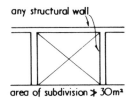

area of subdivision > 30m²

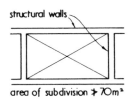

area of subdivision > 70m²

1C 17

V_s is the result of multiplying the basic wind speed (taken from the map in CP3: Chap V: part 2: 1972) by three factors thus:

$$V_s = V \times S_1 \times S_2 \times S_3 \text{ where:}$$

S_1 is the topography factor and is nearly always taken as 1.0.
S_2 covers a number of circumstances (ground roughness, building size etc). A class B size building is to be assumed, which in effect means allowing for a 5 second gust duration. Allowance must also be made for locations near the edge of a cliff or escarpment.

S_3, the probability factor, is to be taken as not less than 1.0. In practice, apart from assessing loads during construction, it never is, nor is it often taken as more than 1.0.

Tables have now been included in the Approved Document of maximum building heights correlated to this value of V_s for various site exposure conditions and basic wind speeds.

The map from CP3 is also included and is reproduced in diagram [1.13].

1C 17 **[1.13]** *Map showing basic wind speeds in m/s.*

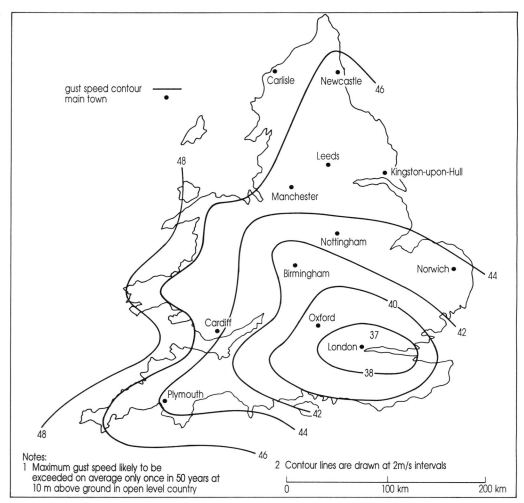

Table   Maximum heights of buildings (metres)

Basic wind speed (m/s)	*Location*			
	Unprotected sites in open countryside with no obstructions	*Open countryside with scattered windbreaks*	*Country with many windbreaks, small towns, outskirts of large cities*	*Protected sites, city centres*
36	15 (8)	15 (11)	15 (15)	15 (15)
38	15 (6)	15 (9)	15 (15)	15 (15)
40	15 (4)	15 (7.5)	15 (14)	15 (15)
42	15 (3)	15 (6)	15 (12)	15 (15)
44	15 0*	15 (5)	15 (10)	15 (15)
46	11 0*	15 (4)	15 (8)	15 (15)
48	9 0*	11 (3)	15 (6.5)	15 (14)

The figures in the left-hand side of the column are for buildings on normal level or slightly sloping sites.

The figures in parentheses are for buildings on steeply sloping sites, including hill, cliff and escarpment sites.

* Part C Guidance is not applicable

NOTE   1A 3 states that provided the specified structural recommendations are met, no special provision should be needed for wind loads.

Conditions relating to the wall

Dimensions and measurement

1C 18/19   The Part does not deal with walls longer or higher than 12 m. Lengths are measured centre to centre of supports (buttressing walls etc). Heights are measured as shown in diagram [1.14].

1C 19 **[1.14]** *Wall and storey heights.*

Key

(a) Measuring storey heights.

A   *is the ground storey height if the ground floor is a suspended timber floor or a structurally separate ground floor slab*

A₁   *is the ground storey height if the ground floor is a suspended concrete floor bearing on the external wall*

B   *is the intermediate storey height*

B₁   *is the top storey height for walls which do not include a gable*

C   *is the top storey height where lateral support is given to the gable at both ceiling level and along the roof slope*

D   *is the top storey height for walls which include a gable where lateral support is given to the gable only along the roof slope*

(b) Measuring wall heights

H₁   *is the height of a wall that does not include a gable*

H₂   *is the height of an internal compartment or separating wall which may extend up to the underside of the roof*

H₃   *is the height of a wall (except a compartment of separating wall) which includes a gable. If the parapet height is more than 1.2 m add the height to H₁*

NOTE   In 1C 11 parapet walls are limited to 860 mm high

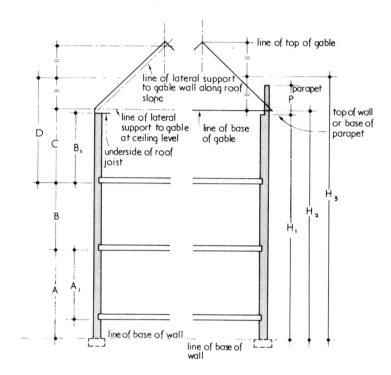

Wall ties

1C 20   These should comply with BS 1243: 1978 (or other not less suitable). In severe exposure conditions austenitic stainless steel or non-ferrous ties are to be used. Refer to BS 5628: Part 3 for definition of 'severe exposure'. (BS 5628 gives a table and graph of exposure categories using a 'local spell index' which is based on meteorological data to show the maximum quantity of wind driven rain falling on vertical surfaces during the worst likely spell of bad weather.)

Brick and block construction

1C 21   Walls should be properly bonded and solidly put together in mortar using:

(*a*)   Clay bricks or blocks to BS 3921: 1974 or BS 6649: 1985, or

(*b*)   Calcium silicate bricks to BS 187: 1978 or BS 6649: 1985, or

(*c*)   Concrete bricks or blocks to BS 6073: Part 1: 1981, or

(*d*)   Square dressed natural stone to relevant parts of BS 5390.

Compressive strength of bricks and blocks

1C 22   The provisions vary according to the location within the building. The strengths, when tested in accordance with the appropriate BS, should be at least those in diagram [1.15].

Mortar

1C 23   Mortar should be:

(*a*)   To the proportions given in BS 5628: Part 1: 1978 designation (iii) or 1:1:6 cement/lime/fine aggregate by volume dry, or

(*b*)   Of equivalent or, if appropriate, greater strength which is compatible with the masonry units and situation.

1C 22 **[1.15]** *Compressive strength of bricks and blocks.*
NOTES
1 *If* H_s *is not greater than 2.7 m, the compressive strength of bricks or blocks should be used in walls as indicated by the key.*
2 *If* H_s *is greater than 2.7 m, bricks or blocks with a compressive strength of at least 7 N/mm² should be used.*
3 *If the external wall is solid construction, the bricks or blocks should have a compressive strength of at least that shown for the internal leaf of a cavity wall in the same position.*
4 *The guidance shown here should only be used to determine the compressive strength of brick and block units for walls of two- and three-storey buildings where the roof construction is of timber.*

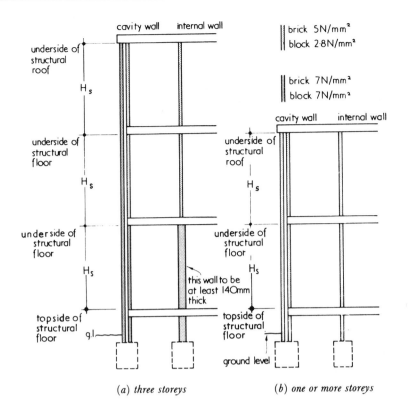

(a) three storeys   *(b) one or more storeys*

Maximum spans of floors
1C 24   These should not exceed 6 m measured centre to centre of bearings (not clear span as used in Section 1B). The sketch illustrating this in the Approved Document is reproduced here as diagram [1.16].
NOTE It is usual for joists built in to bear on the full thickness of the inner leaf and for joist hangers illustrated in BS 5628: Part 1: 1978 as suitable for forming floor-to-wall connections to do the same, being also bent over to provide some effectiveness in tension.

1C 24 **[1.16]** *Span of floors.*

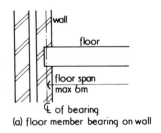

(a) floor member bearing on wall

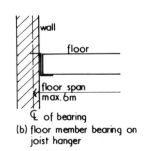

(b) floor member bearing on joist hanger

Other loading conditions
1C 25   Vertical loading on walls should be distributed. This can be assumed for concrete floor slabs, precast or in-situ and timber floors complying with Section 1B. For lintels over 1200 mm span, 150 mm bearing is required, if less 100 mm.
The combined dead and imposed loads at the base of the wall should not exceed 70 kN/m run. Walls should not be subject to any lateral loads, other than from wind or a limited difference in levels of ground or fill at each side: see diagram [1.17].

Buttressing walls, piers and chimneys
1C 26/27/28   The length of a wall, which is limited to 12 m, is measured from centre to centre of end and intermediate supports, which can take the form of buttressing walls, piers or chimneys. These should be provided at each end whatever the length (but see 1C 39 for exception) and in all cases the supports must extend from the base to the full height of the supported wall. Diagrams [1.18] and [1.19] show the criteria for the design of these supports.

1C 25 **[1.17]** *Loading conditions.*

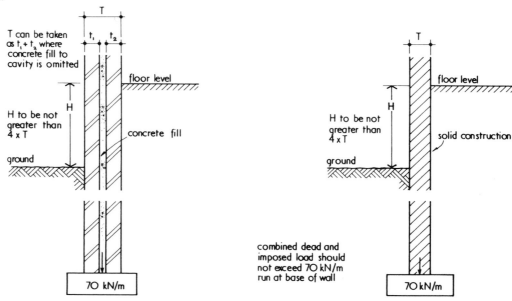

T can be taken
as $t_1 + t_2$ where
concrete fill to
cavity is omitted

floor level

H to be not
greater than
4 x T

ground

concrete fill

70 kN/m

floor level

H to be not
greater than
4 x T

ground

solid construction

combined dead and
imposed load should
not exceed 70 kN/m
run at base of wall

70 kN/m

1C 27 **[1.18]** *Buttressing walls, openings.*

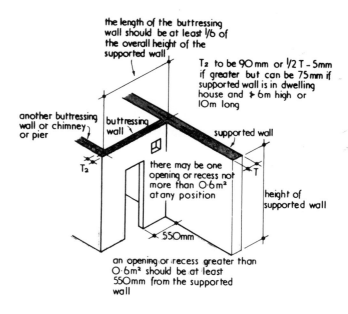

the length of the buttressing
wall should be at least 1/6 of
the overall height of the
supported wall

T_2 to be 90 mm or 1/2 T – 5mm
if greater but can be 75mm if
supported wall is in dwelling
house and ≯ 6m high or
10m long

another buttressing
wall or chimney
or pier

buttressing
wall

supported wall

T_2

there may be one
opening or recess not
more than 0·6 m² at
any position

T

height of
supported wall

550mm

an opening or recess greater than
0·6 m² should be at least
550mm from the supported
wall

NOTES

1   *The buttressing wall should be bonded or securely
   tied to the supported wall and at the other end to a
   buttressing wall, pier or chimney.*

2   *Openings or recesses in the buttressing wall should
   be as shown – the position and shape of the
   openings should not impair the lateral support
   given by the buttressing wall.*

3   *Buttressing walls may themselves be supported
   walls.*

4   *Refer to diagram [1.14] for the rules for
   measuring the height of the supported wall.*

1C 28 **[1.19]** *Buttressing piers and chimneys.*
*The plan area of solid material in a chimney should be
at least equal to that required for a pier.*

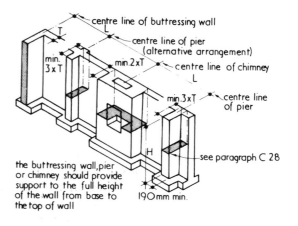

centre line of buttressing wall

centre line of pier
(alternative arrangement)

T

min.
3 x T

min. 2 x T

centre line of chimney

L

min. 3 x T

centre line
of pier

H

see paragraph C 28

the buttressing wall, pier
or chimney should provide
support to the full height
of the wall from base to
the top of wall

190mm min.

Comment

The diagram to 1C 28 shows a depth requirement of only $2 \times T$ for a chimney (including the wall) against $3 \times T$ for a pier. It is questionable whether this makes sense structurally.

Openings and recesses

1C 29/30   The general rule is that the number, size and position of these must not impair the stability of a wall, or the lateral support afforded by a butressing wall: rules about the latter are in 1C 27. Construction above openings must be adequately supported. Specific criteria are given in diagram [1.20]. (NOTE No distinction is made between openings and recesses whatever the depth.)

1C 30 **[1.20]** *Dimensional criteria for openings and recesses.*

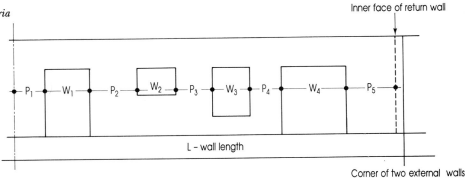

$W_1 + W_2 + W_3 \not> \frac{2L}{3}$

W_1 or W_2 or $W_3 \not> 3\text{m}$

$P_1 \geq \dfrac{W_1}{X}$

$P_2 \geq \dfrac{W_1 + W_2}{X}$

$P_3 \geq \dfrac{W_2 + W_3}{X}$

$P_4 \geq \dfrac{W_3}{X}$

P_5 should be greater than or equal to $\dfrac{W_4}{X}$ but should not be less than 385 mm

value of X is usually 6 but for exceptions see below

Value of X where less than 6

Nature of roof span	Wall or inner leaf min. thickness	Span of floor into wall – max.			
		Timber		*Concrete*	
		4.5 m	*6.0 m*	*4.5 m*	*6.0 m*
Timber into wall	100 mm	6	5	4	3
max 9 m	90 mm	4	4	3	3

NOTES

(a)   *Where roof span is parallel to wall X = 6 except if a concrete floor over 4.5 m spans into wall, when it is 5.*

(b)   *When floor spans are parallel to wall value of X is always 6.*

(c)   *If compressive strength of bricks or blocks is at least 7 N/mm² value of X is always 6.*

Chases

1C 31   The number and position of chases must not be such as to impair stability particularly where hollow blocks are used.

There are limitations as to the depth of vertical and horizontal chases, shown in diagram [1.21]. It is interesting to note that the limitation for horizontal chases if applied to the walls of domestic buildings with 75 mm inner leaf means that such chases are restricted to only 12.5 mm in depth. Clearly, this rule could easily be broken on most domestic work.

1C 31 **[1.21]** *Chases.*

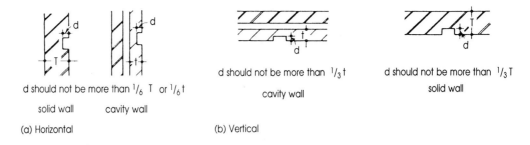

d should not be more than $\frac{1}{6}$ T or $\frac{1}{6}$ t

solid wall   cavity wall

(a) Horizontal

d should not be more than $\frac{1}{3}$ t

cavity wall

d should not be more than $\frac{1}{3}$ T

solid wall

(b) Vertical

Overhangs

1C 32   The amount of any projection should not impair the stability of the wall. This is not very helpful, but there is more guidance in BS 5628: Part 3.

Lateral support by roofs and floors

1C 33/34   Walls should extend the full height of each storey and have lateral supports to restrict movement at right angles, as shown in diagram [1.22].

1C 33/34 **[1.22]** *Floor lateral support and roof lateral support. Connections (c) must be adequate to transmit lateral forces (see* 1C 36, 1C 37*).*

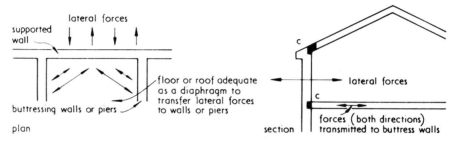

supported wall

lateral forces

buttressing walls or piers

floor or roof adequate as a diaphragm to transfer lateral forces to walls or piers

plan

c

c

lateral forces

forces (both directions) transmitted to buttress walls

section

1C 35   The requirements apply to external, compartment or separating walls at every junction with every floor or roof (but not applicable in the case of floors only if the wall is less than 3 m long), also to internal loadbearing walls at the top of each storey.

NOTE   This rule appears more onerous for internal loadbearing walls below 3 m in length than for external, separating or compartment walls. This is presumably because such walls may be thinner (see 1C 10).

1C 36   Generally, walls should be strapped to all floors above ground level using galvanised mild steel straps 30 × 5 mm cross section. This does not include a suspended ground floor, since the height of a ground storey is taken from foundation level. In a considerable number of cases they are not essential. These are illustrated in diagram [1.23].

1C 36 **[1.23]** *Situations where strapping to floors is not required.*

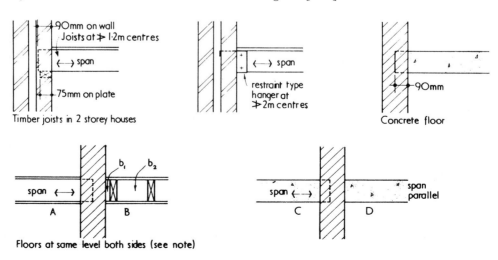

90mm on wall
Joists at $\not>$ 1.2m centres

span

75mm on plate

Timber joists in 2 storey houses

span

restraint type hanger at $\not>$ 2m centres

90mm

Concrete floor

span

b_1 b_2

A   B

Floors at same level both sides (see note)

span

C   D

span parallel

NOTE   Where floors abut on both sides contact should be continuous (eg concrete) or at not more than 2 m intervals. This suggests that in Type B blocking would be needed at b_1 and probably also at b_2, but no   *advice is given. Floors at each side to be about the same level and where contact is intermittent the points of contact should be in line (or almost so).*

Where strapping is required the arrangement should be as indicated in diagram [1.24].
1C 37   Gable walls should be strapped to roofs as indicated in diagram [1.25 (*a*) and (*b*)] which are lateral connections. 1C 37 also requires vertical strapping at eaves level, except where the construction is as shown in (*c*). This in fact will probably cover the majority of cases.

1C 36 **[1.24]** *Strapping.*

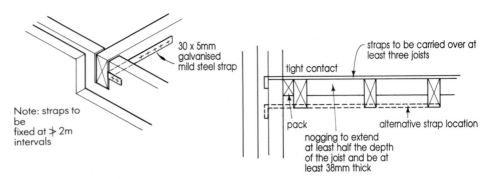

1C 37 **[1.25]** *Wall-to-roof connections.*

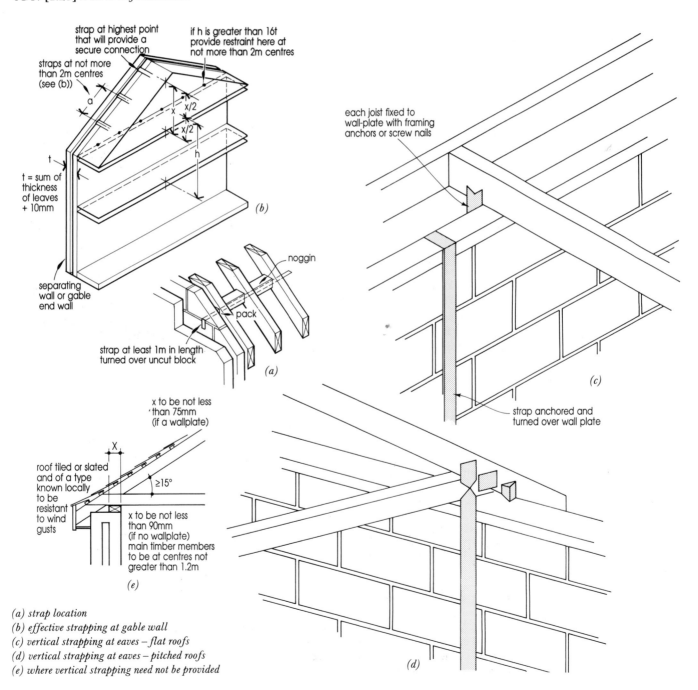

(a) *strap location*
(b) *effective strapping at gable wall*
(c) *vertical strapping at eaves – flat roofs*
(d) *vertical strapping at eaves – pitched roofs*
(e) *where vertical strapping need not be provided*

Comment

The object of strapping in the context of this Section is to ensure interaction between wall and floor or roof in order to provide lateral bracing to the wall. Vertical strapping usually has a different function in preventing roofs from being lifted by wind suction when their self-weight is insufficient, such straps being usually taken down to a joint five or six courses down the wall. This would not necessarily contribute anything to the lateral stiffness of the wall. However, BS 5628: Part 3 does show a vertical strap detail for a flat joisted roof using a twisted strap to connect joist to wall.

Interruption of lateral support

1C 38 An opening for a stairway or the like is permitted adjacent to a supported wall under the circumstances illustrated in diagram [1.26].

1C 38 **[1.26]** *Interruption of lateral support.*

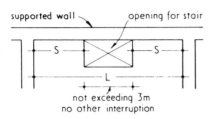

NOTE
Where anchors are not used the conditions along the supported length (S) should be as normal. Where anchors are used the spacing of anchors along the lengths (S) should be reduced to result in the same number as would have been used if full length (L) had been available.

Small single-storey non-residential buildings

1C 39 These are the buildings illustrated in 1C 14 (*b*) and (*c*). They may have single-leaf external walls of bricks or blocks of 90 mm minimum thickness if not subjected to any load apart from the roof and wind loads. They are limited to 2.5 m in length and height unless bonded to piers or buttressing walls as in diagram [1.24] (see also 1C 12) and can only be used where the floor area enclosed does not exceed 36 m².

1C 39 **[1.27]** *Buttressing to single-leaf walls.*

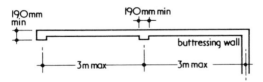

NOTE
The new size limitation on floor area where these walls may be used.

Section 1D Chimney stacks

Application. This is not restricted in the same way as Sections 1B and 1C but 0.2 (a) at the beginning of the document states that Section 1 'is relevant to small buildings of traditional masonry construction', which in the case of Sections 1D and 1E includes buildings of any purpose group.

Where these are not adequately supported by ties or otherwise securely restrained the dimensions are limited as shown in diagram [1.28].

Section 1D **[1.28]** *Chimney stacks. The density of the masonry should be greater than 1500 kg/m³.*

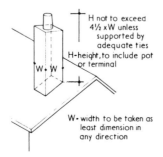

Section 1E   Strip foundations of plain concrete

Application. This also applies to small buildings of any purpose group. This specifies widths and depths of simple strip foundations in relation to loading and type of ground, under the following conditions.

The ground

1E 1

(*a*)   There should be no made ground or wide variation of subsoil type in the loaded area.

(*b*)   No weaker type of soil below the foundation subsoil at a depth which could impair stability.

Design of foundations (diagram [1.29])

1E 2

(*a*)   They should be centrally placed below walls.

(*b*)   They should have minimum widths as shown in diagram [1.30].

(*c*)   Where they are to be laid in chemically aggressive soil conditions, guidance in BS 5328:

1E 2 **[1.29]** *Foundation design.*

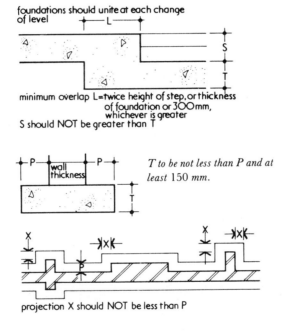

foundations should unite at each change of level

minimum overlap L=twice height of step, or thickness of foundation or 300 mm, whichever is greater

S should NOT be greater than T

T to be not less than P and at least 150 mm.

projection X should NOT be less than P

[1.30] *Foundation dimensions.*

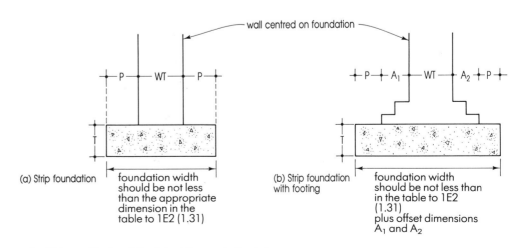

wall centred on foundation

(a) Strip foundation   foundation width should be not less than the appropriate dimension in the table to 1E2 (1.31)

(b) Strip foundation with footing   foundation width should be not less than in the table to 1E2 (1.31) plus offset dimensions A_1 and A_2

The thickness of the foundation T should be equal either to P or 150 mm whichever is greater

Part 1 should be followed. In non-aggressive soils –
Concrete should be of cement to BS 12: 1989
Fine and coarse aggregate to BS 882: 1983
and the mix should be one of 50 g cement: 0.1 m³ fine aggregate: 0.2 m³ coarse aggregate or
Grade ST 1 to BS 5328: Part 2.
(*d*)   The minimum thickness should be 150 mm, or thicker by reference to the Table to
diagrams [1.30] and [1.31],
(*e*)(*f*)   Stepped foundations should overlap as shown [1.29],
(*g*)   Foundations to piers, chimneys etc should project the same distance as for the wall
[1.29].

Minimum widths of strip foundations
1E3   Subject to 1E1 and 1E2 the recommended widths in the table may be used. The table
has been converted into illustrations [1.31] which show the effect of the rules on width and
depth for walls of four thicknesses. Since various masonry units may be used, these have been
chosen to represent walls built up of 100 mm wide units with 10 mm joints or 50 mm cavities.

Comment
As Sections D and E form part of Section 1, they are relevant only to the classes of buildings
described at the beginning (see 0.2).
This is another of those parts which is a handy design tool.

1E 2 **[1.31]** *Foundation dimensions for different
loadings and subsoils.*

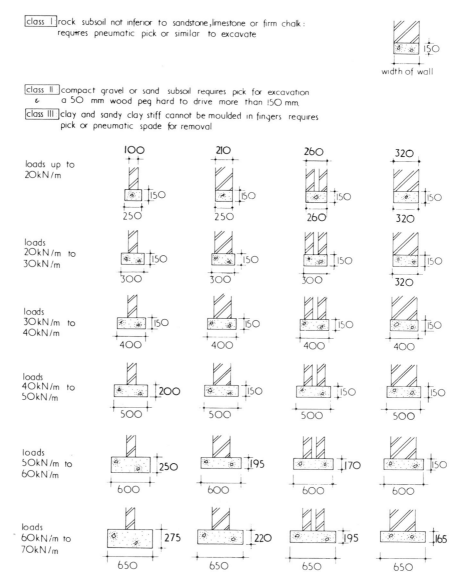

[1.31] *(continued)*

class IV clay or sandy clay, firm : can be moulded by substantial pressure with fingers.
can be excavated with graft or spade

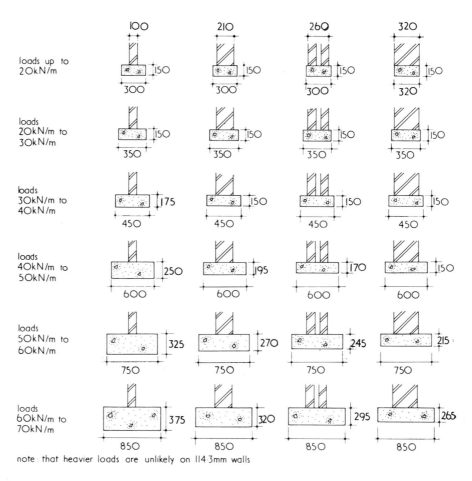

note : that heavier loads are unlikely on 114·3mm walls

class V sand, silty sand, clayey sand, (loose)
can be excavated with spade, 50mm square wood peg can easily be driven in

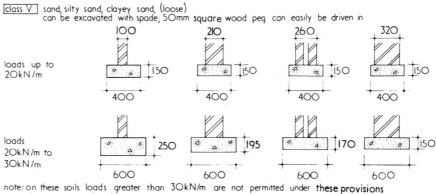

note : on these soils loads greater than 30kN/m are not permitted under these provisions

class VI silt, clay, sandy clay, silty clay (soft)
fairly easily moulded in fingers and readily excavated

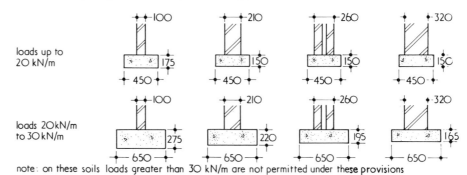

note : on these soils loads greater than 30 kN/m are not permitted under these provisions

[1.31] *(concluded)*

class VII silt, clay, sandy clay, silty clay (very soft)
natural sample in winter conditions exudes between fingers when squeezed in fist

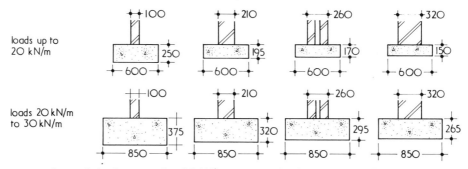

loads up to 20 kN/m

loads 20 kN/m to 30 kN/m

note: on these soils loads greater than 30 kN/m are not permitted under these provisions

---

Note on BS 5628 – CP for structural use of masonry

There are three parts of which only Parts 1 and 3 are referred to.

Part 1: 1978 Unreinforced masonry

This replaces CP 111: 1970 which is withdrawn. It makes use of the 'limit state' philosophy of design (see Section 2), employing partial safety factors and containing guidance on resistance to lateral loading, as well as the limitation of the effects of accidental damage.

It covers the design of unreinforced masonry of bricks, blocks, square dressed natural stone and random rubble.

It assumes that the design will be entrusted to 'chartered structural or civil engineers, or other appropriately qualified persons'.

The contents include sections on:

Materials, components and workmanship.

Design objectives and general recommendations, which deal with stability, loads, partial safety factors and strengths of masonry in compression, shear and flexure.

Detailed design, including slenderness ratios, eccentricity, vertical loads, shear stresses, bearing and lateral loads and accidental damage.

There is a useful appendix on floor connections using metal anchors and joist hangers.

Part 3: 1985 Materials and components, design and workmanship

This covers a different field from Part 1, being concerned primarily with the effectiveness of masonry walls in relation to weather penetration, durability, fire resistance, insulation of heat and sound, as well as structural soundness.

It contains a wealth of useful information, well illustrated where appropriate on the detailing of masonry construction, as well as sections on materials and workmanship on site. Thermal and moisture movement are also well covered and although structural design is left largely for Part 1, there are some useful guidelines which can be applied to small structures without requiring specialist knowledge. It replaces CP 121: Part 1: 1973, which is withdrawn.

Section 2   External wall cladding

2.1   This is a new section giving guidance on the support and fixing of external wall cladding. The type of cladding with which this Section is concerned is that which, because of its weight or height, would present a hazard if it fell from a building. Depending on the type and location of the cladding, an accepted standard can be achieved by different standards of provision. The guidance relates mainly to the heavier forms of cladding such as concrete but some guidance also applies to curtain walling.

2.2   Weather resistance of the cladding is not dealt with here but is in Approved Document C 4.

2.3   Wall cladding will meet the requirements of A 1/2 if:

(*a*)   It will safely sustain and transmit to the structure all dead, imposed and wind loading.

(*b*)   It is securely fixed to and supported by the structure of the building and both vertical and lateral supports are needed.

(*c*)   Provision is made for differential movement.

(Both the cladding and its fixings (including the supports) are durable and the life of the fixings is not less than the cladding. Where the fixings cannot readily be inspected or maintained, particular care will be needed (see Approved Document for Regulation 7).)

Technical approach

Wind loading

2.4   Take from CP3 Chapter V: Part 2: 1972

Class A building size for determining S 2

S 3 should never be less than 1

2.5/2.7   Other forces which should be taken into account are those from –

Ladders and access cradles likely to be used

Support given by the cladding to signboards etc.

Additional imposed loading of cladding if to act as a vehicular barrier or pedestrian guarding to a staircase, ramp etc.

See AD K 2/3.

2.8   In sports stadia where the cladding is required to withstand lateral pressure for crowds, design loading should be based on the Home Office *Guide to Safety at Sports Grounds 1990*.

Fixings

2.9   Strength of fixings should be taken from tests using similar materials to the anchoring material but weaknesses which may affect the fixing such as cracks in concrete due to shrinkage, flexure or voids in masonry construction should also be considered.

The standards and references which should be used are:

BS 5080: *Methods of test for structural fixings in concrete and masonry* Part 1: 1974 and Part 2: 1986, or British Board of Agrément MOAT No. 19: 1981 *The assessment of torque expanded anchor bolts when used in dense aggregate concrete.*

2.10/2.12   The safe working shear and tensile loads should be:

Expanded bolt type fixings

Not more than the lower of:

(*i*)   (the mean shear or tensile failure test load less three times the standard deviation derived from the tests) × 1/3

(*ii*)   the mean of the loads which cause a displacement of 0.1 mm under direct tension and 1 mm under direct shear.

Resin bonded fixings

(*i*)   (the mean shear of tensile failure test load less three times the standard deviation derived from the tests) × 1/3

Certain resin-bonded fixings develop a rapid loss of strength at temperatures above 50°C and this should be taken into account.

2.13   Component parts of mechanical fixings and supports should be lockable or be mechanically fixed together to prevent slippage.

2.14   Eccentricity in imposed loadings should be allowed for, and in such circumstances the possibility of local spalling in which the fixing is anchored should also be allowed for. An increase in eccentricity equal to 0.5 of the diameter of the fixing should be assumed.

Movement

2.15   Guidance on the means of providing for the differential movement of the wall cladding and the supporting structure of the building is given in BS 8200: 1985 and BS 5628: Part 3: 1985.

2.16   Information with regard to the support and fixing of external wall cladding which will meet the requirements of A 1/2 can be found in:

CP3 Chapter V: Part 2: 1972 regarding loading (the factor S 3 should not be taken as less than 1), and

provided the guidance for fixings in paragraphs 2.9–2.14 of this Sectioon has been followed, Clause 38 of BS 8200: 1985

Clauses 6 and 20 of BS 8298: 1989.

Section 3 Re-covering of roofs

It has been a matter of debate in some areas whether re-covering of roofs constituted a material alteration for the purposes of Regulation 3(2)(a). Where roof coverings are replaced with heavier or lighter weight materials than the original covering the loading on the structure will obviously change.

A recommended procedure is set out in the Approved Document and this includes –

(a)　　Compare the proposed imposed roof loading with the original loading. (Allow for water absorption – eg 0.3% for oven-dry slates and up to 10.5% for clay and concrete tiles based on the dry mass per unit area of the existing and new materials.)

(b)　　Arrange for an inspection of the roof structure to be made and check whether:

(i) the roof structure is capable of sustaining the increased load,

(ii) if a lighter material is to be used whether the vertical restraint will be adequate for the wind uplift which may result,

(c)　　Provide appropriate strengthening measures including:

(i) replacing defective timber, fixings and vertical restraints;

(ii) provision of additional structural members as may be found necessary;

(iii) providing restraining straps etc to resist wind uplift.

NOTE It is not expected that a full structural survey will be required in every instance. Carried out practically, this guidance will be satisfactory.

Section 4 Codes, Standards and references

Loading	The CP3: Chapter V series of Codes of Practice on loading are being superseded by BS 6399 *Loading for buildings* BS 6399: Part 1: 1984 *Code of Practice for dead and imposed loads* 　　　　　Part 2　　*Code of Practice for wind loads* 　　　　　Part 3: 1988 *Code of Practice for imposed roof loads.* Part 2 had not been completed when the new AD was published and for wind loads reference should still be made to CP3: Ch. V: Part 2: 1972. See notes on these Codes on the following pages.
Foundations – general	BS 8004: 1986
Structural work of reinforced, prestressed or plain concrete	BS 8110: Parts 1, 2 and 3: 1985
Structural work of steel	BS 5950: Part 1: 1990 or BS 449: Part 2: 1969 BS 5950: Part 2: 1985 BS 5950: Part 4: 1982 BS 5950: Part 5: 1987 NOTE BS 5950 was first published in August 1985. As, however, the BSI has not yet withdrawn BS 449: Part 2: 1969 the reference to this code is not being deleted at this stage.
Structural work of aluminium	CP 118: 1969 using one of the principal or supplementary aluminium alloys designated in Section 1.1 of that code, and for the purpose of Section 5.3 of that code, the structure should be classified as a safe-life structure.
Structural work of masonry	BS 5628: Part 1: 1978 BS 5628: Part 2: 1985

Structural work of timber   BS 5268: Part 2: 1984
BS 5268: Part 3: 1985
BS 5268: Part 6: 1988

References related to Requirement A2 – Ground Movement

4.9   Before proceeding with the design of a building or its foundations known and/or recorded conditions of ground instability, such as faults, landslides or unstable strata, disused mines etc should be taken into account. This information is not always readily available, and this reference draws attention to a series of national reviews of geotechnical conditions carried out for the Minerals and Land Reclamation Division of the Planning Services Directorate of the DoE.

They include county maps and databases and give a general picture of the scale and nature of geotechnical problems and how they may be overcome.

The reviews were:

Review of research into landsliding in Great Britain
Review of mining instability in Great Britain
Review of natural underground cavities in Great Britain
Review of foundation conditions in Great Britain

Contact DPS/2 DoE Room C15/19, 2 Marsham St, London SW1 3EB for availability of these publications.

Appraisal of existing buildings

4.10   One of the major changes in the main regulations is that compliance with Part A is now required in certain cases of 'change of use'. It was previously considered to be too onerous if existing buildings had to be appraised before a change of use could take place. Many architects and designers have always carried out their own assessment of the condition of such buildings but this is now mandatory.

Guidance on structural appraisal is given in

(1)   BRE Digest *Appraisal of Existing Buildings for Change of Use*

(2)   Institution of Structural Engineers Report, *Appraisal of existing structures*. In this Report, in the recommendations for design checks, the choice of partial factors should be made to suit the individual circumstances of each case. For BS Codes and Standards quoted in the Report use the latest version referred to in the AD.

Note on British Standards

As new standards are published, the old ones are phased out, a two-year overlap being allowed for changeover. Apart from those referred to, there are other new standards in the pipeline, but they are not mentioned unless an estimated publication date has been given.

Note also that the old procedure of classifying BSI documents as either British Standard Specifications (coded BS no.) or British Standard Codes of Practice (coded CP no.) has been abandoned and all are now given a BS number, regardless of content. Occasional reference may also be seen to DD numbers, which stands for 'Draft for Development'.

Note on limit state design

Over the past two decades there has been a complete revision of the general approach to structural design in all media. This started in concrete with the proposed redrafting of CPs 114, 115 and 116 (reinforced, precast and prestressed concrete). Guidance became available in the recommendations of the European Concrete Committee published in 1964, which introduced the concept of 'limit states' as opposed to 'single failure' as design criteria.

In this concept, consideration is given to serviceability at all stages of structural behaviour: ie elastic, plastic, cracked and ultimate. Three limit states are normally considered: ultimate strength and the serviceability limit states of deflection and cracking under service loads. Design figures are used which make the chance of reaching the limit state of ultimate strength more remote than those for the two other criteria. The aim of limit state design is that the chance of each limit state being reached is substantially constant for all members in a structure, as appropriate to their situation. Thus is it unlikely the structure will become unfit for use. The method, as distinct from the earlier design load/elastic theory, employs a load factor rather than a stress safety factor. In elastic theory the loads used are the actual loads and the design stresses are the ultimate stresses divided by a factor of safety. In the load factor method, the loads are actual loads multiplied by a load factor, and the stresses are the actual ultimate design stresses. The use of both methods in the same design is prohibited. Lack of statistics has prevented a design method in *complete* accord with the probability theory, but the use of partial safety factor for both loads and stresses had enabled development of a design system which ensures acceptable probability that limit states will not be reached.

This led to the production of CP 110: 1972 which was in general use until its revision, BS 8110: Parts 1, 2 and 3, was published.

Similar changes have been taking place in other fields, and the BSS on structural work of steel and masonry use limit state theory and partial safety factors. BS 5628 for timber does not.

BS 6399: Part 1: 1984 Code of Practice for dead and imposed loads

This Part gives dead and minimum recommended imposed loads for use in designing buildings. It covers:

(*a*)   New buildings and structures.

(*b*)   Alterations and additions to existing buildings and structures.

(*c*)   Existing construction on change of use.

It is, however, *not* applicable to maintenance or replacement of parts where there is no change of use.

Where the actual load is known to be greater than the design loads given in Part 1, the actual load should be used.

The code does not cover:

1 Loads on bridges (see other BS, eg BS 5400).
2 Wind loads (CP3: Ch. V: Part 2).
3 Imposed roof loads ⎱ BS 6399: Part 3.
4 Snow loads ⎰
5 Internal pressure loads (eg bunkers, silos, tanks).
6 Machinery vibration (except some gantry cranes – see later).
7 Loads due to lifts (see BS 2655).
8 Incidental construction loads.
9 Test loads.
10 Accidental loads.

Dead loads

Dead loads are calculated from the unit weights given in BS 648 *Schedule of weights of building materials.*

Partitions

Where these are indicated on plans their weight should be included in the dead loading. Where not so indicated partitions are now considered as imposed loads.

Tanks, receptacles, etc.

The weight of tanks or other receptacles are considered as dead loads and account must be taken of both full and empty conditions in assessing their effect.

Clause 4 Imposed floor loads

The loads appropriate to different uses are split into eight tables, 5 to 12, covering all normal types of building including a vehicle occupancy (table 12). The tables give a distributed load in kN/m² and a maximum concentrated load for each case. The latter are to be considered as acting where they would produce the maximum stress or maximum deflection, whichever is the limiting factor. They are assumed to be acting on a point (whereas previously a square of 300 mm wide was specified) for bending and shear, but for local effects (punching/crushing) to act over the actual area of application [1.32].

[1.32] *Basis for assessing loads. Use distributed or concentrated load – whichever produces greater stress. Do NOT use both together.*

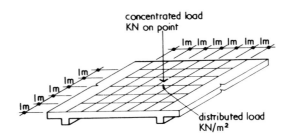

The tables are too extensive to reproduce here. Loads vary from a minimum of $1.5\,kN/m^2$ in dwellings to $20\,kN/m^2$ in foundries. For storage applications a figure per metre of available height is given.

The general recommendations do not apply to atypical usages such as mechanical stacking, plant etc.

For movable partitions the allowance per m^2 is not less than $\frac{1}{3}$ the weight per metre run of partition with a minimum of $1\,kN/m^2$. For office floors the uniformly distributed load should not be less than $1.0\,kN/m^2$.

The distributed loads apply to both slabs and beams. Where no concentrated loads are given, the distributed load is considered an adequate basis for design. Sometimes only concentrated loads are given (eg catwalks – $1\,kN$ at $1\,m$ centres).

[1.33] *Loadings on stairways and landings.*

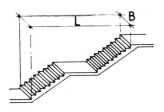

Stairways and landings

The basis of the design is the horizontal area of the stair ($L \times B$). This is not stated in the BS but may be inferred from the general rules applying to the tables [1.33].

Loadings vary according to occupancy and are given in the tables.

Ceilings

For members supporting ceilings, access hatches etc (excluding glazing):

(*a*)   Without access: nil.

(*b*)   With access: $0.25\,kN/m^2$ distributed.
                      $0.9\,kN$ concentrated.

Clause 5 Reduction of imposed loads

When an area of slab ($L \times B$) is supported by a beam reductions in the imposed load for the beam can be made as follows:

exceeding $50\,m^2$	5 per cent
exceeding $100\,m^2$	10 per cent
exceeding $150\,m^2$	15 per cent
exceeding $200\,m^2$	20 per cent
exceeding $250\,m^2$	25 per cent

These are not applicable to roofs except as stated in Clause 4.2 of BS 6399: Part 3. Reductions for intermediate areas may be taken by linear interpolation (diagrams [1.34 and 1.35]).

[1.34, 1.35] *Permissible reduction of imposed loads on beams and vertical supports.*

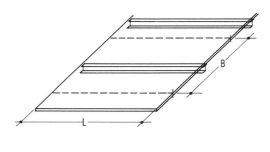

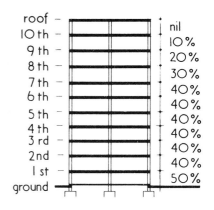

Exceptions

Except as stated below, the reductions shown above can be made in the total calculated imposed load on columns according to the number of floors supported by them.

1   In buildings designed for storage purposes the full load on each floor must be assumed.

2   Where floors are designed for $5\,kN/m^2$ or more the total load calculated in this way must not be less than an average of $5\,kN/m^2$ over the whole area of the building.

3   No reduction shall be made in respect of some areas of office floors (heavy file storage and so on) or buildings used for storage purposes generally.

NOTE   In arriving at column loadings either type of reduction may be used if applicable but both types may *not* be used together on the same member. No reduction shall be made in respect of any fixed plant, machinery or equipment the actual weight of which is specifically allowed for.

Clause 7 Crane gantry girders

The BS gives guidance on allowances to be made in the support system of gantry cranes to cover 'forces set up by vibration, shock from slipping of slings, kinetic action of acceleration and retardation and impact of wheel loads' (diagram [1.36]).

BS 6399: Part 1: Clause 7 **[1.36]** *Gantry cranes.*

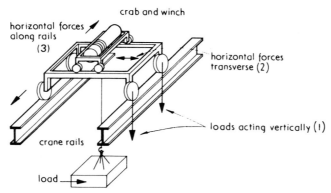

Loads (1) Max static wheel loads increased by 25 per cent for electric crane, 10 per cent for hand crane.
Loads (2) Horizontal force taken as 10 per cent of combined weight of grab and load for electric crane, 5 per cent for hand crane.
Loads (3) Force along rails taken as 5 per cent of static wheel loads whether electric or hand operated.

Forces (2) or (3), but not both, are to be taken as acting simultaneously with force (1). These rules apply only to simple single-gantry cranes. Heavy, high-speed or multiple cranes are to be treated as a special problem. More detailed guidance on crane loading can be found in BS 2573.

Clause 8 Dynamic loading (excluding wind)

The values in the tables allow for small dynamic effects, such as those due to normal movement of people, furniture etc, but not for machinery, fork lift trucks etc, or dynamic loads due to crowds. In such cases, the magnitude of the load effect depends on the response of the structural system, and can be much higher than the normal static load effect. Special design consideration is needed.

Clause 9 Parapets and balustrades

Table 4 gives loads appropriate to the design of parapets and balustrades [1.37].
The loads are expressed as acting horizontally 1.1 m above datum (finished level of platform or pitch of stairs).
Loads are set out relevant to two classes of building – public assembly and all other occupancy classes.
The horizontal UDL per m run is given together with a UDL per m^2 applied to the infill and a point load applied to any part of the infill. (See also Approved Document for K 2/3.)
For design loads in designated stadia (those requiring a safety certificate under the Safety of Sports Grounds Act 1975) reference should be made to the *Green Guide* published by the Home Office.
In addition to a horizontal UDL per m run (as previously) two other figures are given – a UDL per m^2 applied to the infill and a point load applied to any part of the infill (see also Approved Document for K 2/3).

Clause 9 **[1.37]** *Parapets and balustrades.*

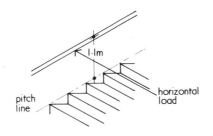

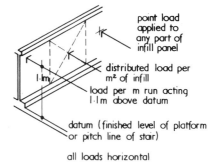

Clause 10 Vehicle barriers for car parks

This section gives a formula for general use, based on vehicle weights etc, and a figure of 150 kN for each 1½ m run for car parks housing cars and light vans up to 2500 kg gross mass. The force is considered as acting horizontally at 375 mm above floor level in this case. For barriers to access ramps the conditions are different, as illustrated in diagram [1.38].

Clause 10 **[1.38]** *Vehicle barriers for car parks (cars and light vans up to 2500 kg gross mass).*

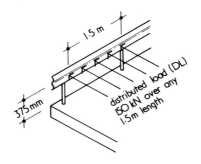

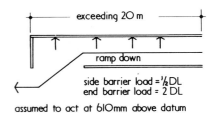

CP 3: Chapter V; Part 2: 1972. Code of practice for wind loads

Although the general policy throughout this guide is to make the necessity for reference back to the Regulations or other publications as infrequent as possible, CP 3: Chapter V: Part 2: 1972 is rather a special case. In the first place, it is due for revision. Secondly, much of the basic design criteria are presented in the form of tables which cannot really be simplified or presented in any better way. This section is, therefore, presented as a general explanation of the principles involved and a description of the method of calculation to be used, with diagrams where appropriate. The reader is, however, referred to the tables in the CP itself when making an assessment of wind forces in a specific case.

The effect of wind

When wind blows against the face of a building it is slowed down, resulting in a build-up of pressure against that face. At the same time, it is deflected and accelerated around the sides and over the roof with a consequent reduction of pressure (ie suction) on those surfaces. A large eddy also forms behind the building, resulting in a negative pressure or suction to the rear wall. The greater the speed at any particular point, the greater will be the resulting suction (diagram [1.39]).

[1.39] *Wind effects.*

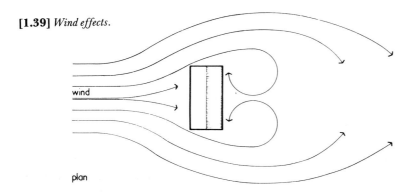

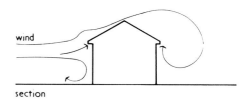

Restricted gaps between or through buildings (eg an open ground storey) can cause higher than normal wind speeds due to the differential pressures on opposite sides of the gap, which in turn results in higher than normal suctions on surfaces facing towards the gap.

The suction on a roof, particularly a low-pitched roof, is frequently the most severe load experienced on any part of the building and may often considerably exceed the dead weight of the structure, requiring firm fixings to prevent it being lifted. Suction or negative pressure will occur even on the windward slope of roofs up to 30° pitch, but roofs of 35° pitch and over usually develop a positive pressure on the windward side. Even then, however, there is a zone near to the ridge where suction occurs and roof coverings may be dislodged. Lee slopes always experience suction. When the wind blows parallel to the ridge, all roofs – regardless of pitch – experience suction, particularly next to the windward gable.

Wind tunnel experiments have shown that external pressures due to the wind vary over the whole surface of the building according to the velocity and direction and the shape and size of the building. These pressures can be shown by means of a contour diagram. Such diagrams would have to be drawn for various wind directions and, since every part of the building has to be designed to resist the forces created by wind from any direction, it is more convenient for practical purposes to make adequate allowances for the increased local pressures which occur at corners and the intersections of surfaces (diagram [1.40]).

[1.40] *Extent of local negative pressures.*

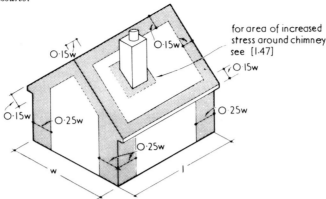

The diagram shows the location of high local pressures. The variation in pressure is expressed for convenience in terms of a coefficient by which the normal dynamic pressure of the wind is multiplied. This can vary between a positive factor of +0.7 in the centre of the windward side and a negative factor of −2.0 near to the windward edges of roofs. Upward positive pressure is generated below the overhangs of roofs and balconies on the windward side. This must be taken into account when assessing the total uplift on a roof, and the intensity is to be taken as the same as that on the adjoining wall surface.

Dynamic pressure of the wind	The forces exerted by the wind on any part of a building may be taken as the product of the dynamic pressure, the area on which it acts, and the coefficient referred to earlier to allow for the situation on the building.

When wind is brought to rest against an obstacle, all its kinetic energy is transformed into dynamic pressure (q) which can be calculated from the formula

$$q = \varrho \frac{V_s^{\,2}}{2}$$

where ϱ = air density
V_s = design wind speed

In SI units the expression becomes

$$q(N/m^2) = 0.613\, V_s^{\,2}\ (m/s)$$

To save calculation, a conversion chart is provided in the CP (Figure 2) from which the pressure q can be directly read off for any relative wind speed (both Imperial and metric units are shown). For greater accuracy or convenience three tables are also provided giving values of q in SI units (N/m^2), metric technical units (kgf/m^2) and Imperial units (lbf/ft^2).

Wind velocity	To enable the pressure to be determined, it is first necessary to establish the appropriate wind velocity to which the building is likely to be subject. This is a complex business bringing in a series of variable factors.

The initial basis for the assessment is a wind speed contour map of the UK (Figure 3 in the CP). Velocities are given in m/s and relate to maximum 3-second gust speed likely to be exceeded, on average, only once in 50 years, measured at 10 m above ground in open level country. They vary from a minimum figure of 38 around the London area to 54/56 in the Orkneys and Hebrides. Generally, the pattern is one of increasing speeds to the north and west. As an example, an average figure of 46/48 occurs in the Border Country, the extreme west of Wales, Cornwall and roughly across the centre of Ulster. This basic wind speed figure is referred to as V.

It has to be adjusted for three factors which are described as:
S1   Local topographic influences.
S2   Surface roughness of the environment, gust duration appropriate to size and the height of the structure.
S3   The design life of the building.
The design wind speed (V_s) can then be calculated from: $V_s = V \times s1 \times s2 \times s3$.

S1 Topography

Height above sea level does not in itself affect wind speed but exposed hills rising well above their surroundings may cause accelerated wind, as also may some valleys so shaped as to cause funnelling of the wind. Conversely, in steep-sided enclosed valleys wind speed may be less than normal.

For all normal sites a factor of 1.0 is recommended, but in cases such as those quoted above, higher or lower values within the range 1.1 to 0.9 may be appropriate. Caution is necessary when using a reducing factor. In extreme cases a value of 1.2 may possibly be justified. If doubt exists the Meteorological Office may be consulted.

S2 Surface roughness, duration of gust, and height of building

This factor really combines three separate considerations which are grouped together simply because their effects can all be represented in a single table (table 3).

Surface roughness
Any strong wind speeds near to the ground are affected by ground roughness, which tends to reduce speed. Four categories are described:
1   Open country with no shelter (eg fens, airfields, moorland, farmland without hedges, coastal fringes, etc). Mean level of obstruction taken as zero.
2   Open country with scattered wind breaks (eg most farmland and country estates, except well-wooded parts. Mean level of obstruction assumed to be 2 m.
3   Country with many wind breaks (eg well-wooded parkland and forest areas, small towns and suburbs). Generally, the top level of obstructions is assumed to be about 10 m. This category includes all built-up areas except those in category 4.
4   Surfaces with large and numerous obstructions (eg the centres of large towns and cities). The general roof height assumed to be about 25 m or more.
Where buildings are sited near to the edge of an area having a particular category, it may be necessary to assume that the adjacent lower category applies – the effect of surface roughness not being instantaneous. The principles are illustrated in diagram [1.41].

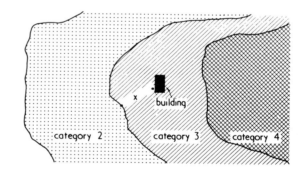

[1.41] *Change in surface roughness.*
x is the shortest distance (in any direction)
Building considered as within Category 2 if x is less than the following
If building is above general level of obstruction
x = 1 km
otherwide depends on ground coverage
          if not less than: 10 per cent: x = 500 m
                              15 per cent: x = 250 m
                              30 per cent: x = 100 m

Gust duration
The maximum wind speed assumed also depends on the length of the gust being considered. The shorter the gust period, the higher will be the average speed over that period. With larger buildings a longer period can be assumed since it is unlikely that the maximum gust effect will be applied to the whole building at once. Three alternatives are given in table 3 to be applied as follows:
3-second gust for all glazing, cladding and roofing. For structural design of the whole building use a 5-second or 15-second gust according to the size, as shown in diagram [1.42]. These are known as Classes A, B and C respectively, as listed in table 3 of the CP.

[1.42] *Gust duration in relation to size.*

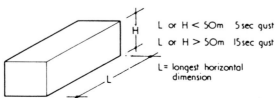

Height

Table 3 also provides a series of values graduated according to the total height of the structure above ground level. When calculating the total overturning effect of the wind, a single wind strength can be assumed relating to the total height of the building. Alternatively, the building may be divided into several parts and advantage taken of the reduced effect on the lower sections. The principles are illustrated in diagram [1.43]. The same rule applies to pitched roofs. Buildings close to a cliff or escarpment need special consideration and the CP provides rules for assessing an effective height to be used in calculations. The method varies according to the angle of the escarpment on which the building is situated, and the principles are illustrated in diagram [1.44].

[1.43] *The S 2 factor: subdivision of height.*

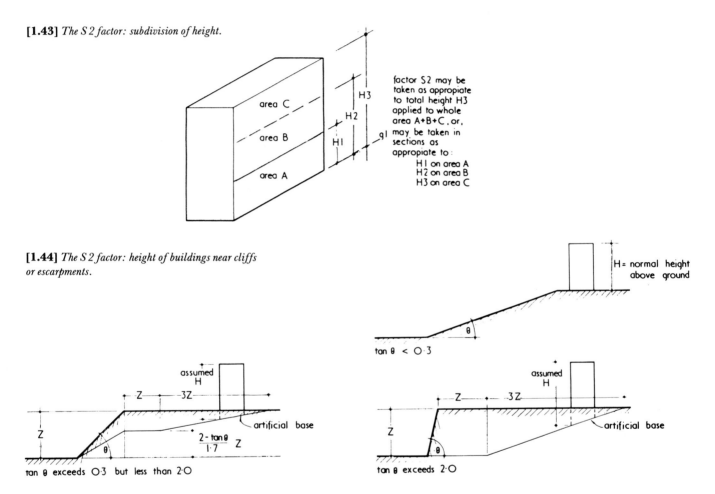

[1.44] *The S 2 factor: height of buildings near cliffs or escarpments.*

S3 Building life

The S3 factor is related to the probability that the basic wind speed will be exceeded in any particular length of time. The basic speeds shown on the map are maximum 3-second gust speeds likely to be exceeded only once in 50 years. This factor, however, is based on statistical concepts, and it can be shown mathematically that the probability (P) that a value greater than x (basic wind speed) will occur in any period of N years is governed by the formula:

$$P = 1 - \left(1 - \frac{1}{T}\right) N$$

where T represents the return period (ie the period in which the basic wind speed is likely to be exceeded only once).

For a period of 50 years, which is the normal situation, the probability level is 0.63 and not 1.00 as might be expected.

The CP provides a simple chart which gives value for the factor S3 using four different probability levels and exposure periods from two years to 200 years (Fig. 1). It also states that S3 should be taken as 1.00, with certain exceptions which include temporary or short-life structures and, conversely, structures where an abnormally long life is expected, or greater than normal safety is required. The matter is explained in greater detail in Appendix C, which does suggest that a period of two years, giving an S3 value of 0.77 at the normal probability level of 0.63, would be acceptable for assessing wind loads during construction. The Approved Document itself, however, overrules this suggestion by a proviso that 'in no case shall the factor S3 be taken as less than 1'.

The other probability levels shown in Fig. 1 of the CP are unlikely to be much used. They are 0.1, 0.01 and 0.001. Appendix C gives an example of the use of level 0.01 giving S3 = 1.35 at 50 years. Although not evident from the diagram, this converts the once in 50 years wind to once in about 5000 years. Clearly, as records have only been kept for a fraction of that time, this must give rise to speculation as to the accuracy of statistical methods in such examples. Unless circumstances are exceptional, therefore, factor S3 will be taken as 1.00, which means it will have no effect on calculations.

This seems the least realistic part of the CP since statistics of this sort are always difficult to accept. Clearly, if it is accepted that during the normal life of a building the design wind speed will be exceeded once, there would seem little reason to worry if this happened more than once, in which case it is hard to understand why doubling the design life of a building to, say, a hundred years should have any real influence on the design's basis. Equally, although a structure may even be classed as temporary, it may still be subject to the maximum design wind speed during its short life.

Pressure coefficients

As explained earlier, these are simply a means of expressing the variation in the normal dynamic pressure of the wind relating to various directions and situations. Tables 7 and 8 in the CP give details of external pressure coefficients to be applied to walls, roofs and monopitches respectively. The abbreviation used for the term 'external pressure coefficient' is 'Cpe'. This is to differentiate it from 'internal pressure coefficient' for which the abbreviated term is 'Cpi'. Figures are given in the tables for three different height/width ratios and two alternative length/width ratios which should cover the majority of cases.

It is emphasised that all structures must be checked, with each face being considered in turn as the windward face.

The tables also give figures for high local pressure coefficients which must be used for calculating the local loads on cladding, roofs, etc in the appropriate situations but *not* for determining the total load on the building.

Local coefficients

Areas around projections, such as chimney stacks or surface areas in passages through buildings and so on, should be given a local Cpe of −1.2. Parapets are also a case requiring special consideration because the wind pressures are considerably reduced below the average at the top of the windward face. The sketch [1.45] illustrates these points.

[1.45] *Local coefficients for projections, narrow openings and parapets. Note that reduced figures may be used for parapets.*

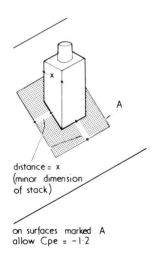

distance = x
(minor dimension of stack)

on surfaces marked A allow Cpe = −1·2

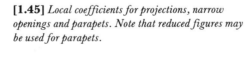

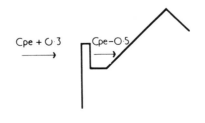

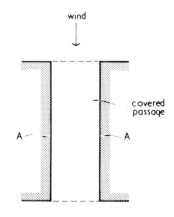

wind

covered passage

A — — A

Internal pressures

The total force on any cladding element depends upon the difference between the internal and external pressures. Internal pressures depend on the permeability of each face of the building. This can be expressed as a percentage of opening in relation to the total area of the face. Even with all doors and windows shut, the gaps which occur around them provide a passage for air. When all doors and windows are shut, the permeability of the average office or domestic block is in the range 0.01 to 0.05 per cent. This is quite a low figure and one open window even in quite a large facade will increase the percentage dramatically. The position of openings in relation to

[1.46] *Internal pressures:*
general principles.

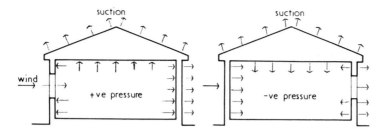

A. Opening on windward side. Positive internal
pressure increases effect of external suction and
decreases effect of external pressure.

B. Opening on leeward side. Negative internal pressure
increases effect of external pressure and decreases effect
of external suction.

wind direction will decide whether or not the internal pressure is positive or negative, with a correspondingly varying effect upon the loads sustained by the roof and cladding. A simple illustration of the principles involved is given in sketch [1.46].

Since facades where windows are provided may be subject to wind effects from any direction, it is necessary to allow for the most severe conditions. In the CP, such openings (windows, doors, and so on) are referred to as 'dominant openings' and rules are given for calculating the C_{pi} in relation to the size and position of such openings in comparison with the total normal permeability of the building. This, however, presumes that it is possible to know with reasonable accuracy where and to what extent a dominant opening will occur, and also to be able to assess accurately the total distributed permeability of the other faces of the building. It is possible to envisage circumstances where the design of a building is clearly controlled by a dominant opening (eg aircraft hangars, factories with large sliding doors, and so on). For normal occupied buildings, however, it would clearly be impossible to state how many windows or doors might be opened during a gale, and the CP therefore gives some general rules for guidance where specific information is not available.

There are two main conditions:

1   Where no dominant opening is likely to occur. The sketch indicates the principles to be followed (diagram [1.47]).
2   Where a dominant opening will exist. If there is only a small possibility of a dominant opening during a storm, the C_{pi} should be taken as the more onerous of $+0.2$ or -0.3. If a dominant opening is likely to occur during a storm, the principles to be followed are indicated in the sketch [1.47].

[1.47] *Internal pressures: assumed C_{pi} for various*
conditions.

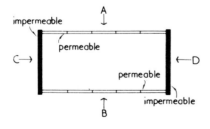

Wind direction A or B: cpi = $+ 0.2$
Wind direction C or D: cpi = $- 0.3$

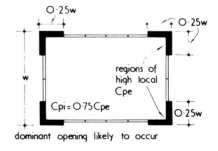

dominant opening likely to occur

Where openings can occur only as shown, normal values
of cpe to be used. If openings can occur in regions of high
local cpe, then the higher value must be taken.

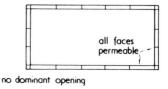

no dominant opening

For all wind directions: cpi = $- 0.3$

Total load on structural elements

Having arrived at a value for the design wind speed (V_s) and, from this, having determined the appropriate dynamic pressure (q) and finally having settled the critical values for the external and internal pressure coefficients (Cpe and Cpi), the total wind load (F) on any flat wall or roof panel of given area (A) is:

$$F = A.q. (Cpe - Cpi)$$

In cladding which is composed of several layers (eg a roof with tiles, felt and boarding), the pressure between the layers will be at some intermediate level between the Cpe and Cpi. Care must be taken to ensure that the whole pressure difference is not brought to bear on some thin membrane not designed to resist it. In the same way, there may be a pressure gradient across the interior of a building which could impose a load on partitions.

To keep down the effect of Cpi on elements of structure, the internal pressure is sometimes controlled by deliberately introducing permeability. A simple example is indicated in diagram [1.48].

[1.48] *Deliberate control of internal pressure. Note: ventilator reduces positive Cpi and hence upward load on roof.*

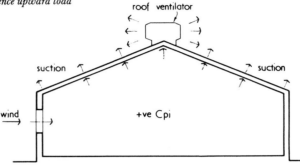

Total wind loads on the whole structure

The total load on a building is obtained by taking the vectorial summation of the loads on the individual surfaces. The principles are indicated in sketch [1.49].

It is important to use only those loads which can occur simultaneously (ie for a given wind direction) and not the maxima used for the individual design of walls, roofs, etc. For simple calculations a single height figure is often taken, but with tall buildings designers will usually prefer to calculate using a series of height zones to avoid applying the maximum wind speed over the whole face of the building. In buildings of irregular outline this will always be necessary.

[1.49] *Summation of individual loads on surfaces.*

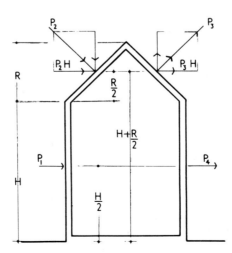

P_2H and P_3H are the horizontal components of the roof wind loads which act normally to the slope. Total overturning force =

$$\left[P_1 \times \frac{H}{2}\right] + \left[P_2H \times \left(H + \frac{R}{2}\right)\right] +$$

$$\left[P_3H \times \left(H + \frac{R}{2}\right)\right] + \left[P_4 \times \frac{H}{2}\right]$$

plus the effect of the vertical components of P_2 and P_3 and frictional drag if applicable.

Force coefficients

For simple structural shapes the CP has provided a simplified method of calculation.

Instead of having to add together the various forces acting on individual parts using differing pressure coefficients, a single coefficient is provided to represent the combined effect on the whole structure. These are known as 'force coefficients' (Cf) and table 10 of the CP gives a series of these for rectangular buildings of varying plan shapes from square to long and narrow and varying height/breadth ratios. The range of shapes in table 10 varies from a square to a plan length/width ratio of 4:1 in five stages, with a height/breadth ratio from ½ up to 6:1 in five stages, which for winds in both directions (90° between) gives a total of 45 values for Cf, ranging from a minimum of 0.7 to a maximum of 1.6. The CP also states (paragraph 7.1) that these tables may be used for other buildings of similar shape, presumably by interpolation or, to a reasonable degree, by extrapolation.

One omission from the CP which was included in BRS Digest 119 is a note on the effect of small projections or recesses in otherwise rectangular plan forms. It states that small projections or recesses do not invalidate the use of force coefficients, providing these do not exceed 10 per cent of the floor area (diagram [1.50]). The Code states that values for buildings of other shapes will be published later as an addendum. In the meantime, the guidance given by BRS Digest 119 is presumably still valid. The same might be said for circular and polygonal buildings which are dealt with in table 6 of the Digest but omitted from the CP, presumably being the subject of further research.

The general formula for the use of force coefficients is

F = Ae.q. Cf when

F is the force in the direction of the wind

Ae is the effective frontal area (projected area on a plane normal to the wind)

q is the dynamic pressure

Cf is the force coefficient in the direction of the wind.

[1.50] *Use of force coefficients in table 10: permitted variations from plain rectangle as recommended in BRS Digest 119.*

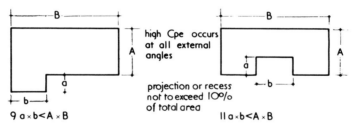

Circular structures

The force coefficients for the special case of circular and polygonal structures (eg chimneys) are given in table 6 of BRS Digest 119. These vary according to shape, surface roughness, and height/diameter ratios. Simple circular structures of low height ratio offer the least resistance. They are not mentioned in CP 3: Chapter V: Part 2: 1970 other than to say that special investigations may be necessary.

Frictional drag

In most cases frictional drag may be ignored but, when the surface over which the wind blows is large in relation to the frontal area (eg single-storey factories), the force created by frictional drag must be considered. The simple formula given in BRS Digest 119 has been abandoned and there are now two formulae depending in whether the breadth (b) (dimension at right angles to the wind) is greater or less than the height (h). With rectangular buildings, the frictional drag need only be considered if the depth (d), ie the dimension in the direction of the wind, is more than four times the height or the breadth (d/h or d/b>4). In such cases the frictional drag (F') can be calculated as follows:

if   h ⩽ b   F' = Cf' qb (d−4h) + Cf' 12h (d−4h)

but if h ⩾ b   F' = Cf' qb (d−4h) + Cf' 12h (d−4b)

The expression Cf' represents a coefficient of friction which is varied according to the surface across which the wind blows – that is, the roof in the first formula and the side walls in the second. The values of Cf' are given as:

Cf' = 0.01 for smooth surfaces without corrugations.

CF' = 0.02 for surfaces with corrugations across the wind direction.

Cf' = 0.04 for surfaces with ribs across the wind direction.

q is of course the normal dynamic pressure and b, d and h are breadth (across wind), depth (in direction of wind) and height: expressions used in tables 7, 8, 9 and 10 for pressure and force coefficients. The formulae could be slightly simplified to

Cf' q (b+2h) (d−4h) when b exceeds h and

Cf' 1 (b+2h) (d−4b) when h exceeds b.

As a prerequisite depth (d) must always be more than four times b or h, the expression (d–4h) or (d–4b) must always exceed unity; also, as b and d are multiplied (after adjustment) the final answer must be related to the plan area modified by the effect of the height (diagram [1.51]).

Frictional drag is additional to any other forces calculated using force or pressure coefficients.

[1.51] *Frictional drag.*

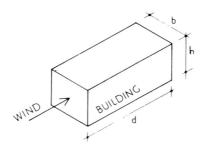

Loads during construction

Pressure coefficients which apply to completed buildings are not relevant during construction, when special conditions will apply. A typical example is the extremes of internal pressure which can arise when a building is partly clad. It is necessary to consider these possibilities and to arrange programmes to avoid dangerous conditions arising.

Another example is the case of a structure standing complete with frame and floors but without cladding, when critical loads can arise. The loads on such a structure can be calculated using coefficiencies as in sketch [1.52].

In making these calculations, the Code states that it is permissible to assume a reduced S3 factor for the life of the building, based on the length of the site construction period, but with a minimum of two years. Using the graph in the CP, this would give an S3 factor of about 0.77 for a building in which the normal probability level was assumed. However, the Approved Document itself states that in no case shall the S3 factor be taken as less than 1.0 and, although not specifically stated, this presumably applies to temporary states during construction, as well as completed buildings.

The response of buildings to the wind – oscillation

Although not included in the Code, BRS Digest 119 deals briefly with such things as deflection due to wind and the oscillation of slender structures. Buildings generally are relatively stiff and trouble from excessive deflection has been rare. Recently, however, situations have been reached where blocks of flats of about thirty storeys have been subject to sway and wind vibration which, although not structurally dangerous, has been beyond the limit for residential occupancy.

With slender structures, oscillation can arise when the natural frequency of the structure is less than the shedding frequency of the wind at maximum velocity. In such cases, structural damping or the use of devices to reduce aerodynamic excitation is necessary. The CP merely states that such oscillations may require further investigation and observes that they may occur at wind velocities below the maximum.

[1.52] *Loads during construction: force coefficients.*

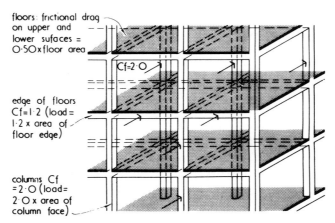

BRE Digests 119 and 346	BRE Digest 119 has been superseded by Digest 346 – The assessment of wind loads. The new Digest is compatible with the proposed BS 6399 Part 2 which will replace CP3, Chapter V, Loading, Part 2. The Digest has 8 parts: Part 1: Background and method Part 2: classification of structures Part 3: wind climate in the UK Part 4: terrain and building factors and gust peak factors Part 5: assessment of wind speed over topography Part 6: loading coefficients for typical buildings Part 7: wind speeds for serviceability and fatigue assessments Part 8: internal pressures

BS 6299 Part 3 1988	BRE Digest 332 which replaces Digest 290 is entitled 'Loads on roofs from snow drifting against vertical obstructions and in valleys'. The calculation of snow loads using this Digest can be used for the design of new buildings, extensions and structural appraisal. Local snow loads on roofs are caused by specific architectural features such as: valleys abrupt changes in roof height local projections and obstructions The calculation applies to: (*a*) most roofs more than 200 m^2 on plan having one or more of the above features (*b*) roofs smaller than 200 m^2 on plan which have an abrupt change in height deeper than 1 m and where the lower part of the roof is larger than 35 m^2 on plan (*c*) structures built at less than 500 m above sea level A map in the Digest shows basic snow load on the ground – this is in kN/m^2 and ranges between 0.8 and 0.3. The local loads caused by drifting snow on roofs can be calculated by determining from the map the basic snow load on the ground and the appropriate snow load shape coefficient. The Digest contains diagrams on calculation of drift length, etc together with examples of calculation and design.

A 3/4   DISPROPORTIONATE COLLAPSE

The Requirement is:

Requirement	Limits on application
Disproportionate collapse A 3 The building shall be constructed so that in the event of an accident the building will not suffer collapse to an extent disproportionate to the cause.	This requirement applies to a building having five or more storeys (each basement level being counted as one storey); excluding a storey within the roof space where the slope of the roof at eaves does not exceed 60° to the horizontal.
A 4 The building shall be constructed so that in the event of failure of any part of the roof including its supports, the building will not suffer collapse to an extent disproportionate to the cause of the local failure.	This requirement applies to any part of a public building, shop or shopping mall which has a roof with a clear span exceeding 9 m between supports.

A 3   Disproportionate collapse may be limited by the appropriate choice of measures which
(*a*)   avoid or reduce hazards to which the building is exposed, and
(*b*)   reduce the sensitivity of the building to disproportionate collapse should an accident occur.
The guidance describes ways of achieving (*b*) and gives three options.

Option 1: Effective horizontal and vertical ties
If these are provided in accordance with the Codes and Standards listed at the end of this section, no further measures are needed.

Option 2: Effective horizontal tying but no vertical tying
If it is not feasible to tie any of the vertical loadbearing members –
(*a*)   each untied member should be considered to be notionally removed
(*b*)   one at a time
(*c*)   in each storey in turn
to check that its removal would allow the remainder of the structure to bridge over that missing member albeit in a substantially deformed condition. If it is not possible to bridge over then that member should be designated as a *protected member*.
Certain areas such as cantilevers or simply suspended floor panels will be vulnerable to collapse and the area at risk of collapse should be limited as in Option 3.

Option 3: No effective horizontal or vertical tying
If no effective horizontal or vertical tying of any of the loadbearing members is provided –
(*a*)   each support member should be considered to be notionally removed
(*b*)   one at a time
(*c*)   in each storey in turn
to check that on its removal the area at risk of collapse of the structure within the storey and the immediate adjacent storeys is limited to
(*i*)   15 per cent of the area of the storey
(*ii*) $70\,\mathrm{m}^2$
whichever is the less.
The area at risk of collapse is the area of the floor supported by the member and not necessarily the entire area supported by the member in conjunction with the other members.
If on removal of a member the area put at risk of collapse is greater than that shown above, the member should be designated as a *protected member*.

Protected members (or key elements)
These should be designed in accordance with the codes and standards set out at the end of this Section.

Alternative approach
The performance can also be met by following the relevant recommendations in the following:
(*a*)   Structural work of masonry: Clause 37 of BS 5628: Part 1: 1978.
(*b*)   Structural work of steel: Clause 2.4.5.3 of BS 5950: Part 1: 1990.
(The accidental loading referred to in clause 2.4.5.5 should be chosen having particular regard to the importance of the key element and the consequences of failure, and the key element should always be capable of withstanding a load of at least $34\,\mathrm{kN/m}^2$ applied from any direction.)
(*c*)   Structural work of reinforced, prestressed or plain concrete:
Clause 2.2.2.2 of BS 8110: Part 1: 1985 and
Clause 2.6   of BS 8110: Part 2: 1985.

Requirement A3 applies to any type of building which has five or more storeys (basement storeys are included) and Requirement A4 applies to any part of a public building shop or shopping mall which has a roof clear span of more than 9 m.
A public building is defined in the main regulations – Regulation 2(2) as a theatre, hall or other place of public resort, a non-exempted school or a place of public worship.
It will no doubt be of interest and assistance to the reader to understand the need for these special requirements, even though it is not possible, or necessary, to go into detail. Requirement A3 started with the partial collapse of a block of flats known as Ronan Point in the 1960s. This block, being system-built, of large storey-height panels, was proved to be highly susceptible to a gas explosion, which resulted in a house of cards type collapse. During the resulting enquiry it was realised that, although such structures were most susceptible to progressive collapse unless adequately tied in, other more normal types of structure could also be at risk. The earlier regulations were amended to apply to all buildings of 5 or more storeys, and proposed two possible methods to avoid collapse. The first required that the structure be designed so that if any single structural member were removed, the loads which it supported would be transferred to others, which had to be capable of sustaining such transferred loads (the transference of load

principle). The alternative was to make members which could not be removed strong enough to sustain the design load plus a possible accidental load (the key element principle).

The regulations specified a limit to the extent of any collapse after the removal of any one member not designed as a key element. The new AD does the same. The extent is illustrated in diagram [1.53].

[1.53] *Limitation of structural failure.*

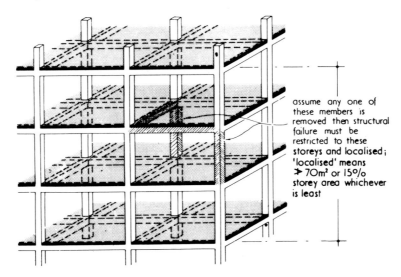

assume any one of these members is removed then structural failure must be restricted to these storeys and localised; 'localised' means ➤ 70m² or 15% storey area whichever is least

The alternative basis required that the key elements, being members the removal of which would involve a larger collapse than that permitted above, must be designed to withstand a load of at least $34\,kN/m^2$ (originally $5\,lb/in^2$) applied from any direction, in addition to the design loads. This load could (and frequently would) be transmitted to the member by another element connected to it, which could be considerably greater than a load applied directly to the member itself. An obvious example is that of a floor slab supported by a beam, which would have to be designed to accept a load of $34\,kN/m^2$ over the whole floor area, not merely over the flange area of the member itself. This type of accidental load could be caused by an explosion similar to that at Ronan Point. There could, however, be other types of accidental loading such as a vehicle colliding with a column.

A4 Roof structure with clear span of over 9 m. This requirement applies to public buildings, shops and shopping malls.

Each member of the roof structure and its immediate supports should be considered to be notionally removed to check that the building would not collapse (see diagram [1.54]).

6.1 **[1.54]** *Example of disproportionate collapse in the event of a local failure in the roof structure or its supports.*

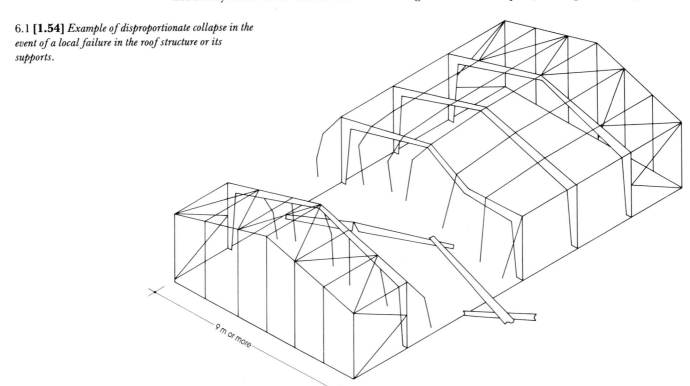

9 m or more

It may be acceptable that other members supported by the notionally removed member collapse and/or substantial deformation of the building occurs.

NOTE   The risk of local failure of the roof structure may be reduced by

(*i*)   Protecting the structure from foreseeable physical damage and from adverse environmental conditions.

(*ii*)   Assessing and providing for movement and deformation.

(*iii*)   Providing access for inspection of the main structural components and joints.

Requirement A 4 has been added because there has been concern over the few collapses of roof structures in relatively modern buildings. There were some fatalities although a large number of persons can be at risk. Investigation of these failures revealed that failure of one or two beams in certain structures could lead to the collapse of the whole roof.

Buildings with long span roofs (typically in excess of 9 m) showed a greater susceptibility to disproportionate collapse compared with those with short span roofs. Some of the reasons were thought to be that the roof decking may not be stiff enough to brace long spans, components may be more susceptible to permanent deformation due to dead loads, and bearings and joints may not be normally designed to accommodate movements which may be significant in long span roof structures. There are also usually fewer major structural components and therefore fewer alternative paths to load resistance.

APPENDIX A

Tables of sizes of timber floor, ceiling and roof members in single-family homes

A 1   The Appendix must be used in conjunction with Sections 1A and 1B.

A 2   The section sizes are, in the case of floor joists, ceiling and flat roof joists either regularised from BS 4471 basic sawn sizes or CLS/ALS sizes with in each case tolerances to BS 4471. For roof members the section sizes are either BS 4471 sawn sizes or CLS/ALS sizes each with BS 4471 tolerances.

A 3   All spans are measured as the clear dimension between supports (except floorboards) and all spacings are measured betweeen centres of members.

The tables each present a formidable block of dimensions which are anything but easy for quick reference. Furthermore, they give no visual impression of the relationship between the four variables of size, span, load and spacing. The graphs which follow do, however, give an immediate picture of these relationships, and they should be useful for making a rapid assessment of the alternative possibilities available in any particular element of structure.

In the interests of clarity not all of the tabulated figures are charted. For example, the joist tables give sizes for dead load values of under $0.25 \, kN/m^2$, $0.25 \, kN/m^2$ to 0.5 and 0.5 to $1.25 \, kN/m^2$, and for spacings of 400 mm, 450 mm, and 600 mm centres. The graphs show directly only the 0.25 to 0.5 kN and 0.5 to $1.25 \, kN/m^2$ figures and the 400 mm and 600 mm figures, but it is a simple matter visually to interpolate between the appropriate graph lines whenever an intermediate value is desired. Even the tables do not cover all possibilities, and spacing of joists frequently has to be something in between the figures given. The figure of 0.25 to $0.5 \, kN/m^2$ has been chosen as the lower of the two dead load figures in preference to under $0.25 \, kN/m^2$, as the lower figure would be unlikely to occur often in practice. Similar principles have been adopted in other tables where different dead load brackets are used: ie in each case one load classification is left out and the other two brackets only are shown. The tables also show a 47 mm timber width which has been omitted, as have the three Northern American sizes which are intermediate between some of the 25 mm depth increases. Here again, using the graphs it is easy to interpolate for any intermediate size.

The graphs relating to timber roof members only show the $0.75 \, kN/m^2$ imposed loading.

Table A1. Floor joists: SC3
Imposed load 1.5 kN/m²
Dead load 0.5 kN/m² and 1.25 kN/m²
Spacing:
——————— *400 mm centres*
---------- *600 mm centres*

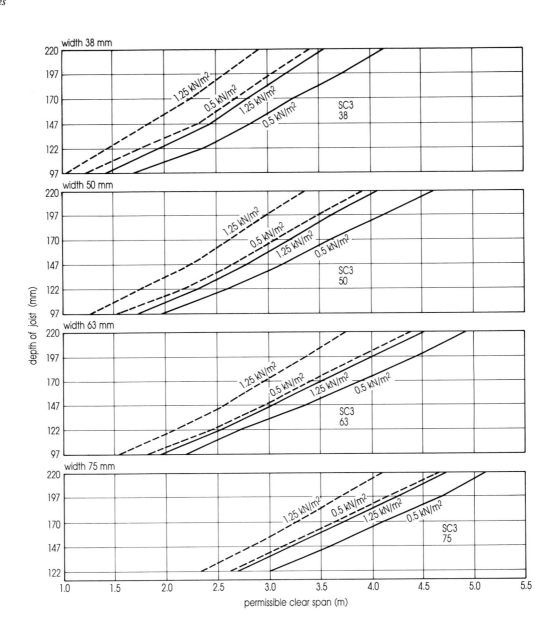

Table A2. Floor joists: SC4
Imposed load 1.5 kN/m²
Dead load 0.5 kN/m² and 1.25 kN/m²
Spacing:
——————— *400 mm centres*
----------- *600 mm centres*

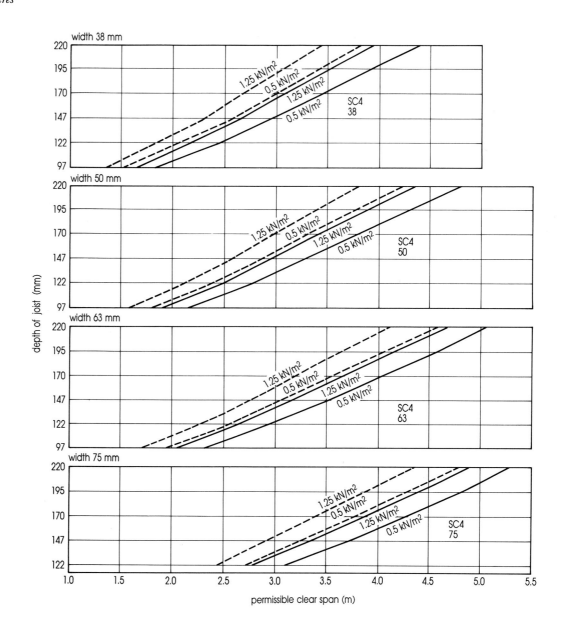

Table A3. Ceiling joists: SC3
Imposed load 0.25 kN/m²
or concentrated load 0.9 kN
Dead load 0.25 kN/m² and 0.5 kN/m²
Spacing:
——————— *400 mm centres*
----------- *600 mm centres*

— · — · {
    400 mm spacing with 0.5 kN/m²
    dead load
    600 mm spacing with 0.25 kN/m²
    dead load
}

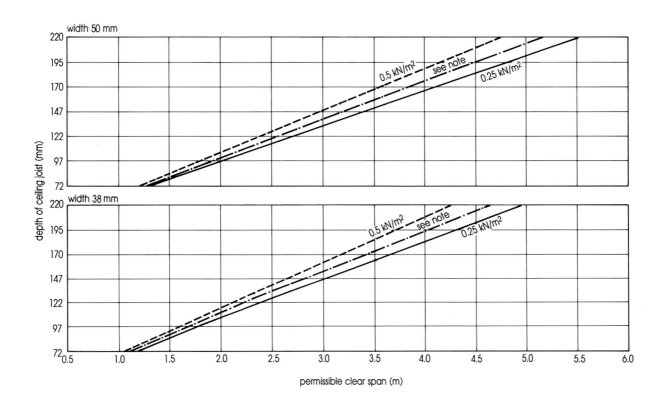

Table A4. Binders supporting ceiling joists (Table
A3): SC3 imposed load 0.25 kN/m²
or concentrated load 0.9 kN
Dead load 0.25 kN/m² and 0.5 kN/m²
Spacing:
——————— *400 mm centres*
----------- *600 mm centres*

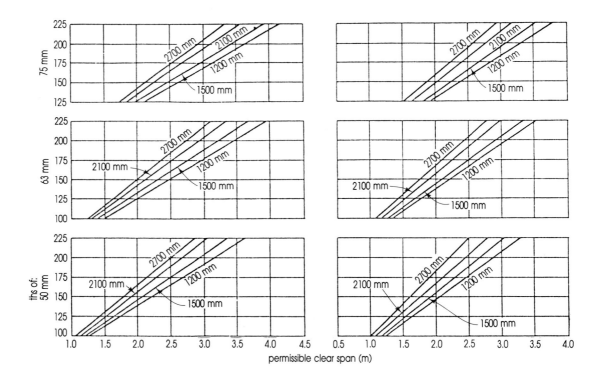

Table A3. Ceiling joists: SC4
Imposed load 0.25 kN/m²
or concentrated load 0.9 kN
Dead load 0.25 kN/m² and 0.5 kN/m²
Spacing:
——————— *400 mm centres*
----------- *600 mm centres*

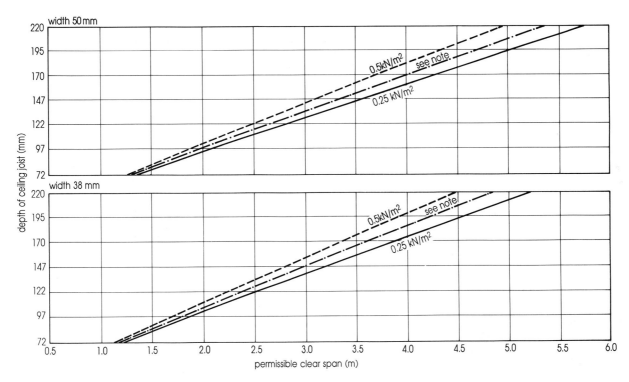

Table A4. Binders supporting ceiling joists (Table
A3): SC4
Imposed load 0.25 kN/m²
or concentrated load 0.9 kN
Dead load 0.25 kN/m²
and 0.5 kN/m²
Spacing as shown

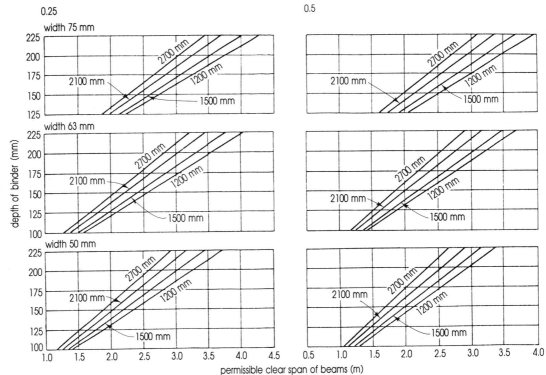

Table A5. Common or jack rafters: SC3
Imposed load 0.75 kN/m²
or concentrated load 0.9 kN
Dead load 0.5 kN/m² or 1.0 kN/m²
Spacing:
——————— *400 mm centres*
----------- *600 mm centres*
Roof pitch 15–22½°

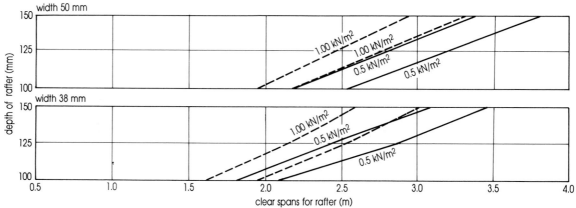

Table A9. Common or jack rafters: SC3
Imposed load 0.75 kN/m²
or concentrated load 0.9 kN
Dead load 0.5 kN/m² and 1.0 kN/m²
Spacing:
——————— *400 mm centres*
----------- *600 mm centres*
Roof pitch 22½°–30°

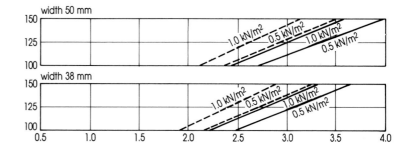

Table A13. Common or jack rafters: SC3
Imposed load 0.75 kN/m²
or concentrated load 0.9 kN
Dead load 0.5 kN/m² and 1.0 kN/m²
Spacing:
——————— *400 mm centres*
----------- *600 mm centres*
Roof pitch 30–45°

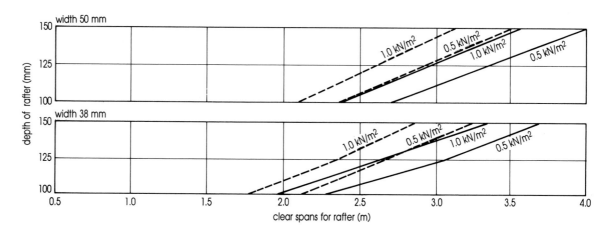

Table A6. Purlins supporting rafters (Table A5):
SC3
Imposed load 0.75 kN/m²
or concentrated load 0.9 kN
Dead load 0.5 kN/m² and 1.0 kN/m²
Spacing as shown
Roof pitch 15–22½°

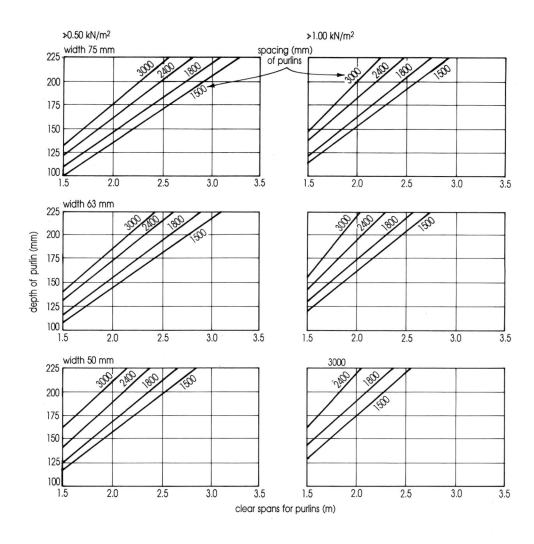

Table A10. Purlins supporting rafters (Table A9):
SC3
Imposed load 0.75 kN/m²
or concentrated load 0.9 kN
Dead load 0.5 kN/m² and 1.0 kN/m²
Spacing as shown
Roof pitch 22½–30°

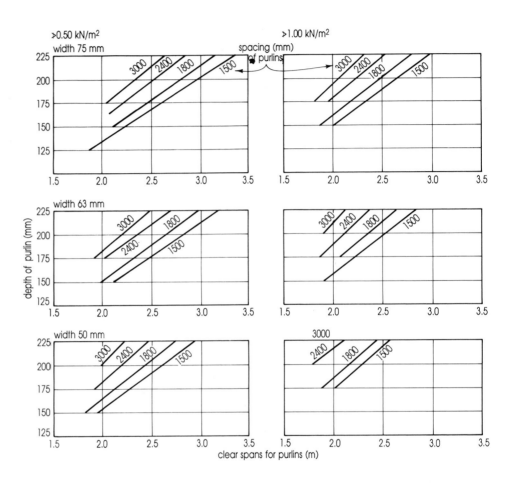

Table A14. Purlins supporting rafters
(Table A13): SC3
Imposed load 0.75 kN/m²
or concentrated load 0.9 kN
Dead load 0.5 kN/m²
and 1.0 kN/m²
Spacing as shown
Roof pitch 30–45°

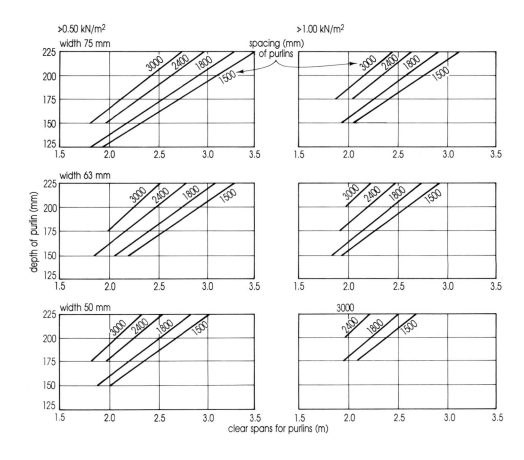

Table A5. Common or jack rafters: SC4
Imposed load 0.75 kN/m²
or concentrated load 0.9 kN
Dead load 0.5 kN/m² and 1.0 kN/m²
Spacing:
——————— 400 mm centres
----------- 600 mm centres
Roof pitch 15–22½°

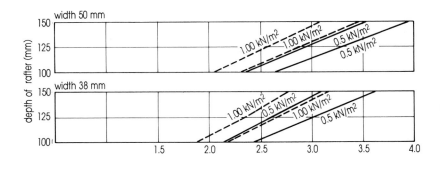

Table A9. Common or jack rafters: SC4
Imposed load 0.75 kN/m²
or concentrated load 0.9 kN
Dead load 0.5 kN/m² and 1.0 kN/m²
Spacing:
——————— *400 mm centres*
---------- *600 mm centres*
Roof pitch 22½°–30°

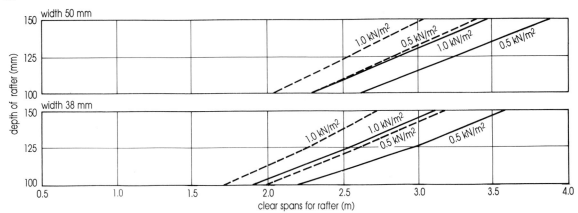

Table A13. Common or jack rafters: SC4
Imposed load 0.75 kN/m²
or concentrated load 0.9 kN
Dead load 0.5 kN/m² and 1.0 kN/m²
Spacing:
——————— *400 mm centres*
---------- *600 mm centres*
Roof pitch 30–45°

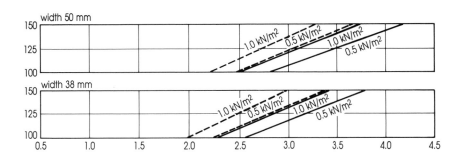

GBR-91 – Table A13(2)

Table A6. Purlins supporting rafters
(Table A5): SC4
Imposed load 0.75 kN/m²
or concentrated load 0.9 kN
Dead load 0.5 kN/m²
and 1.0 kN/m²
Spacing as shown
Roof pitch 15–22½°

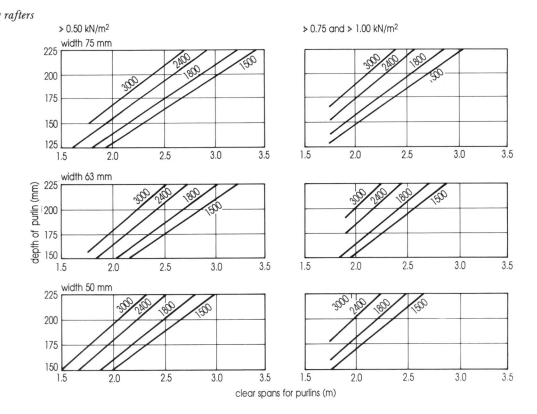

*Table A10. Purlins supporting rafters
(Table A9): SC4
Imposed load 0.75 kN/m²
or concentrated load 0.9 kN
Dead load 0.5 kN/m²
and 1.0 kN/m²
Spacing as shown
Roof pitch 22½–30°*

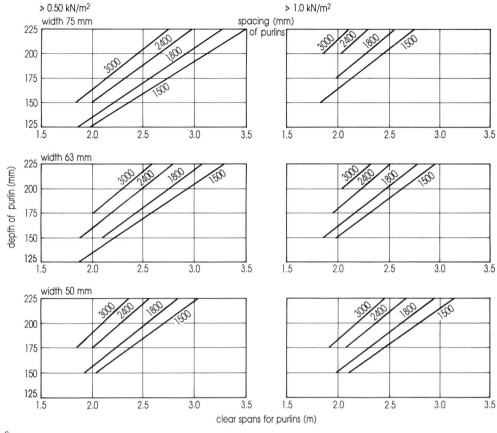

*Table A14. Purlins supporting rafters
(Table A13): SC4
Imposed load 0.75 kN/m²
or concentrated load 0.9 kN
Dead load 0.5 kN/m² and 1.0 kN/m²
Spacing as shown
Roof pitch 30–45°*

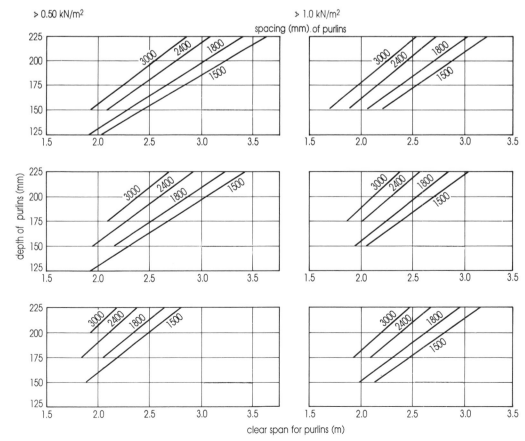

Table A17. Joists for flat roofs (access for
maintenance only): SC3
Imposed load 0.75 kN/m²
or concentrated load 0.9 kN
Dead load 0.5 kN/m² and 1.0 kN/m²
Spacing:
————— 400 mm centres
----------- 600 mm centres

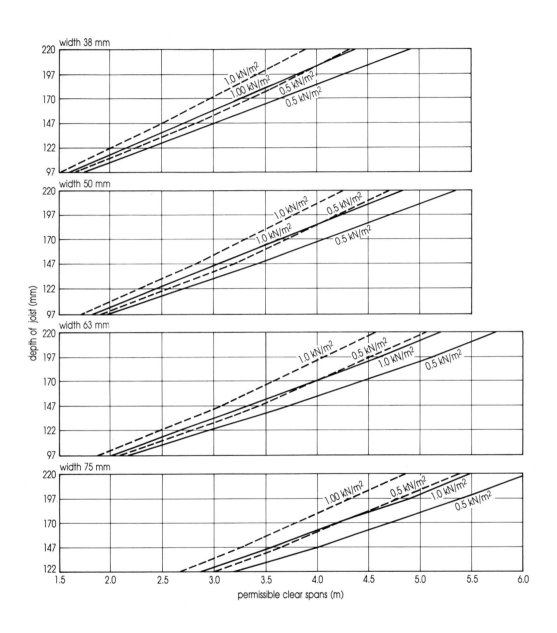

Table A18. Joists for flat roofs (access for
maintenance only): SC4
Imposed load 0.5 kN/m² and 1.0 kN/m²
or concentrated load 0.9 kN
Spacing:
——————— *400 mm centres*
---------- *600 mm centres*

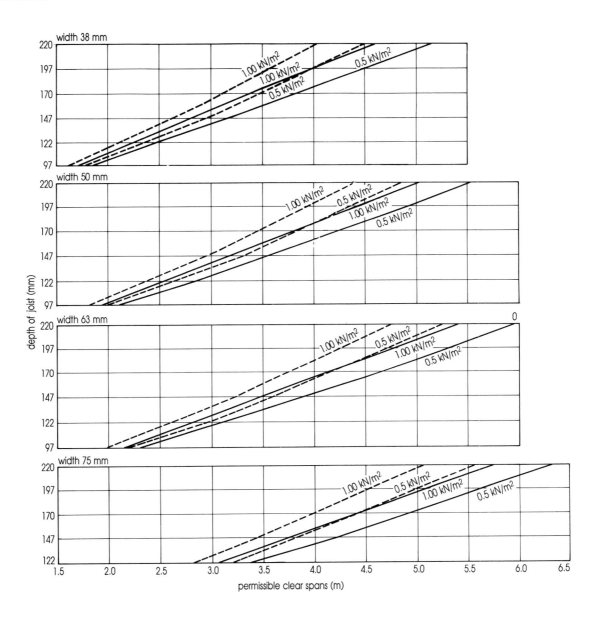

Table A21. Joists for flat roofs (full access): SC3
Imposed load 1.5 kN/m²
Dead load 0.5 kN/m² and 1.0 kN/m²
Spacing:
——————— *400 mm centres*
----------- *600 mm centres*

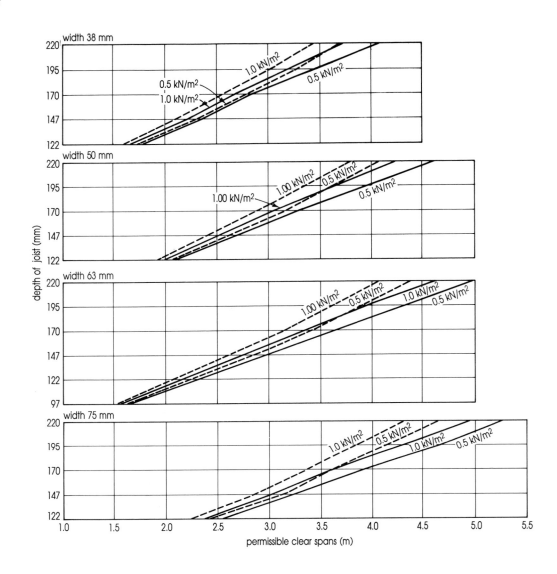

Table A22. Joists for flat roofs (full access): SC4
Imposed load 1.5 kN/m²
Dead load 0.5 kN/m² and 1.0 kN/m²
Spacing:
——————— *400 mm centres*
---------- *600 mm centres*

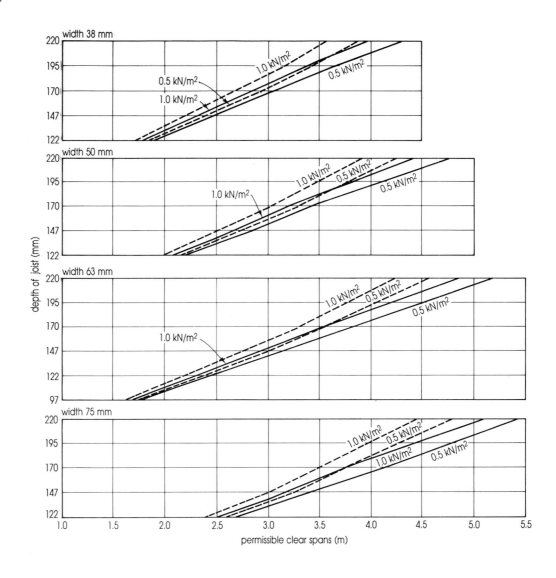

Table A23. Purlins supporting sheeted or decked roofs: SC3
Imposed load 0.75 kN/m²
or concentrated load 0.9 kN
Dead load 0.25 kN/m², 0.5 kN/m² and 0.75 kN/m²
Spacing as shown
Roof pitch 10–35°

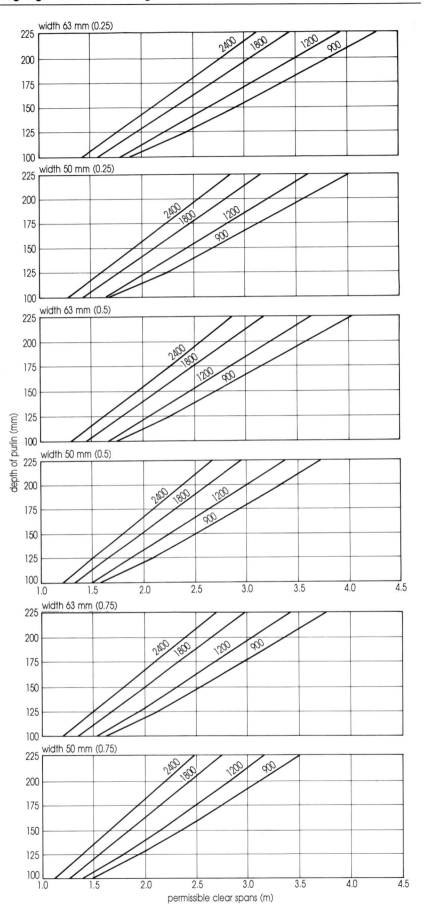

Table A23. Purlins supporting sheeted or decked roofs: SC4
Imposed load 0.75 kN/m²
or concentrated load 0.9 kN
Dead load 0.25 kN/m², 0.5 kN/m² and 0.75 kN/m²
Spacing as shown
Roof pitch 10–35°

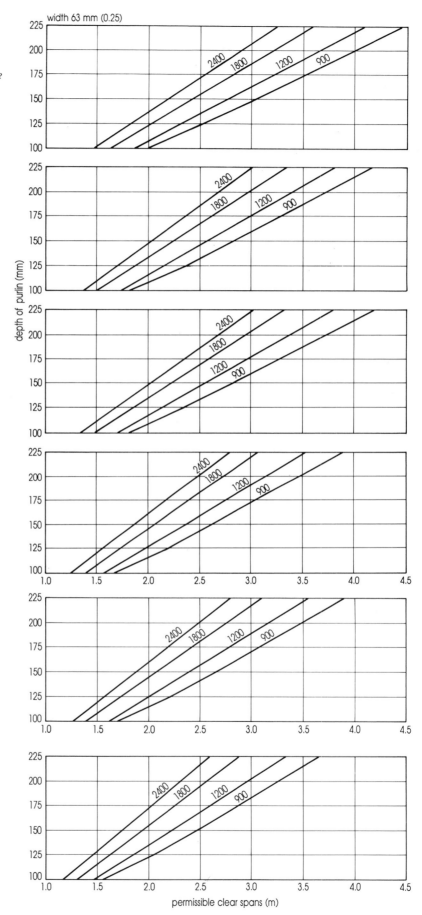

References

British Standards and other documents referred to in the AD.

BS 12: 1989 *Specification for Portland cements.*

BS 187: 1978 *Specification for calcium silicate (sandlime and flintlime) bricks* Amendment 1: AMD 5427.

BS 449 *The use of structural steel in building* Part 2: 1969 *Metric units.* Amendment 1: AMD 416, 2: AMD 523, 3: AMD 661, 4: AMD 1135, 5: AMD 1787, 6: AMD 4576, 7: AMD 5698, 8: AMD 6255.

BS 882: *1983 Specification for aggregates from natural sources for concrete* Amendment 1: AMD 5150.

BS 1243: 1978 *Specification for metal ties for cavity wall construction* Amendment 1: AMD 3651, 2: AMD 4024.

BS 1297: 1987 *Specification for tongued and grooved softwood flooring.*

BS 3921: 1985 *Specification for clay bricks.*

BS 4471: 1987 *Sizes of sawn and processed softwood.*

BS 4978: 1988 *Specification for softwood grades for structural use.*

BS 5268: *Code of practice for the structural use of timber* Part 2: 1989 *Code of practice for permissible stress design, materials and workmanship* Part 3: 1985 *Code of practice for trussed rafter roofs* Amendment 1: AMD 5931. Part 6: Section 6.1: 1988 *Code of practice for timber framed walls – dwellings not exceeding three storeys.*

BS 5328: *Concrete.* Part 1: 1990: *Guide to specifying concrete.* Part 2: 1990 *Methods for specifying concrete mixes.*

BS 5390: 1976 *Code of practice for stone masonry* Amendment 1: AMD 4272.

BS 5628 *Code of practice for the structural use of masonry* Part 1: 1978 *Structural use of unreinforced masonry* Amendment 1: AMD 2747, 2: AMD 3445, 3: AMD 4800, 4: AMD 5736, Part 3: 1985 *Materials and components, design and workmanship.* Amendment 1: AMD 4974.

BS 5950 *Structural use of steel work in building* Part 1: 1990: *Code of practice for design in simple and continuous construction; hot rolled sections,* Part 2: 1985: *Specification for materials, fabrication and erection; hot rolled sections,* Part 3: *Code of practice for design in composite construction,* Section 3.1: 1990 *Code of practice for design of simple and continuous composite beams,* Part 4: 1982 *Code of practice for design of floors with profiled steel sheeting.*

Part 5: 1987: *Code of practice for design in cold formed sections* Amendment 1: AMD 5957.

BS 6073 *Precast concrete masonry units* Part 1: 1981: *Specification for precast concrete masonry units* Amendment 1: AMD 3944, 2: AMD 4462.

BS 6399: *Loading for buildings.* Part 1: 1984 *Code for dead and imposed loads,* Amendment 1: AMD 4949, 5881 and 6031.

BS 6649: 1985: *Specification for clay and calcium silicate modular bricks.*

BS 6750: 1986: *Specification for modular coordination in building* AMD 6033.

BS 8004: 1986: *Foundations.*

BS 8110: *Structural use of concrete.* Part 1: 1985: *Code of practice for design and construction* AMD 5917 and 6276. Part 2: 1985: *Code of practice for special circumstances* AMD 5914.

Part 3: 1985: *Design charts for single reinforced beams, doubly reinforced beams and rectangular colums* AMD 5918.

BS 8200: 1985: *Code of practice for design of non-load bearing external vertical enclosure of buildings.*

BS 8298: 1989: *Code of practice for design and installation of natural stone cladding and lining.*

CP 3: Chapter V: *Loading.* Part 2: 1972 *Wind loads.*

Amendment 1: AMD 4952, 2: AMD 5152, 3: AMD 5343, 4: AMD 6028.

CP 118: 1969 *The structural use of aluminium* Amendment 1: AMD 1129.

Chapter 2

Approved Document B: Fire Safety

Arrangement of sections and provisions common to more than one requirement of Part B.

0.1/0.4   The structure of this package of ADs is very different from the 1985 edition. There are now five separate ADs, each covering one of the functional requirements B 1 to B 5 but each AD is in sections and the section numbers run throughout the documents as indicated below.

B 1: Sections 1 to 5 – means of escape in case of fire.

This is no longer subject to Mandatory Rules but is a functional requirement in line with all the other ADs.

B 2: Section 6 – internal fire spread – linings

B 3: Sections 7–11 – internal fire spread – structure

B 4: Sections 12–14 – external fire spread

B 5: Sections 15–18 – access and facilities for the fire service.

This is a new area of control although similar powers exist in many Local Acts.

Some items are common to one or more requirements and these have been set out in the Appendices.

Appendix A: Fire performance of materials and structures

Appendix B: Provisions regarding fire doors

Appendix C: Methods of measurement

Appendix D: Classification of purpose groups

Appendix E: Definitions

When the 1985 Regulations were drafted it was considered that the provisions should be arranged in a series of sections relating to specific building types. A user study showed, however, that it was preferable to return to a layout where each AD covers the specific requirements, and this has been achieved.

The introduction refers to all the parts and draws attention to the fact that many of the provisions are closely interlinked. Interaction between the different requirements should be recognised where variations in the standard of provision are contemplated. The provisions in the document as a whole should be considered as a package which is designed to give an acceptable standard of fire safety.

The provisions for means of escape for dwellings have been separated from those for other types of building. Dwelling houses are dealt with in Section 1 and flats in Section 2.

0.5/0.9   These paragraphs set out the content of the Appendices.

Fire safety engineering

0.10   An alternative approach to providing fire safety can be used and perhaps may be the only viable way in some large and complex buildings. This is a fire safety engineering approach which takes into account the total fire safety package.

0.11/0.12   In the case of existing buildings, a rigid application of Part B may be unduly restrictive. Buildings of architectural or historic interest may need particular attention. A range of fire safety features could be taken into account and these could be set against an assessment of the hazard and risk in a particular case. Matters to be taken into account could include anticipated risk of a fire occurring, its severity, the ability of the structure to resist the effect of fire and danger to persons who may be in and about the building.

0.13   It is suggested that a wide range of measures could be considered and incorporated to a variable extent depending on the circumstances. These include whether fire prevention measures are adequate, ie

Fire warning systems

Means of escape

Smoke control

Control of the rate of growth of fire

The adequacy of the structure to resist the effects of fire

Fire containment and separation between buildings

Active measures for fire extinguishment and control

Facilities to assist the fire service

Availability of powers to require staff training, eg under the Fire Precautions Act or licensing procedures

Availability of continuing control through legislation.

0.14   Quantitative techniques can be used to evaluate risk and hazard but assumptions so made need careful assessment.

0.15   BS 5588: Part 10: *Code of practice for shopping complexes* is an example of an overall approach to fire safety. Buildings which contain an atrium penetrating compartment floors also need special fire safety measures.

Property protection

0.16   The protection of property including the building itself may require additional fire safety measures and insurers may ask for higher standards. Building Regulations are made to ensure an adequate standard of life safety in the event of fire.

NOTE When considering these amendments to Part B, careful consideration was given to whether life safety requirements included the safety of firemen who may be carrying out rescue or firefighting in the interests of life safety. The Fire Services Act 1947 requires fire authorities to make provision for fighting fire for the purpose of life safety and property protection. It was decided that the requirements of the Regulations should include the safety of firemen in their life safety role of rescue.

The Loss Prevention Council has published a revised set of rules for the construction of buildings* and these require a higher standard of fire protection than the Regulations. They, of course, are acting in the best interests of the insurance industry who are very much concerned with the continuing high property loss in fire.

Designers should ensure that measures required by insurers to enable them to accept the insurance risk are incorporated into buildings.

Material alteration

0.17   This is a reminder that although there are no powers under Building Regulations to ensure that standards set under them can be maintained throughout the life of a building, any alterations affecting B 1, B 3, B 4 and B 5 which result in a less satisfactory standard are controllable as a material alteration (Regulations 3 and 4).

B 1   MEANS OF ESCAPE

The requirement is as follows:

Requirement	Limits on application
Means of escape B 1. The building shall be designed and constructed so that there are means of escape in case of fire from the building to a place of safety outside the building capable of being safely and effectively used at all material times.	Requirement B 1 does not apply to any prison provided under Section 33 of the Prisons Act 1952 (power to provide prisons etc)

The change to this requirement was the greatest change to take place in the 1991 amendments. No longer are there mandatory rules for means of escape; this requirement is a functional requirement in line with all the others. It will be noted that the only limits on the application of B 1 relate to prisons. With this exception B 1 applies to *all* new buildings as well as to alterations and extensions and material changes of use.

*LPC Rules for the construction of buildings, The Loss Prevention Council, Melrose Avenue, Borehamwood, Hertfordshire WD6 2BJ.

The legal requirements in the Fire Precautions Act to consult the fire authority on matters affecting fire safety still apply but the building control authority has the final say in implementing means of escape requirements.

Consultation with the fire authority takes many forms, but a document prepared by the Department of the Environment and the Home Office giving guidance should be followed to avoid any conflicting advice being given, particularly in the case of those buildings which will require a fire certificate. These are buildings of designated use, ie hotels and boarding houses, offices, shops, railway premises and factories. There are provisions within the Housing Act 1985 concerning houses in multiple occupation but even these are now included within the scope of Regulation B 1.

The decision to limit the application to exclude prisons may seem somewhat unusual, as prisons are Crown property and are at present exempt because Section 44 of the Building Act 1984 has not yet been brought into operation. Should a commencement order be made to remove Crown property exemption, the limitation will be more meaningful.

Performance
The requirement will be met if there are routes:
Of sufficient number, capacity and which are suitably located to enable persons to escape to a place of safety in the event of fire;
Sufficiently protected from the effects of fire by enclosure where necessary;
Adequately lit;
To exits which are suitably signed.

Appropriate facilities should be provided to either limit the ingress of smoke to the escape routes or to restrict the fire and remove the smoke. The extent of these measures will depend on the use, size and height of the building.

NOTE Readers of Approved Document B will notice that the introductory paragraphs for each section run in sequence throughout the Document. Paragraphs 0.1–0.17 can be found in the main introductory remarks at the beginning of the AD.

Introduction

0.18 The structural fire precautions in B 1 are only those necessary to safeguard escape routes.

Reliance should not be placed on external rescue by the fire service and B 1 has been written on the basis that, in an emergency, the occupants of a building should be able to escape safely without any external assistance. Evacuation without assistance is obviously not practicable in some institutional buildings where people may be bedridden or unable to assist themselves and special considerations are given in these cases.

For one- and two-storey dwellings the guidance is limited to the provision of openable windows in an emergency and the provision of smoke alarms.

0.19 Although a fire certificate is required for buildings of designated use, in the case of certain smaller premises which do not require a fire certificate there is a statutory duty on occupiers to provide reasonable means of escape in case of fire.

The point is made that Building Regulations do not require the provision of some means of giving warning in case of fire, but this is essential in the overall strategy for fire safety in an occupied building.

There are, however, requirements under other legislation to provide appropriate means of giving warning in case of fire in most places of work, public assembly buildings, institutional and residential care buildings. British Standard 5839: Part 1 gives guidance on suitable fire warning devices for various types of premises.

Interaction with other legislation

0.20 Now that regulations have been made for means of escape from all buildings the implications of the *statutory bar* (as it is known) have changed.

Where an application is made for a fire certificate for a building which is subject to building regulations for means of escape, the fire authority cannot make the issue of a fire certificate conditional on making alterations concerning means of escape unless Regulations made under Section 12 of the Fire Precautions Act 1971 are in force.

Section 12 allows regulations to be made about fire precautions but none have yet been made. If the fire authority considers that the means of escape are inadequate because of matters which were not required to be supplied with the Building Regulations deposit of plans, the fire authority can make their own requirements.

The Fire Precautions Act also requires things like first aid and firefighting equipment which is beyond the scope of the Building Regulations.

NOTE It is vitally important for the designer to ensure that all fire precaution measures are incorporated into the building.

The guidance document, previously mentioned, will endeavour to describe a system of operation where the designer can consult with one authority (the building control authority) who, after consultation with the fire authority, will be able to advise the designer of all the necessary requirements.

As mentioned in the introductory chapter, building regulations now require the building control authority to issue a completion certificate for all premises which are put to a designated use (where notice of completion is given). If proper consultation has taken place during the early stages of a project, the fire authority should be able to take note of the Building Regulations completion certificate when considering the issue of a fire certificate.

The designer will only need to consult with one authority and will then not be in a position to receive advice from both authorities, which has sometimes been contradictory in the past.

0.21 Under the Health and Safety at Work etc Act 1974 certain highly specialised industrial and storage premises have to be certified by the Health and Safety Executive.

0.22 The Housing Act 1985 requires Local Authorities to ensure adequate means of escape in houses in multiple occupation, and compliance with this AD will enable a newly constructed or converted HMO to achieve an acceptable standard of fire safety.

0.23 Occupied premises may be subject to other statutes enforced by either the Local Authority or the fire authority.

Management of premises

0.24 Proper management of premises is essential and B 1 assumes that this will be effected. Premises which are not properly managed risk prosecution for the building owner or occupier under other legislation which may also result in prohibition of the use of the premises.

Analysis of the problem

0.25 Design of means of escape should take into account:

The form of the building;

The activities of the occupants;

The likelihood of fire;

The potential sources of fire; and

The potential for fire spread.

0.26 Fires do not normally start in different places in a building at the same time, so initially fire will create a hazard only where it starts and in the early stage will be unlikely to involve a large area.

Subsequently it may spread to other parts of the building, usually along circulation routes.

Furnishings and other items not controlled by the Regulations are most likely to be ignited first. Fire is less likely to start within the structure itself, and the risk of it starting in circulation areas is also limited provided the combustible content of these areas is restricted.

0.27 Smoke and noxious gases are a greater danger than flame. They cause most casualties and may obscure the way to escape routes and exits. Measures to limit the rapid spread of smoke fumes must be of paramount importance in the design of safe means of escape.

Criteria for means of escape

0.28 (*a*) Alternative means of escape from most situations;

(*b*) Where there is no direct escape to a place of safety, it should be possible to reach a place of relative safety such as a protected stairway, which is on a route to an exit within a reasonable travel distance. Then the means of escape will consist of two parts;

1   Unprotected in accommodation and circulation areas.

2   Protected in protected stairways and, in some instances, protected corridors.

The ultimate place of safety is in open air, clear of the effects of fire. In large buildings, reasonable safety may be reached within the building, provided suitable planning and protection measures have been incorporated.

0.29 *Not* acceptable for means of escape are

(*a*) Lifts: but a suitably designed and installed evacuation lift for use by disabled people can be accepted;

(*b*) Portable ladders and throw-out ladders;

(*c*) Fold down ladders and similar manipulative appliances.

Escalators should not be counted in calculations for stair capacity although they may be used during escape.

Mechanised walkways can be accepted on the basis of their use as a walking route when not in operation.

Alternative means of escape	**0.30** In the event of fire, people should be able to turn their backs on it and travel away from it to a final exit or protected escape route leading to a place of safety. Although there is a possibility of a single escape route being rendered impassable by fire, smoke or fumes, a single escape route (dead end) can in limited circumstances be acceptable as providing reasonable safety. Use of a dead-end situation depends on the use, associated fire risk, size and height of the building, the extent of the dead end and the numbers of persons who may be within the dead end.
Unprotected and protected escape routes	**0.31/0.32** People should not have to travel excessive distances while exposed to smoke and fire in unprotected escape routes so these must be limited in extent. Also in protected horizontal escape routes some limitation is necessary because the structure will not give indefinite protection. Protected stairways should provide 'fire sterile' areas which will enable persons to be safe from immediate danger and then proceed at their own pace to places of safety outside the building. These stairways should have fire resisting construction or have a smoke control system (eg pressurisation) or a combination of both, so that, as far as possible, flames, smoke and gases cannot enter. Unprotected or 'accommodation' stairs can be used for normal daily use but these can only play a very limited role in means of escape terms.
Means of escape for disabled people	**0.33** Part M of the Regulations requires reasonable provision to be made for access by disabled persons to certain buildings. It does not give any specific guidance on means of escape in case of fire. Buildings to which disabled people have access should have management arrangements to provide assistance with escape. BS 5588 *Fire precautions in the design and construction of buildings: Part 8: Code of practice for means of escape for disabled people* gives guidance and introduces the concept of refuges and the use of an evacuation lift. It also stresses the need for effective management of evacuation procedures.
Health care and other institutional premises	**0.34** In hospitals and similar premises the principle of total evacuation may not be appropriate because of the immobility of numbers of the inhabitants. The guidance in AD B 1 may not be suitable for the specialised nature of health care premises and the Department of Health has published guidance under the general title of 'Firecodes'. Means of escape in new hospitals should be to one of the following Firecodes: *Nucleus Fire Recommendations*, or *Health Technical Memorandum 81* The Home Office *Draft Guide for Fire Precautions in Hospitals* should be used in connection with means of escape work to existing NHS hospitals or NHS trust hospitals. The *Draft Guide to Fire Precautions in existing Residential Care Premises* also provides useful information. Where a one- or two-storey house is converted to use as an unsupervised Group home for not more than seven mentally ill or mentally handicapped people it should be regarded as Purpose Group (1c) if means of escape are provided in accordance with Health Technical Memorandum 88.
Security	**0.35** Conflict can occur with the control of entry, and exit and entry for the fire service can be hindered by measures to prevent unauthorised entry. These potential problems should be identified and resolved at the design stage, and it is suggested that architectural liaison officers of the police force can offer useful advice.
Use of B 1	**0.36** Sections 1 and 2 deal with dwellings and Sections 3, 4 and 5 are on buildings other than dwellings. Section 1 – dwelling houses Section 2 – flats and maisonettes Section 3 – the design of means of escape on one level, ie the horizontal phase in multi-storey buildings Section 4 – stairways and the vertical phase of the escape route Section 5 – matters common to all parts of the means of escape, other than houses.

Methods of measurement   **0.37/0.40**   These methods of measurement apply specifically to AD B 1 (see diagram [2.1]).

0.37 **[2.1]** *Measurement: travel distance and width.*

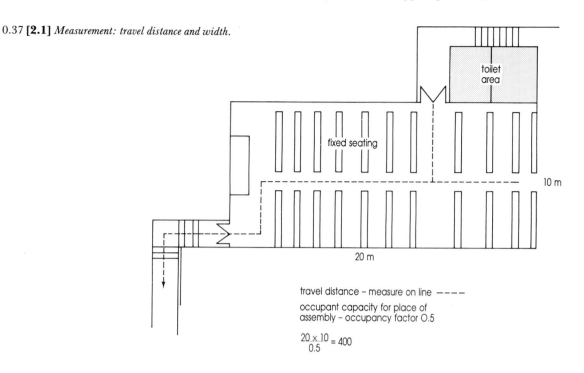

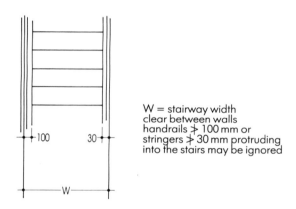

Occupant capacity

(*i*)   Of a room or storey – is the maximum number of persons it is designed to hold (where this is known) or

The number calculated using the occupancy load factors in the Table to 0.38. This is

$$\frac{\text{area of room or storey (m}^2)}{\text{floor space factor m}^2/\text{person}}$$

Area excludes stair enclosures, lifts and sanitary accommodation.

(*ii*)   Of a building or part of a building – the sum of the number of occupants of the storeys in the building or part.

Travel distance

This is the shortest route which if:

(*i*)   There is fixed seating or other fixed obstructions – is along the centre line of the seatways and gangways

(*ii*)   Includes a stair – is along the pitch line of the centre of travel.

Width

Doorway – width of the opening leaf (or the sum of the widths if there are double doors). It is *not* the clear width between door stops.

Escape route – is the width at 1.5 m above the floor or the stair pitch line when defined by walls or elsewhere, the minimum width of passage between any fixed obstructions.
Handrails fixed to walls may be ignored.
Stair – clear width between the walls or balustrades. Stringers and handrails intruding not more than 30 mm and 100 mm respectively may be ignored.

Table to 0.38 Floor space factors

Type of accommodation[1][6]	Floor space factor (m²/person)
1 Standing spectator areas	0.3
2 Amusement arcade, assembly hall (including a general-purpose place of assembly), bar (including a lounge bar), bingo hall, dance floor or hall, club, crush hall, venue for pop concert and similar events, queueing area	0.5
3 Concourse or shopping mall[2]	0.75
4 Committee room, common room, conference room, dining room, licensed betting office (public area), lounge (other than a lounge bar), meeting room, reading room, restaurant, staff room, waiting room[3]	1.0
5 Exhibition hall	1.5
6 Shop sales area[4], skating rink	2.0
7 Art gallery, dormitory, factory production area, office (open-plan exceeding 60 m²), workshop	5.0
8 Kitchen, library, office (other than in 7 above), shop sales area[5]	7.0
9 Bedroom or study bedroom	8.0
10 Bed-sitting room, billiards room	10.0
11 Storage and warehousing	30.0
12 Car park	Two persons per parking space

NOTES
[1] Where accommodation is not directly covered by the descriptions given, a reasonable value based on a similar use may be selected.
[2] Refer to Section 4 of BS 5588: Part 10 for detailed guidance on the calculation of occupancy in common public areas in shopping complexes.
[3] Alternatively, the occupant capacity may be taken as the number of fixed seats provided, if the occupants will be seated.
[4] Shops, excluding those under item 8 but including supermarkets and department stores (all sales areas), shops for personal services such as hairdressing and shops for the delivery or collection of goods for cleaning, repair or other treeatment or for members of the public themselves carrying out such cleaning, repair or other treatment.
[5] Shops (excluding those in covered shopping complexes and excluding department stores) trading predominantly in furniture, floor coverings, cycles, prams, large domestic appliances or other bulky goods, or trading on a wholesale self-selection basis (cash and carry).
[6] If there is to be a mixed use, the most onerous factor(s) should be applied.

Section 1 Dwelling houses

1.1/1.3 Each habitable room should:
(*a*)   Open directly onto a hallway or stair leading to the entrance, or
(*b*)   have a window or door through which escape could be made and means are provided for giving early warning in the event of fire. More complex provisions are needed with increasing height because escape through windows becomes more hazardous.
It is then necessary to protect the internal stairway.
Floors above 7.5 m from ground level present a greater risk because the stairs may become impassable before occupants in the upper part of the house have escaped, and here an alternative route from those upper parts is called for.
Measures that significantly interfere with the day-to-day convenience of the occupants cannot be relied upon in the long term.

As previously mentioned, AD B 1 is also applicable to HMOs. The definition in Section 345 of the Housing Act 1985 is 'a house which is occupied by persons who do not form a single household'.

There are many local interpretations of this definition and guidance on the meaning of the term (which may be equally unhelpful) is given in the joint DOE/Home Office/Welsh Office Circular (DOE12/86; HO39/86; WO23/86) entitled *Memorandum on overcrowding and houses in multiple occupation.*

General provisions

1.4 The installation of self-contained smoke alarms or automatic fire detection and alarm systems can significantly increase the level of safety by giving an early warning of fire.

1.5 If no automatic fire detection and alarm system at least to the L3 standard in accordance with BS 5839: Part 1 has been installed, dwellings should be provided with a suitable number of mains-operated self-contained smoke alarms conforming to BS 5446: Part 1 installed as stated in paragraph 1.8. Mains units with a secondary power supply are acceptable, but those operated only by primary batteries are not.

1.6 In large dwellings, if the circulation route from one room to another is more than 30 m in length, a system of discrete detectors and alarms connected to a control and indicating unit should be installed. The installation should be to the L3 standard of BS 5839: Part 1.

1.7 Dwellings which are part of a sheltered housing scheme with a warden should have detection equipment connected to a central monitoring point so that either a central alarm relay station or the person in charge is aware that fire has been detected and can identify the dwelling concerned. This does not apply to communal lounges or other common parts of sheltered housing development or to sheltered accommodation in the Institutional or Other Residential purpose groups.

Installation of self-contained alarms

1.8 Smoke alarms should be positioned in circulation areas. They should be near enough to places where fires are most likely to start, to pick up smoke in the early stages and also close enough to bedroom doors for the alarm to be effective when the occupants are asleep.

1.9/1.10 Alarms should be positioned:

(*a*) within 7 m of the doors to kitchens and living rooms (these are the rooms where fire is most likely to start);

(*b*) within 3 m of bedroom doors (distances are measured horizontally) (see diagram [2.2]).

If (*a*) and (*b*) cannot be satisfied, a second unit should be installed.

Where more than one self-contained smoke alarm is installed they should be interconnected so that detection of smoke by one unit operates the alarm signal in all of them. Manufacturers' instructions should be followed regarding the number of alarms which can be so connected.

1.9 **[2.2]** *Smoke alarms.*

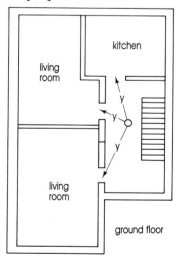

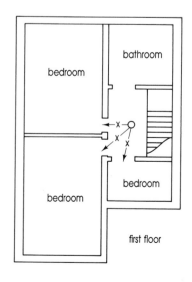

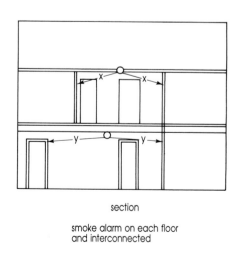

section

smoke alarm on each floor
and interconnected

plan

o smoke alarm
x not more than 3 m from the bedroom doors
y not more than 7 m from the kitchen or living room doors
distances are measured horizontally

1.11/1.15   Other provisions regarding smoke alarms are:

Single-storey houses with accommodation at one level – one alarm is sufficient unless the circulation route exceeds 15 m;

With accommodation on more than one level – at least one alarm per storey.

Fix to ceiling, preferably in a central position at least 300 mm from any light fitting.

Wall-mounted units should be fixed between 150 and 300 mm below the ceiling.

Access will be needed for testing and cleaning. Therefore safety alarms should not be fitted directly over a stairwell.

Smoke alarms should *not* be fixed:

> Next to or directly above heaters or air conditioning outlets in bathrooms, showers, cooking areas, garages, saunas or wherever steam, condensation or fumes could give false alarms;
>
> In places that get very hot or very cold (eg in an unheated porch);
>
> To surfaces which are normally warmer or colder than the rest of the space (air currents may stop smoke from reaching the unit).

The electrical wiring installation should conform to the IEE Regulations but need have no special fire-survival properties.

NOTE   These provisions should not be applied to the common parts of blocks of flats or to maisonettes.

The building control authority cannot make any conditions concerning maintenance, and builders and developers should ensure that occupants have information on the use and maintenance of these systems. Part 1 of BS 5839 recommends that occupiers should receive the manufacturer's operation and maintenance instructions.

Smoke Detectors Act 1991

Attention is also drawn to the provisions of the Smoke Detectors Act 1991, which imposes a requirement on persons, who, in the course of a business, construct or arrange for the construction of a dwelling.

The requirement is that all new dwellings shall be fitted with one or more smoke detectors in such a manner as to make adequate provision for the early detection of the outbreak of a fire in the dwelling.

This was a Private Member's Bill which, in view of the number of lives lost in domestic fires, received government support.

A separate AD may be issued giving guidance on how the requirements of the Act can be implemented.

There could be a certain amount of confusion between the requirements of the Act and the guidance given in AD B1 and it is to be hoped that the guidance will be combined into one Approved Document.

It should be noted that the Smoke Detectors Act only applies to those persons who *in the course of business* construct or arrange for the construction of dwellings. It does not apply to DIY or, presumably, self-build houses, but in these instances the guidance in AD B1 will apply.

Inner rooms

1.16   Where the only escape route from a room (an inner room) is through another room (an access room), the occupants are at risk if a fire starts in the access room.

The only rooms which can be acceptable as inner rooms are:

kitchens, laundry or utility rooms, dressing rooms, bathrooms, wc's, shower rooms or any other room on the basement, ground or first storey which has an openable window or external door suitable for rescue and which complies with the conditions set out in paragraph 1.18.

Basements

1.17   Combustion products tend to rise, so there is a danger that persons escaping from a fire in a basement may have to move into a layer of smoke if they have to use an internal stair.

If a basement contains a habitable room and does not have its own external entrance at basement level there should be an external door or window suitable for escape. The door or window should comply with the conditions set out in paragraph 1.18. If basements are not separated from the rest of the house (and they do not have to be if the house has no floor more than 4.5 m above ground level) rooms in other storeys are effectively inner rooms and should be subject to the provisions of paragraph 1.16.

Windows and external doors for escape

1.18   The minimum size of the unobstructed opening (diagram [2.3] is

Height 850 mm

Width 500 mm

1.18 **[2.3]** *Unobstructed opening.*

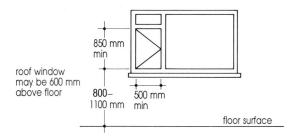

1.18 **[2.4]** *Ground/basement storey exit into enclosed space.*

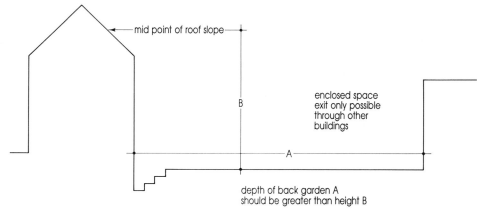

Bottom of window opening – between 800 mm and 1100 mm above the floor (roof windows may be 600 mm above the floor)

At basement or ground level persons escaping should be able to reach a place free from danger from fire (diagram [2.4]).

Means of escape from rooms above ground-storey level, dormer windows or roof windows should be as shown in diagram [2.7]. (See also note 2 after 1.31.)

1.19   Guarding may be needed where a flat roof or balcony is provided for means of escape purposes. In these cases any guarding should meet the provisions of AD K, Stairs, ramps and guards.

Additional provisions for houses with a floor more than 4.5 m above ground level

1.20/1.21   There are separate provisions for houses:

(*a*)   With one storey having a floor more than 4.5 m above ground level, and

(*b*)   With more than one floor over 4.5 m above ground level.

In the case of (*a*) the upper storeys (those above the ground storey) should have a protected stairway which should either:

(*i*)   extend to a final exit (diagram [2.5(a)]) or

(*ii*)   give access to at least two escape routes at ground level (diagram [2.5(b)]).

1.18/1.20/1.24 **[2.5]** *Alternative arrangements for final exits.*

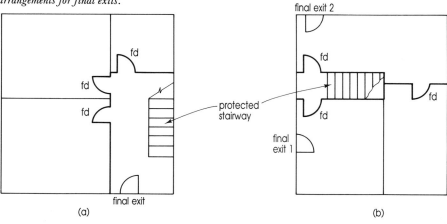

(a)   (b)

fd – FD20 self-closing firedoor
 30 minute fire resistance

The top storey should be separated from the lower storeys by fire-resisting construction and be provided with an alternative escape route leading to its own final exit.

In the case of (*b*) additional measures may be needed.

Guidance in Clause 4.4 of BS 5588: Part 1: 1990 *Code of practice for residential buildings* should be followed.

Ducted warm air heating systems – houses with a floor more than 4.5 m above ground level

1.22   In houses with a floor more than 4.5 m above ground level, precautions may be needed against the possibility of ducted warm air heating systems allowing smoke or fire to spread into a protected stairway.

Guidance can be found in Clause 6 of BS 5588: Part 1. This recommends that transfer grilles should not be fitted in any part of a protected stairway.

Ductwork passing through a protected stairway should have all joints sealed.

Where warm air is ducted into a protected stairway, the return air from the protected stairway should be ducted back to the heater.

Warm air and return air grilles or registers should be at a height not exceeding 450 mm above floor level.

A room thermostat with a maximum setting of 27°C should be mounted in the living room between 1370 mm and 1830 mm above the floor.

Loft conversions

1.23   Paragraphs 1.23 to 1.31 refer to the conversion of the roof space of a two-storey dwelling house into habitable rooms and is an alternative to using the guidance in paragraph 1.20. These alternatives do not apply if:

(*a*)   The work involves raising the roofline above existing ridge level;

(*b*)   The new second storey exceeds 50 m² in floor area;

(*c*)   The new second storey is to contain more than two habitable rooms.

Enclosure of existing stair

1.24   The stair on the ground and first storeys should be enclosed with fire-resisting construction and the enclosure should either:

(*i*)   extend to a final exit (diagram [2.5(a)]) or

(*ii*)   give access to at least two escape routes at ground level (diagram [2.5(b)]).

Doorways and glazing

1.25/1.26   Within the enclosure, every doorway to habitable rooms should be fitted with a self-closing device, and any glazing, including doors, should be fire resisting. Glazing to bathroom or WC is excluded.

New stair and fire separation

1.27/1.28   The new storey should be served by a stair which complies with Part K (alternating tread stairs may be used) (see diagram [2.6(a)]).

The stair may be either in a continuation of the existing stairway or in an enclosure separated from the existing stairway and from ground and first-floor accommodation, but which opens into the existing stairway at first-floor level (diagram [2.6(b)]).

The new storey should be separated from the rest of the house by fire-resisting construction as shown in paragraph 7.7 in Section 7.

A self-closing door set in fire-resisting construction should be provided either at the top or the bottom of the new stairway to prevent smoke and fire in the stairway from entering the new storey (diagram [2.6(c)]).

1.27/1.28 **[2.6]** *New stair and fire separation.*

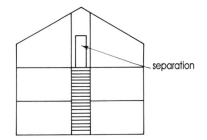

(a) continuation of existing stairway
separation at top level

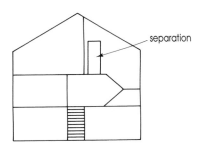

(b) stairway separated from first-floor accommodation
separation at top level

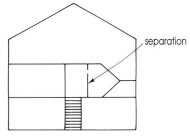

(c) stairway separated from first-floor accommodation
but new storey open to stairway
separation from original stair at first-floor level

Escape windows   **1.29/1.31**   The room or rooms in the new storey should each have an openable window or rooflight for escape or rescue purposes (see diagrams [2.3] and [2.7]).
A door to a roof terrace is also acceptable.

1.29 **[2.7]** *Dormer windows and rooflights suitable for escape purposes.*

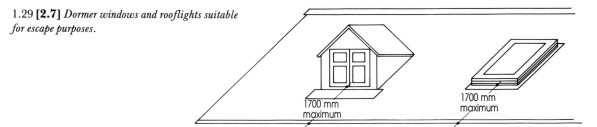

The 1700 mm distance is measured on the roof surface from the eaves to the vertical plane of the dormer

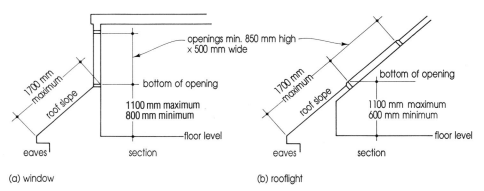

(a) window   (b) rooflight

A window may be in the end wall of the house instead of the roof as shown

The window should be located so as to allow rescue by ladder from the ground. For this to be possible there should be access to carry the ladder from a rescue vehicle to the point where it can be set up, although it should not be assumed that the fire service may make the rescue. This is a departure from the principle that escape should be without outside assistance, but in the case of a three-storey domestic residential loft conversion it is considered that these provisions are reasonable as an emergency measure.

NOTE 1   The 1985 AD was silent on access for a ladder to be set up, and consequently many relaxations and appeals were considered on this particular point.

NOTE 2   In a two room loft conversion, a single escape window can be accepted provided both rooms have their own access to the stairs. A communicating door between the rooms must be provided so that it is possible to gain access to the escape window without passing through the stair enclosure.

Section 2   Flats and maisonettes

Introduction   **2.1**   The means of escape from flats generally ensure that each habitable room either:
(a)   opens directly onto a hallway or stair leading to the entrance, or
(b)   has a window or door through which escape can be made, and that means are provided for giving early warning in the case of fire.
As with houses, the higher the building, the more hazardous is the means of escape and more complex provisions have to be made. Also in maisonettes internal stairs require a higher level of protection.

2.2   This Section deals with the more common arrangements for flats. Guidance on flat arrangements such as flats entered above or below accommodation is given in Clauses 9 and 10 of BS 5588: Part 1.

Clause 9.5 refers to flats entered from below the floor of the flat, Clause 9.6 to flats entered from the floor above the flat and Clause 9.7 deals with flats with galleries. Clause 10 deals with maisonettes.

2.3   Assumptions upon which means of escape from flats are based:

(*a*)   The fire is generally in the dwelling.

(*b*)   No reliance on external rescue (eg by a ladder).

(*c*)   There should be a low probability of fire spread beyond the dwelling where fire originates, because Section 8 of B 3 requires a high degree of compartmentation.

(*d*)   Simultaneous evacuation of the building is not likely to be necessary.

(*e*)   Although fires may occur in the common parts of the building the materials and construction used should prevent the fabric being involved beyond the immediate vicinity of the fire.

2.4   There are two distinct parts to consider in planning means of escape from flats and maisonettes:

1   Escape from within each dwelling (set out in paragraphs 2.7–2.17);

2   Escape from each dwelling to the final exit from the building (paragraphs 2.18–2.45).

2.5   The guidance also applies to HMOs – see comment in Section 1.

Sheltered housing

2.6   Some types of sheltered housing may be treated in accordance with the guidance in Sections 1 and 2, but where additional fire protection measures are necessary there is further guidance in Clause 17 of BS 5588: Part 1: 1990.

Automatic smoke detection and alarms

2.7   The guidance given in Section 1 is equally applicable to flats, but it should be noted that the provisions are not intended to be applied to the common parts of blocks or maisonettes, and that a flat with accommodation on more than one level such as a maisonette should be treated in the same way as a house with more than one storey.

Inner rooms and basements

2.8/2.10   Guidance in Section 1 on inner rooms, basements and balconies and flat roofs is also applicable to flats. The relevant paragraphs are 1.16, 1.17 and 1.19.

Flats where the floor is not more than 4.5 m above ground level

2.11   No flat should be planned to have a habitable room as an inner room unless that room has an external door or window complying with Section 1, paragraph 1.18.

Flats and maisonettes with a floor more than 4.5 m above ground

Internal planning

2.12   The internal planning of these flats should:

(*a*)   Provide a protected entrance hall serving all habitable rooms with a travel distance from the entrance door to the door of any habitable room of not more than 9 m (diagram [2.8(a)]), or

(*b*)   Have a travel distance from the entrance door to any point in any of the habitable rooms of not more than 9 m with the cooking facilities remote from the entrance door and not in a position to prejudice the escape route from any point in the flat (diagram [2.8(b)], or

(*c*)   Provide for an alternative exit which complies with paragraph 2.13.

2.13   Where any flat has an alternative exit and all habitable rooms do not have direct access to the entrance hall:

(*a*)   The bedrooms should be separated from the living accommodation by fire-resisting construction and self-closing fire doors, and

(*b*)   The alternative exit should be located in the part of the flat containing the bedroom(s) (diagram [2.8(c)]).

Internal planning of maisonettes

2.14   A maisonette with its own external entrance at ground level is similar to a dwelling house, so the means of escape can be as either Section 1, paragraphs 1.20 or 1.21, depending on height of the top storey above ground level.

2.15   If a maisonette does not have its own external entrance at ground level but has a floor more than 4.5 m above ground level, the following are acceptable:

(*a*)   Provide an alternative exit from each habitable room which is not on the entrance floor (diagram [2.9(a)]), or

(*b*)   Provide an alternative exit from each floor (other than the entrance floor) with a protected landing entered directly from all the habitable rooms on that floor (diagram [2.9(b)]).

2.12/2.13 **[2.8]** *Planning of flats.*

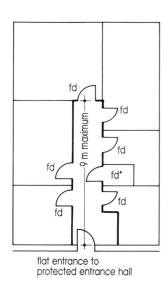

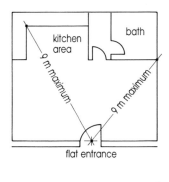

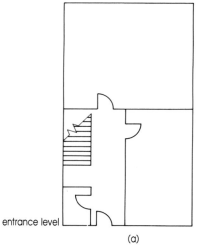

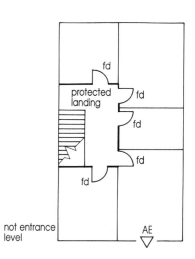

KEY
fd   self closing FD20 fire door
fd*   a cupboard door need not be self-closing
───   30 minute fire-resisting construction
      to entrance hall

(a) all habitable rooms with access to entrance hall

(b) travel distance not more than 9 m
cooking facilities remote and not
near escape route

fd   self-closing FD20 fire door
───   30 minute fire-resisting
      construction between living
      and bedroom accommodation

(c) all habitable rooms not having access
directly to entrance hall

2.15 **[2.9]** *Maisonettes with floor more than 4.5 m*
above ground level: alternative layouts.

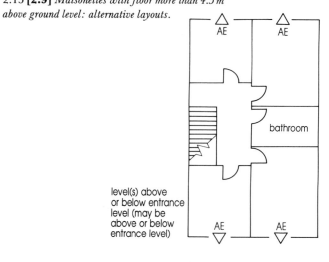

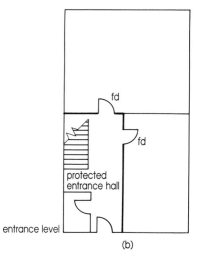

level(s) above
or below entrance
level (may be
above or below
entrance level)

not entrance
level

AE   alternative exit
fd   self-closing FD20 fire door
───   30 minute fire-resisting
      stair enclosure

(a)   (b)

Alternative exits

2.16 An alternative exit from a flat or maisonette should:
(*a*) Be remote from the main entrance door to the dwelling;
(*b*) Lead to a final exit or common stair through:
(*i*) A door on to an access corridor or common balcony, or
(*ii*) An internal private stair leading to an access corridor or common balcony at another level, or
(*iii*) A door on to an external stair, or
(*iv*) A door on to an escape route over a flat roof.

Ducted warm air heating systems in flats and maisonettes with a floor more than 4.5 m above ground level

2.17 Guidance is given in Clause 15 of BS 5588: Part 1 and is similar to that for houses with similar floor levels. For convenience of the reader it is repeated here.

The recommendation is that transfer grilles should not be fitted in any wall, floor or ceiling bounding the entrance hall of a dwelling or stairway within a maisonette. Ductwork passing through such a wall, floor or ceiling should have all joints sealed.

Where warm air is ducted into the entrance hall of the dwelling or stairway within a maisonette through such a wall, floor or ceiling bounding the hall or stairway, the return air from the hall or stairway should be ducted back to the heater.

Warm air and return air grilles or registers should be at a height not exceeding 450 mm above floor level.

A room thermostat with a maximum setting of 27°C should be mounted in the living room between 1370 mm and 1830 mm above the floor.

Means of escape in the common parts of flats and maisonettes

2.18/2.20 These paragraphs deal with the means of escape from the entrance doors from dwellings and from the common parts of the building to a final exit. Generally, every dwelling should have alternative means of escape so that when confronted by an outbreak of fire a person can turn away from it and make a safe escape. Paragraphs 2.18/2.21 only apply where the top floor is more than 4.5 m above ground level.

A single escape route is acceptable, however, if either:
(*a*) The dwelling is in a storey served by one common stair and
(*i*) Every dwelling is separated from the common stair by a protected lobby or common corridor (diagram [2.10]), and
(*ii*) The limitations on the distance of travel in the Table to 2.21 for escape in one direction only are met, or

2.18(a) **[2.10]** *Flats or maisonettes served by one common stair.*

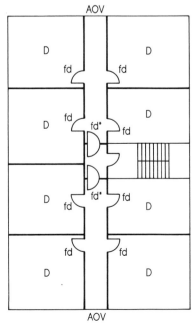

(a) corridor access dwellings

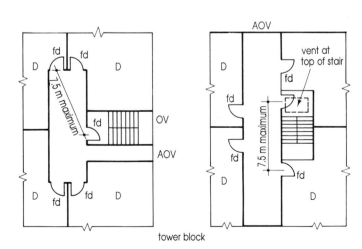

tower block

OV openable vent for (fire service use)
AOV automatic opening vent – 1.5 m² minimum free area
D   dwelling
fd   self-closing FD30s fire door
fd* self-closing FD20s fire door

(b) stair by external wall   (c) internal stair

2.18(b) **[2.11]** *Flats or maisonettes served by more than one common stair.*

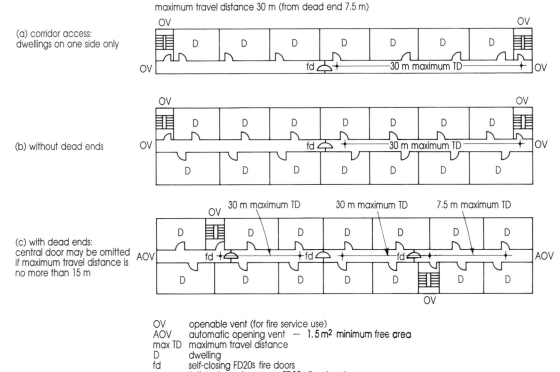

OV openable vent (for fire service use)
AOV automatic opening vent — 1.5 m² minimum free area
max TD maximum travel distance
D dwelling
fd self-closing FD20s fire doors
(other doors shown are FD30s fire doors)

2.20 **[2.12]** *Common escape routes in small single-stair building.*

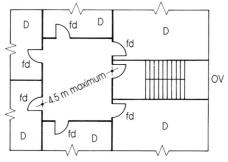

(a) small single-stair building
* if an automatic opening vent is provided
in the lobby, the travel distance can be
increased to 7.5 m maximum (see diagram (2.10(b))

—— fire-resisting construction
fd self-closing FD30S fire door
OV openable vent for fire service
use (it may be replaced by a vent
over the stair)
D dwelling

(b) small single-stair building
with no more than two
dwellings per storey
the door between stair and lobby
should be free from security fastenings.

if the dwellings have protected entrance
halls, the lobby between the common stair
and dwelling entrance is not essential.

(*b*)   The dwelling is in a dead-end part of a common corridor served by two or more common stairs and the travel distance does not exceed that shown in the Table to 2.21 (see diagram [2.11]).

A building may be served by a single stair protected in accordance with diagram [2.12] if all the following are observed:

(*a*)   The top floor of the building is not more than 11 m above ground level.

(*b*)   There are not more than three storeys above the ground-level storey.

(*c*)   The stair does not connect to a covered car park, except if the car park is open sided.

These provisions may also be modified in the case of flats and maisonettes with a balcony or deck approach in accordance with the guidance given in Clause 13 of BS 5588: Part 1.

Common escape routes

2.21   Escape routes in the common areas generally should not involve a distance of travel greater than that shown in the Table to 2.21, but there may be circumstances where some increase may be reasonable. Escape routes should be planned so that people do not have to pass through one stairway enclosure to reach another, but it is acceptable to pass through a protected lobby of one stair to reach another.

Table to 2.21   Limitations on distance of travel in common areas of flat and maisonette buildings

Maximum distance of travel (m) from the dwelling entrance door to a common stair, or to a door to a lobby in corridor access single stairs (diagram [2.10(a)])

Escape in one direction only 7.5 m [1,2]	Escape in more than one direction 30 m [2]

[1] Reduced to 4.5 m in the case shown in diagram [2.12(a)].
[2] Where all dwellings on a storey have independent alternative means of escape, the maximum distance of travel does not apply. However, all parts of the building need to comply with the provisions for fire mains in the guidance on Regulation B 5 (Sections 15–18).

Protection of common escape routes

2.22   Common corridors should be protected corridors and the wall between each dwelling and the corridor should be a compartment wall (see B 3, Section 8).

Ventilation of common escape routes

2.23   Some smoke will inevitably get into a common corridor, if only when the entrance door is open when the occupants escape. It is therefore necessary to provide ventilation for the common escape routes to disperse the smoke as follows:

(a)   (i)   In single-stair buildings other than small ones as in diagram [2.12],
         (ii)   In any dead-end portion of a building with more than one stair – provide in the common corridor or lobby an automatic opening ventilator, triggered by automatic smoke detection located in the space to be ventilated.
         The ventilator should have a free area of at least $1.5\,m^2$ and be fitted with a manual override (see also diagrams [2.10] and [2.11(c)]).
(b)   In buildings with more than one stair –
Common corridors should extend at both ends to the external face of the building where there should be openable ventilators, which operate automatically for fire service use (see diagrams [2.11(a)] and [2.11(b)]).
The free area of the ventilators should be at least $1.5\,m^2$ at each end of the corridor.

Sub-division of common escape routes

2.24/2.25   A common corridor that connects two or more storey exits should be sub-divided by a self-closing fire door and any necessary fire-resisting screen (diagram [2.11]). The door should be positioned so that smoke will not affect access to more than one stairway.
A dead-end portion of a common corridor should be separated from the rest of the corridor by a self-closing door and, if necessary, any associated fire-resisting screen (diagrams [2.10(a)] and [2.11(c)]).

Pressurisation of common escape routes

2.26   Where the escape stairway and corridors/lobbies are protected by a smoke pressurisation system to BS 5588: Part 4, the cross-corridor fire doors and the openable and automatically opening vents should be omitted.

Ancillary accommodation

2.27   Stores and other ancillary accommodation should not be located within or entered from any protected lobby or protected corridor forming part of an escape route. There are special provisions for refuse chutes and storage areas and these are in B 1 Section 5, paragraphs 5.47 to 5.50.

Escape routes over flat roofs

2.28   If there is more than one escape route, one of these routes may be over a flat roof, provided that:
(a)   The roof is part of the same building from which escape is being made;
(b)   The route across the roof leads to a storey exit;

(c)   The part of the roof forming the escape route and its supporting structure, together with any opening within 3 m of the escape route, is fire resisting (see Appendix A, Table A1), and

(d)   The route is adequately defined and guarded by walls and/or protective barriers in accordance with AD K, Stairs, ramps and guards.

Common stairs

2.29/2.30   Except in the cases mentioned in paragraphs 2.18 and 2.19, there should be access to more than one common stair for escape purposes and the minimum width should be 1 m. If the stair is a firefighting stair it should be at least 1.1 m wide (paragraph 0.40 gives guidance on measurement of width).

Enclosure of common stairs

2.31/2.34   Common stairs should be situated within a fire-resisting enclosure, ie a protected stair so as to make the stair less hazardous by reducing the risk of smoke and heat.

Appendix A, Tables A1 and A2 give the appropriate levels of fire resistance. There is guidance in B 3 Section 8 on the enclosure of stairs and on firefighting stairs in B 5 Section 17.

Protected stairways

2.35/2.39   Protected stairways should discharge:

To a final exit, or

By way of a protected exit passageway to a final exit.

Where two protected stairways (or exit passageways leading to different final exits) are adjacent, they should be separated by an imperforate enclosure.

Protected stairways can include a lift well but should not be used for anything else. Provisions for lifts are in paragraphs 5.37 to 5.42.

Where a protected stairway projects beyond or is recessed from, or is in an internal angle of, the adjoining external wall of the building, a fire in one part of the building could subject the external wall of a protected stairway to heat.

To safeguard the stairway the distance between any unprotected area in the external enclosures to the building and any unprotected area in the enclosure to the stairway should be at least 1.8 m (see diagram [2.13]).

Gas service pipes and meters should not be incorporated into a protected stairway unless the gas installation complies with the Gas Safety Regulations, ie

Gas Safety Regulations 1972 (SI 1972. 1178)

Gas Safety (Installation and Use) Regulations 1984 (SI 1984/1358) as amended by the

Gas Safety (Installation and Use) (Amendment) Regulations 1990.

2.38 **[2.13]** *External protection to protected stairways: stairs in relation to external walls.*

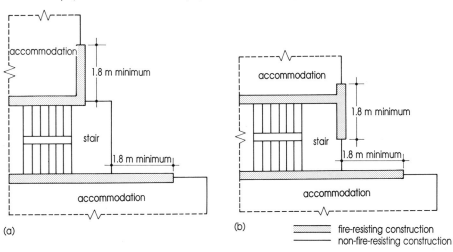

Basement stairs

2.40/2.42   An escape stair which forms part of the only escape route from an upper storey of a building or part should not be continued down to serve a basement storey. The basement should be served by a separate stair. This is to prevent a basement fire endangering upper storeys by filling upper stairways with smoke.

However, if there is more than one escape stair in a building, only one of the stairs serving the upper storeys need be terminated at ground level.

The other stairs may continue down provided there is a ventilated protected lobby or a ventilated protected corridor between the stair(s) and the accommodation at each basement level.

Stairs serving accommodation ancillary to flats and maisonettes

2.43/2.44 Common stairs which form part of the only escape route from a dwelling should not also serve a covered car park, boiler room fuel storage space or other ancillary accommodation likely to be a fire risk. Where such stairs do not form part of the only escape route they may also serve such accommodation but should be separated from it by a protected lobby.

External escape stairs

2.45 If there is more than one escape route from a storey (or part of a building), one of the routes may be by way of an external escape stair provided that:

2.45 **[2.14]** *Fire resistance of areas adjacent to external stairs.*

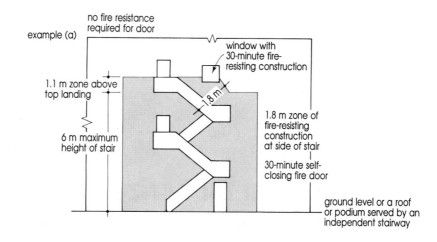

example (a)

no fire resistance required for door

window with 30-minute fire-resisting construction

1.1 m zone above top landing

1.8 m

1.8 m zone of fire-resisting construction at side of stair

6 m maximum height of stair

30-minute self-closing fire door

ground level or a roof or podium served by an independent stairway

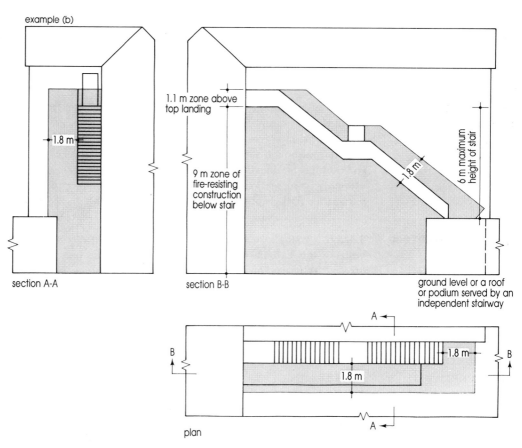

example (b)

section A-A

1.8 m

1.1 m zone above top landing

9 m zone of fire-resisting construction below stair

section B-B

1.8 m

6 m maximum height of stair

ground level or a roof or podium served by an independent stairway

plan

1.8 m

1.8 m

(*a*)   The stair serves a floor not more than 6 m above either the ground level or a roof or podium which is itself served by a protected stairway (see diagram [2.14]);

(*b*)   All doors giving access to the stairway should be fire resisting and self-closing, but a fire-resisting door is not required at the head of any stair leading downwards where there is only one exit from the building onto the top landing;

(*c*)   Parts of the external walls near the stair should be of fire-resisting construction (see diagram [2.14]);

(*d*)   Any part of the building within 3 m of the escape route to a place of safety (including doors) should be of fire-resisting construction.

Flats in mixed-use buildings

2.46   In buildings with not more than three storeys above ground level, stairs may serve dwellings and non-residential occupancies if the stairs are separated from each occupancy by protected lobbies at all levels.

2.47   If a flat is ancillary to the main use of the building, the stair serving the flat may also serve other parts of the building provided:

(*i*)   The stair is separated from such other parts on lower storeys by protected lobbies;

(*ii*)   An independent alternative escape route is provided from the flat; and

(*iii*)   Any automatic fire detection and alarm system fitted in the main part also covers the flat.

Section 3   Design for horizontal escape – buildings other than dwellings

Introduction

3.1   This Section (and Section 4) deals with means of escape from all buildings other than dwelling houses, flats and maisonettes. Section 3 should be read in conjunction with Section 4 (Vertical Escape) and the General provisions in Section 5.

Number of escape routes and exits

3.2/3.4   The number of escape routes and exits depends on the number of occupants in the room, tier or storey and the travel distance to the nearest exit. Where more than one stair is needed for escape (see Section 4) every part of each storey will need to have access to more than one stair, although some access may be by way of a dead-end condition.

In buildings of mixed use, the means of escape from any residential part and any part used for assembly or recreation purposes should be independent of the means of escape from the other parts. (See paragraphs 2.46 and 2.47.)

Single escape routes and exits

3.5/3.6   A single route is acceptable where the travel distance to a storey exit is within the limits in the Table to 3.6 for travel in one direction only:

(*a*)   Where no one room in this situation has an occupant capacity of more than 30 people, if it is a building in institutional use (purpose group 2a) or 50 people in any other case. See paragraph 0.38 for calculation of occupant capacities;

(*b*)   Where a storey has an occupant capacity of not more than 50 people (except a storey used for in-patient care in a hospital).

In many instances at the beginning of an escape route there will be only one direction in which to travel, eg in a room to the only doorway and then from the doorway there may be an alternative route.

This is acceptable provided the escape in one direction only does not exceed the limits in the Table to 3.2 for escape in one direction and the overall distance does not exceed the limit where there are alternative routes (see diagram [2.15]).

3.6 **[2.15]** *Travel distance: dead-end condition.*

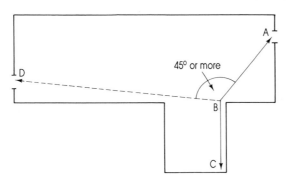

If angle DBA is 45° or more BA and BD can
be considered as alternative routes from B.
Travel distance CA or CD (whichever is less)
should not exceed that shown in the Table
to 3.6 for travel in more than one direction
and CB should be no greater than that
shown for travel in one direction

Table to 3.6   Limitations on travel distance

Purpose group	Use of the premises or part of the premises	Maximum travel distance[1] where travel is possible in:	
		One direction only (m)	More than one direction (m)
2(a)	Institutional[2]	9	18
2(b)	Other residential:		
	(a) in bedrooms[3]	9	18
	(b) in bedroom corridors	9	35
	(c) elsewhere	18	35
3	Office	18	45
4	Shop and commercial[4]	18	45
5	Assembly and recreation		
	(a) buildings primarily for the handicapped except schools	9	18
	(b) elsewhere	15	32
6	Industrial[5]	25	45
7	Storage and other non-residential[5]	18	45
2,3,4,5,6 or 7	Places of special fire risk[6]	9[3]	18[3]
2,3,4,5,6 or 7	Plant room or rooftop plant:		
	(a) distance within the room	9	35
	(b) escape route not in open air	18	45
	(c) escape route in open air	60	100

NOTES

[1] The dimensions in the Table are travel distances. If the internal layout of partitions, fittings, etc is not known when plans are deposited, direct distances may be used for assessment. The direct distance is taken as two thirds of the travel distance.

[2] If provision for means of escape is being made in a hospital or other health care building by following the detailed guidance in the relevant part of the Department of Health 'Firecode', the recommendations about travel distances in the appropriate 'Firecode' document should be followed.

[3] Maximum part of travel distance within the room.

[4] Maximum travel distances within shopping malls are given in BS 5588: Part 10: 1991 (see diagram [2.16]). Guidance on associated smoke control measures is given in a BRE report *Design principles for smoke ventilation in enclosed shopping centres* (BR 186).

[5] In industrial buildings the appropriate travel distance depends on the level of fire risk associated with the processes and materials being used. Control over the use of industrial buildings is exercised through the Fire Precautions Act. Attention is drawn to the guidance issued by the Home Office's *Guide to fire precautions in existing places of work that require a fire certificate – Factories, Offices, Shops and Railway Premises*. The dimensions given above assume that the premises will be of 'normal' fire risk as described in the Home Office guidance. If the building is high risk, as assessed against

the criteria in the Home Office guidance, then lesser distances of 12 m in one direction and 25 m in more than one direction would apply.

6 Places of special fire risk are listed in the definitions in Appendix E.

NOTE (to Table to 3.6)   BS 5588: Part 10: 1991 gives the following travel distances (other than in malls):

With the exception of engineering services, engineering rooms, boiler rooms, fuel storage rooms, battery and switchgear rooms, the maximum travel distance within a room or area and to the nearest storey exit is:

In one direction only: 18 m

In more than one direction: 45 m (this may include 18 m in one direction only)

For the exceptions, the distances are 9 m and 18 m respectively.

The maximum travel distance for malls is shown in diagram 2.17 in the British Standard.

Table to 3.6 **[2.16]** *Covered malls: travel distance.*

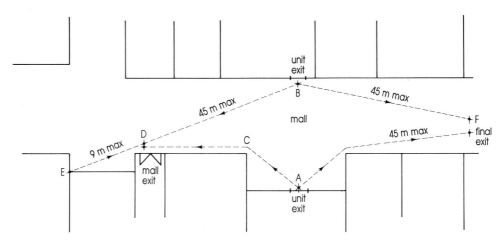

travel distance AF, BF, BD, AD 45 m maximum
ED 9 m maximum (dead end)

NOTE In uncovered malls dead ends may exceed 9 m if the total travel distance to the mall exit is not more than 25 m.

3.8 **[2.17]** *Alternative escape routes.*

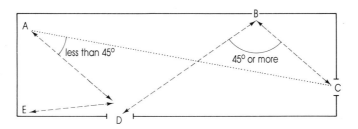

alternative routes – from B – BC and BD
because DBC = 45° or more
No alternative route from A because DAC is less than 45°
∴ AD (and ED) must not exceed travel distance in one direction

Number of occupants and exits

3.7   Use either the design occupancy numbers or, if this is not known, the capacity calculated in accordance with paragraph 0.38 and the Table below. The Table gives the minimum number of escape routes but this is likely to be increased by the need to observe travel distances etc.

Table to 3.7   Minimum number of escape routes and exits from a room, tier or storey

Maximum number of persons	*Minimum number of escape routes/exits*
500	2 [1]
1 000	3
2 000	4
4 000	5
7 000	6
11 000	7
16 000	8
more than 16 000	8 [2]

NOTES
[1] See paragraph 3.5 about the circumstances in which single exits and escape routes are acceptable.
[2] Plus 1 per 5000 persons (or part) over 16 000.

Alternative escape routes

3.8   If all escape routes are likely to be simultaneously disabled, they will be of little value. They should therefore be in directions:
(*a*)   45° or more apart (see diagram [2.17]) or
(*b*)   45° or less apart but separated from each other by fire-resisting construction.

Inner rooms

3.9   An inner room is one from which escape can only be made through another room – the access room. An inner room situation is acceptable only if:
(*a*)   The occupant capacity is not more than 50 (30 for PG 2a buildings – Institutional);
(*b*)   The inner room is not a bedroom;
(*c*)   Escape from the inner room does not pass through more than one access room;
(*d*)   The travel distance from any point in the inner room to the exit of the access room is within the appropriate limits;
(*e*)   The access room is in the control of the same occupier and is not a place of special fire risk; *and*
(*f*)   One of the following arrangements is made:
    (*i*)   The walls/partitions of the inner room are stopped 500 mm minimum below the ceiling;
    (*ii*)   There is a vision panel in the door or walls of the inner room (approx. $0.1 \, m^2$) to enable occupants of the inner room to see if a fire has started in the access room; or
    (*iii*)   The access room is fitted with an automatic fire detection and alarm system.

Planning of exits in a central core

3.10   Where buildings have more than one exit to the central core, storey exits should be remote from one another and so that no two exits are approached from the same lift hall, common lobby or unventilated corridor, or linked by any of these (see diagram [2.18]).

Access to storey exits

3.11   If a storey has more than one escape stair, the arrangement should be that it is not necessary to pass through one stairway to reach another, but it is acceptable to pass through the protected lobby of one stairway to reach another stair.

Separation of circulation routes from stairways

3.12   A protected stairway should not form part of the primary circulation route between different parts of the building at the same level. This is because the necessary self-closing doors may be ineffective if they are a nuisance to the occupants and, as often happens with doors in constant use, the 'standard wedge' is used to keep them open or the closers are removed.

Storeys divided into different occupancies

3.13   Where there are separate ownerships or tenancies in the same storey:
(*a*)   The means of escape from any one occupancy should not pass through another occupancy; and
(*b*)   If the means of escape include a common corridor/circulation space it should either be a protected corridor or the storey should be fitted with an automatic fire detection and alarm system.

3.10 **[2.18]** *Exits in central core.*

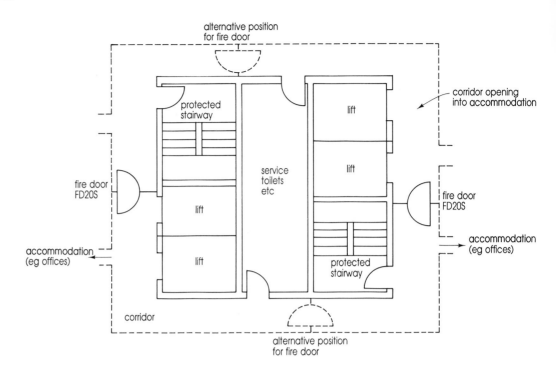

Height and width of escape routes

3.14/3.16   The clear headroom should be at least 2 m except in doorways. The width depends on the number of persons needing to use them and should be in accordance with the Table to 3.15. If the numbers are not known, calculate using paragraph 0.38. Methods of measurement of width are given in paragraph 0.40.

Table to 3.15   Width of escape routes and exits

Maximum number of persons	*Minimum width (mm)* [1]
50	800 [2]
110	900
220	1100
more than 220	5 per person

NOTES
[1] See guidance in the AD to Part M on minimum widths for areas accessible to disabled people.
[2] May be reduced to 530 mm for gangways between fixed storage racking, other than in public areas of PG 4 (shop and commercial).

Discounting of exits

3.17   When there are two or more exits to a storey, it has to be assumed that in the event of fire, the occupants may be prevented from using one of the exits. The remaining exit or exits need to be wide enough to enable the occupants to leave quickly and safely. It is therefore necessary when calculating the total width of exits needed (by using the Table to 3.15) to discount the exit which has the largest width. This may also have implications on the width of stairways because they should be at least as wide as any storey exit leading on to them.
Although paragraph 4.11 indicates some stairways which are not subject to discounting, storey exit width should always be subjected to this guidance on discounting.
3.18   See BS 5588: Part 6 for guidance on spacing of fixed seating for auditoria etc (diagram [2.19]).

3.18 **[2.19]** *Spacing of fixed seating in auditoria.*

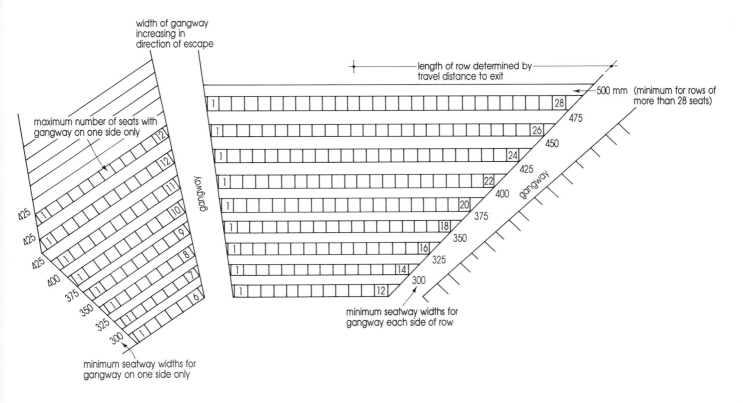

Corridors

Protected corridors

3.19   The following should be protected corridors:

(*a*)   Corridors within residential accommodation;

(*b*)   Dead-end corridors; and

(*c*)   Corridors common to two or more occupancies.

Corridors which are not protected

3.20   Where a corridor is used for means of escape and is not a protected corridor, the enclosing partitions should be carried up to the structural floor above or to a suspended ceiling. Openings into rooms from the corridor should be fitted with doors which need not be fire doors. Partitions provide some defence against the spread of smoke. Open planning, of course, does not, but it has the advantage that occupants become quickly aware of a fire.

Sub-division of corridors

3.21/3.22   Corridors which provide access to alternative escape routes should be sub-divided by self-closing fire doors (and screens where necessary) where the length of the corridor exceeds 12 m so that:

(*a*)   No length of undivided corridor is common to two storey exits; and

(*b*)   Having regard to the layout and any adjacent fire risks, the fire door(s) are positioned to protect the route from smoke.

If corridors are not sub-divided in this way there is a risk that the spread will make both routes impassable before all the occupants have escaped.

Unless they are protected by a pressurisation system to BS 5588: Part 4, dead-end corridors longer than 4.5 m should be separated by self-closing fire doors (and screens where necessary) from any part of the corridor which:

(*a*)   Provides two directions of escape, or

(*b*)   Continues past one storey exit to another.

(See diagram [2.20].)

External escape routes

3.23/3.25   That part of an external wall which is within 3 m of an external escape route, other than a stair, should be of fire-resisting construction up to a height of 1.1 m above the floor level of the route. (See also paragraph 4.35.)

3.21 **[2.20]** *Dead-end corridors.*

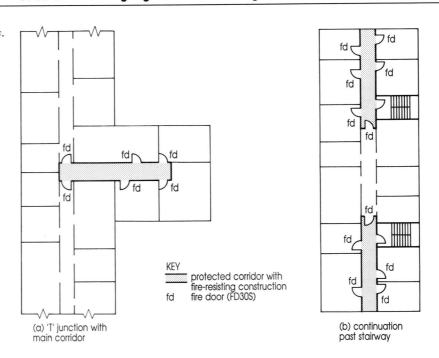

KEY

protected corridor with fire-resisting construction

fd   fire door (FD30S)

(a) 'T' junction with main corridor

(b) continuation past stairway

Where one of the escape routes from a storey or part of a building (other than an institutional building or a building intended to be used by members of the public) is over a flat roof:

(a)   The roof should be part of the building from which escape is being made;

(b)   The route across the roof should lead to a storey exit;

(c)   The roof forming the escape route and any opening within 3 m of it should be fire-resisting (see Appendix A, Table A1); and

(d)   The route should be clearly defined and guarded by walls and protective barriers in accordance with AD K, Stairs, ramps and guards.

Hospitals and other residential care premises – purpose group 2a

General

3.26/3.27   One of the features in the Department of Health ('Firecode') documents is the concept of progressive horizontal evacuation. This allows escape to be made in those areas of in-patient care by evacuation into adjoining compartments or sub-divisions of compartments. This can provide a place of relative safety within a short distance from where further evacuation can be made should it become necessary.

Planning for progressive horizontal evacuation

3.28/3.29   Horizontal evacuation could also be used in some other residential care buildings and the following conditions should be observed:

(a)   Compartments into which the evacuation may take place should have sufficient space for the needs of their own occupants and the needs of those who may arrive from the adjoining compartment. The space needed should be calculated on the design occupancy basis.

(b)   Each compartment should have at least one other escape route independent of the route into the adjoining compartment.

This route may be by way of a third compartment provided the third compartment has an exit independent of the exits from the other compartments (see diagram [2.21]).

3.28 **[2.21]** *Progressive horizontal evacuation.*

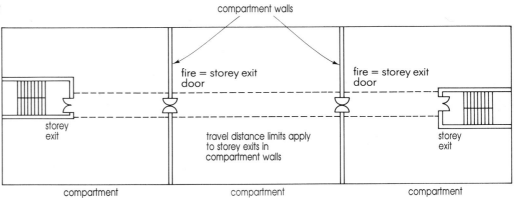

compartment walls

fire = storey exit door

fire = storey exit door

storey exit

travel distance limits apply to storey exits in compartment walls

storey exit

compartment   compartment   compartment

3.30   Every upper storey used for in-patient care should be divided into at least two compartments so as to allow progressive horizontal evacuation of each compartment.

Assembly buildings

3.31   Difficulties may arise with escape where fixed seating is installed and guidance on means of escape from assembly buildings is in BS 5588: Part 6, sections 3 and 5. Where the Safety of Grounds Act 1975 applies, the Green guide – *Guide to safety at sports grounds* – should be followed.

Schools and other educational buildings

3.32   Means of escape in schools should be designed in accordance with *Building Bulletin* 7 published by the Department of Education and Science.

3.33   Certain specialised buildings found on some educational premises may be outside the scope of *Building Bulletin* 7, and in these cases the guidance in the appropriate BS or in another relevant reference should be followed.

Small shops

3.34   Guidance on means of escape for small shops can be found in clause 9 of BS 5588: Part 2 and may be followed instead of the provisions in this Section. A small shop is one having no storey larger than $280\,m^2$ and no more than two storeys plus a basement storey.

BS 5588: Part 10 (*Shopping complexes*) applies more restrictive provisions to units with only one exit.

Shopping complexes

3.35   Shopping complexes present a different set of means of escape problems, and it may be preferable to follow the guidance in BS 5588: Part 10.

Offices

3.36   As an alternative, BS 5588: Part 3 may be used, but if this is done, all the provisions of Sections 2, 3, 4 and 5 of the Code should be followed and not a mixture of parts of the Code and parts from Sections 3–5 of this document.

Section 4   Design for vertical escape from buildings other than dwellings

Introduction

4.1   Adequately sized and protected escape stairs are an important aspect of means of escape from multi-storey buildings. This section deals with escape stairs including measures necessary to protect them.

As with Section 3, this section applies to all types of building other than dwelling houses, flats and maisonettes but should be read in conjunction with Section 5.

Number of escape stairs

4.2/4.3   This is determined by:
(*a*)   The provisions of Section 34 regarding the design of horizontal escape routes;
(*b*)   Whether independent stairs are required for mixed-occupancy buildings;
(*c*)   Whether a single stair is acceptable;
(*d*)   Provision of adequate width for escape with the possibility of a stair having to be discounted because of fire and smoke;
(*e*)   In large buildings whether firefighting stairs are required.

4.4   Where a building contains parts which are in different purpose groups and one of those is either assembly and recreation or residential, there should be a means of escape separate from that serving any other purpose group.

Single escape stairs

4.5   Subject to the provisions of paragraph 4.4, a building or part may be served by a single escape stair in the following:
(*a*)   From a basement which is allowed to have a single escape route (see paragraph 3.5);
(*b*)   From a building having no storey with a floor level more than 11 m above ground level provided every storey is allowed to have a single escape route (see Section 3.5);
(*c*)   In offices where the recommendations of Clause 8 of BS 5588: Part 3: 1983 are followed.

Width of escape stairs

4.6/4.8   The width:

(*a*)   should not be less than the width of any exit giving access to them;

(*b*)   should conform with the Table to 4.6;

(*c*)   should not exceed 1400 mm if they rise more than 30 m, unless the stairs are at least 1800 mm wide and have a central handrail;

(*d*)   should not reduce in width at any point on the way to a final exit.

If the width of stair needed is more than 1800 mm it should have a central handrail for reasons of safety, and the stair width on each side of the central handrail should be considered separately when calculating stair capacity.

Where the exit route from a stair is also part of the escape route from the ground storey and/or basement storeys the width may need to be increased.

NOTE   Research indicates that people prefer to stay within reach of a handrail when making a prolonged descent, so the centre part of a wider stair could be hazardous, and is little used. Therefore additional stairs may be needed. Buildings with a floor more than 30 m above ground level may also be designed for phased evacuation if the provisions of paragraph 4.19 are met.

Table to 4.6   Minimum width of escape stairs

Situation of stair	Max. number of people served[1]	Minimum stair width (mm)
1. In an institutional building (unless it will only be used by staff)	150	1000
2. In an assembly building and serving an area used for assembly purposes (unless the area is less than 100 m^2)	220	1100
3. In any other building and serving an area with an occupancy of more than 50	over 220	[2]
4. Any stair not described above	50	800

NOTES
[1] Assessed as likely to use the stair in a fire emergency.
[2] See Table to 4.17 for sizing stairs for total evacuation and Table to 4.23 for phased evacuation.

Calculation of stair width

4.9/4.10   The following should be considered in calculating stair width.

The escape stair should:

(*a*)   Be wide enough to accommodate the number of persons needing to use it in case of emergency;

(*b*)   Be designed according to the escape strategy – whether total evacuation of the building or part of the building or phased evacuation;

(*c*)   Be calculated, where the number of persons likely to use the stair is not known, on the basis of occupant capacity (paragraph 0.38).

Discounting of stairs

4.11/4.14   Where two or more stairs are provided, one of the stairs could become unusable because it may be affected by fire or smoke. It is therefore necessary to discount each stair in turn in order to ensure that the remaining stair(s) have adequate capacity for the number of persons who may need to escape.

However, if the escape stairs are approached on each storey (but not necessarily the topmost storey) through a protected lobby there is less likelihood that the stair will be affected by smoke or fire and it is not necessary to discount one stair.

Discounting is also unnecessary if the stairways are either protected by a smoke control system to BS 5588: Part 4. If the building is fitted throughout with a sprinkler system to BS 5306: Part 2, the discounting rule applies unless the stairs are lobbied or protected by a smoke control system.

Total evacuation

4.15/4.18   With total evacuation, all floors will be evacuated simultaneously and the calculations must take into account the number of people within the stairways during the time the evacuation takes place.

Escape based on total evacuation should be used for all stairs which serve:

(*a*)   Basements;

(*b*)   Open-planned buildings;

(*c*)   Other Residential or Assembly and Recreation buildings.

The capacity of stairs of widths from 1 m to 1.8 m serving buildings of up to 10 storeys is given in the following table.

Table to 4.17

No. of floors served	Maximum number of persons served by a stair of width (mm):								
	1000	1100	1200	1300	1400	1500	1600	1700	1800
1.	150	220	240	260	280	300	320	340	360
2.	190	260	285	310	335	360	385	410	435
3.	230	300	330	360	390	420	450	480	510
4.	270	340	375	410	445	480	515	550	585
5.	310	380	420	460	500	540	580	620	660
6.	350	420	465	510	555	600	645	690	735
7.	390	460	510	560	610	660	710	760	810
8.	430	500	555	610	665	720	775	830	885
9.	470	540	600	660	720	780	840	900	960
10.	510	580	645	710	775	840	905	970	1035

NOTE   The capacity of stairs serving more than 10 storeys may be obtained by using the formula in paragraph 4.18.

For taller buildings stair widths should be derived from the formula:

$$P = 200w + 50(w - 0.3)(n - 1)$$

P is the number of people that can be accommodated
w is the width of the stair
n is the number of storeys in the building.

Worked example
Stair width needed (after discounting any one stairway) for:
Population of building excluding those on ground floor 1400
Number of storeys 14 – total simultaneous evacuation.

$$P = 1400$$
$$n = 14$$
$$1400 = 200w + 50(w - 0.3(14 - 1)$$
$$= 200w + (50w - 15)(13)$$
$$= 200w + 650w = 195$$
$$1595 = 850w$$
$$w = 1.88 \text{ m}$$

Discounting the stair with greatest width, three stairs at 1.1 m would be sufficient.

Phased evacuation

4.19/4.23   In phased evacuation the first people to be evacuated are those of reduced mobility and those on the storeys most immediately affected by fire, normally those on the floor of origin and the floor above.

If it is then subsequently necessary for further evacuation to take place, this is done two floors at a time.

Phased evacuation cannot be used in every type of building, and it depends on the provision (and maintenance) of supporting facilities such as fire alarms. The advantages are that it reduces disruption in large buildings and enables narrower stairs to be incorporated.

Phased evacuation should not be used for open-planned buildings, Other Residential and Assembly and Recreation buildings but should be used for all other types of buildings over 30 m high. It can be used for buildings less than 30 m high if the conditions set out below are met:

(*a*)   The stairways should be approached through a protected lobby or protected corridor at each storey, except a top storey consisting exclusively of plant rooms.

(*b*)   If the building has a storey with a floor more than 30 m above ground level, the whole building should be protected by an automatic sprinkler system to BS 5306: Part 2. This will be the occupancy rating together with the additional requirements for life safety, but this provision would not apply to any purpose group 1(a) (flats) part of a mixed-use building.

(*d*)   The building should be fitted with an appropriate fire warning system conforming at least to the L3 standard in BS 5839: Part 1.

(*e*)   A telephone or intercom system should be provided to permit conversation between the control point at fire service access level and a fire warden on every storey.

The minimum stair width needed for evacuation is given in the table below and assumes a phased evacuation of not more than two floors at a time.

Table to 4.19   Minimum aggregate width of stairs designed for phased evacuation

Maximum number of people in any storey	*Stair width[1] (mm)*
100	1000
120	1100
130	1200
140	1300
150	1400
160	1500
170	1600
180	1700
190	1800

NOTES

[1] Stairs with a rise of more than 30 m should not be wider than 1400 mm unless provided with a central handrail (see paragraph 4.6).

As an alternative to using this table, provided that the minimum width of a stair is at least 100 mm, the width may be calculated from: $[(P \times 10) - 100]$ mm where P = the number of people on the most heavily occupied storey.

Protection of escape stairs

Enclosure

4.24/4.25   To fulfil the role of providing areas of relative safety, escape stairs should have a satisfactory standard of fire protection. Every internal escape stair should be a protected stair, ie it should be within a fire-resisting enclosure.

An unprotected stair may form part of an internal route to a storey exit or final exit provided that the distance of travel and the number of people involved are very limited. Clause 9 of BS 5588: Part 2, for instance, gives recommendations in this regard for small shops.

If the protected stairway is also a protected shaft or is a firefighting shaft, additional measures may be necessary (see Sections 8 and 17).

Access lobbies and corridors

4.26   An escape stair needs the added protection of a protected lobby or corridor in the following cases:

(*a*)   Where the stair is the only one serving a building or part which has more than one storey above or below the ground storey; or

(*b*)   Where the stair serves any storey at a height greater than 20 m; or

(*c*)   Where the building is designed for phased evacuation; or

(*d*)   In a sprinklered building in which the stair width has not been based on discounting one stairway (see paragraph 4.11).

In these cases protected lobbies or protected corridors are needed at all levels except the top storey, and at all basement levels.

Where there is a place of special fire risk, a protected lobby should be provided between it and an escape stairway. The lobby should have not less than 0.4 m² of permanent ventilation or be protected by a mechanical smoke control system.

Exits from protected stairways	**4.28/4.29** Protected stairways should discharge:
	(a) Directly to a final exit, or
	(b) By way of a protected exit passageway to a final exit.
	The exit from a protected stairway should be at least as wide as the stair leading to it.

Exits from protected stairways

4.28/4.29 Protected stairways should discharge:
(a)   Directly to a final exit, or
(b)   By way of a protected exit passageway to a final exit.
The exit from a protected stairway should be at least as wide as the stair leading to it.

Separation of adjoining stairways

4.30   An imperforate enclosure should separate two adjacent protected stairways and any protected exit passageways linking them to final exits.

Use of space within protected stairways

4.31   Because a protected stairway needs to be free from potential sources of fire, only the following may be incorporated into such a stairway:
(a)   Sanitary accommodation or washrooms, but not
if this accommodation is to be used as a cloakroom, or
if a gas appliance is to be installed, other than a gas water heater or a sanitary towel incinerator;
(b)   A lift well, if the stairway is not a firefighting stair;
(c)   A reception desk or enquiry office area at ground or access level if:
it is not in the only stair serving the building or part and in any case is not more than 10 m² in floor area;
(d)   Cupboards enclosed with fire-resisting construction, but not in the only stair serving the building or part.

Other provisions for protected stairways

4.32/4.34   The provisions regarding external walls of protected stairways, the installation of gas service pipes and the guidance on basement stairs given in Section 2 apply equally to buildings other than dwellings.
The references are in paragraphs 2.38 to 2.42.

External escape stairs

4.35/4.36   If there is more than one escape route from a storey or part of a building, one of the routes may be by way of an external escape stair, provided that:
(a)   In Assembly and Recreation buildings –
the route is not intended for members of the public; or
(b)   In Institutional buildings –
the route serves only office or residential staff accommodation.
Where external escape stairs are installed they should be protected from the weather as well as from fire. The guidance in paragraph 2.45 regarding fire protection should be followed, but the external escape stair for buildings other than dwellings may be more than 6 m high provided it is protected from the weather. The greatest difficulties arise from snow and ice, but the document states that where weather protection is necessary it does not necessarily imply full enclosure. Much, of course, will depend on where the stair is sited and the degree of protection which the building may give to the stair.

Section 5   General provisions common to buildings other than dwelling houses

5.1
This section gives general guidance mainly by referring to other parts of the Approved Document and pointing out other relevant sources of information on the construction and protection of escape routes and other design matters.
It is applicable to all buildings other than dwelling houses and should be considered in conjunction with Section 2 (flats and maisonettes), Section 3 (horizontal escape) and Section 4 (vertical escape).

Protection of escape routes

5.2/5.9

Fire protection	*Reference*
Fire-resistance test criteria etc	Appendix A
Although a 30-minute standard is sufficient for the protection of means of escape, there are greater	

fire-resistance requirements in	AD B 3, AD B 5
and also in	AD B 1, Sections 3 and 4
Walls, partitions and other fire-resistant enclosures	Appendix A, Tables A1 and A2
Glazed elements in fire-resistant enclosures	
– satisfying integrity only	Appendix A, Table A4
– satisfying integrity and insulation	No restriction
– glass in firefighting stairs/lobbies	B 5, Section 17 and
	BS 5588: Part 5
– safety of glazing	AD, Part N
Fire-resistance test criteria for doors	Appendix B
Performance of fire-resisting doors	Appendix B, Table B1

Doors on escape routes

5.10/5.18 Doors on escape routes within and from the building should be readily openable, so that there will be no undue delay in escaping.

Whether or not they are fire doors they should either:

(a)   Not be fitted with a lock latch or bolt or

(b)   Be fitted with simple fastenings which can be easily opened from the side approached by people making the escape, and

(c)   Be operated without the use of a key and without having to manipulate more than one mechanism

In buildings such as some Assembly and Recreation or shop and commercial uses, where security of final exit doors is important, panic bolts may be used. Appendix B contains details of opening devices.

Doors should be generally hung to open in the direction of escape, but should always do so if the number of persons likely to use the door for escape purposes will exceed 50.

Doors should:

(a)   Be hung to open through 90°;

(b)   Have a swing clear of any change in floor level, other than a threshold or single step;

(c)   When open, not reduce the effective width of any escape route;

(d)   Have vision panels where they are on escape routes which sub-divide corridors, or where they are hung to swing both ways.

See also AD to Part M regarding vision panels in doors to which disabled persons have access.

(e)   If they are revolving doors, automatic doors or turnstiles, not be placed across escape routes unless they fail safely in the open position or can easily be opened in an emergency, or, alternatively, swing doors should be provided immediately adjacent to the revolving or automatic door.

Construction of escape stairs

5.19/5.23 An escape stair and its associated landing should be of materials of limited combustibility in the following cases but except in (e) below may have combustible material added to the upper surface:

(a) If it is the only stair serving the building or part;	Does not apply to dwelling houses (PG1a)
(b) If it is in a basement storey;	Does not apply to a private stair in a maisonette.
(c) If it serves any storey having a floor level more than 20 m above ground or access level; or	
(d) If it is external;	Except where it connects with a floor or flat roof not more than 6 m high.

(e)   If it is a firefighting stair.

See also AD to Part K (Stairs, ramps and guards) for other constraints on design generally.

Single steps are considered to be a source of danger and should only be used on escape routes where they are properly marked, although a single step on the line of a doorway is acceptable.

Helical stairs, spiral stairs and fixed ladders may form part of an escape route if:

(a)   In the case of helical stairs, they are designed in accordance with BS 5395: Part 2, and, if to be used by members of the public, be of Type E;

(b)   In the case of fixed stairs, they are used only where it is not practical to provide a conventional stair such as in providing access to plant rooms not normally occupied. They should be of non-combustible materials. Fixed ladders should not be used as a means of escape for members of the public.

See the AD to Part K for guidance on the design of these stairs and ladders.

General

Height of escape routes
5.24   There should be a clear headroom of not less than 2 m except for door frames, with no other projection below this height.

Floors of escape routes
5.25   Floor surfaces should be such that they have minimal slipperiness when wet.

Ramps and sloping floors
5.26/5.28 Ramps should have an easy gradient – no steeper than 1 in 12. Sloping floors or tiers should not have a pitch greater than 35°.
See also ADs to Parts K and M for the design of ramps and landings and aisles and gangways where there is fixed seating and BS 5588: Part 6: Section 3 for the design of means of escape from places with fixed seating.

Final exits
5.29/5.32   Final exits should:
(*a*)   Have a width not less than the escape routes they serve;
(*b*)   Be sited to ensure rapid dispersal of persons from the vicinity of the building;
(*c*)   Give direct access to a street, passageway, walkway or open space;
(*d*)   Have a clearly defined route with guarding as necessary;
(*e*)   Be apparent to the persons needing to use them (particularly important where the exit opens off a stair that continues down or up beyond the level of the final exit);
(*f*)   Be sited to be clear of risk from fire and smoke from a basement or from openings to risks from such places as boiler rooms etc.
(See Section 18 regarding outlets to basement smoke vents.)

Lighting of escape routes
5.33   Escape routes should have adequate artificial lighting and areas requiring escape lighting are shown in the Table to 5.33. The lighting to escape stairs should be on a separate protected circuit from that supplying any other part of the escape route.
BS 5266: Part 1 gives recommendations on the installation of escape lighting in entertainment premises other than cinemas and CP 1007: 1955 deals with maintained lighting for cinemas.

Table to 5.33   Provisions for escape lighting

Purpose group of the building or part	*Areas requiring escape lighting*
Residential	All common escape routes
Office, shop and commercial[1] Industrial, storage, other non-residential	(a) Underground or windowless accommodation (b) Stairways in a central core, or serving storeys more than 20 m above ground level (c) Internal corridors more than 30 m long (d) Open-plan office areas of more than 60 m^2
Shop and commercial[2] Car parks to which the public are admitted	All escape routes and accommodation (except into shops of three or fewer storeys with no sales floor more than 280 m^2 floor area provided that the shop is not a restaurant or bar)
Assembly and recreation	All escape routes and accommodation except for: (a) Accommodation open on one side to view sport or entertainment during normal daylight hours (b) Toilet accommodation having a gross floor area of more than 8 m^2
Any purpose group	(a) Electricity generator rooms (b) Switch room/battery room for emergency lighting system (c) Emergency control room

NOTES
[1] Those parts of the premises to which the public are not admitted.
[2] Those parts of the premises to which the public are admitted.

Exit signs

5.34   In all buildings other than dwellings, every doorway or other exit providing access to a means of escape should be marked with an exit sign in letters of adequate size. Exits in normal use do not require to be so signed.

Under other legislation additional signs may be needed. See BS 5499: Part 1 for details of exit signs.

Protected power circuits

5.35   Where it is critical that electrical circuits are able to function during a fire, a protected circuit should be installed. This should comprise cable for operation of the equipment which meets the requirements for the classification CWZ in accordance with BS 6387. The route followed by the cable should pass through only those parts of the building where the fire risk is negligible and the circuit should be separate from all other circuits in the premises.

Lifts

Evacuation lifts

5.36   Generally lifts are not appropriate to use when there is a fire in a building. The lift could become immobilised as a result of fire and people could be trapped.

However, in some circumstances a lift may be used for evacuating disabled people as part of the management plan for the building. Such lift installation needs to be properly sited and protected and will require a number of safety features to be installed so that the lift remains usable while disabled people are being evacuated in an emergency.

BS 5588: Part 8 gives guidance on the necessary measures.

Fire protection of lift installations

5.37/5.42   Lifts which rise within a large volume such as a mall or atrium and do not have a conventional well may be at risk if they run through a smoke reservoir. Where these wall climber or feature lifts are installed the integrity of the smoke reservoir should be maintained to protect the occupiers of the lift. Lift wells should be either contained within a protected stairway or be enclosed throughout their height with fire-resisting construction if they are sited so as to prejudice the means of escape. A lift well connecting different compartments should form a protected shaft (see Section 8).

In basements and enclosed car parks, unless the lift is within the enclosure of a protected stairway it should be approached only by a protected lobby or protected corridor. There should also be a protected lobby approach to a lift in any storey containing high fire-risk areas where the lift alllso delivers directly into corridors serving sleeping accommodation. Fire risk areas here include kitchens, lounges and stores.

A lift should not continue down to serve a basement storey where it is:

(*a*)   In a building or part served by only one escape stair; or

(*b*)   Within the enclosures to an escape stair which terminates at ground level.

Lift machine rooms, wherever possible, should be sited over the lift well. If the machine room cannot be sited over the lift well within a protected stairway which is the only stairway serving the building, to avoid smoke spread from a fire in the machine room, it should be located outside the stairway.

Mechanical ventilation and air conditioning systems

5.43/5.46   In recirculation systems, the relevant recommendations for recirculating distribution systems of BS 5588: Part 9, in terms of operation under fire conditions, should be followed. Any system of mechanical ventilation should be designed to ensure that in a fire the movement of air will be directed away from protected escape routes and exits or that appropriate parts of the system are closed down.

BS 5588 gives guidance on the use of mechanical ventilation in places of assembly.

Where a pressurisation system is installed, ventilation and air conditioning systems should be compatible when operating under fire conditions.

Guidance on the design and installation of mechanical ventilation and air conditioning plant will be found in BS 5720 and on ventilation and air conditioning ductwork in BS 5588: Part 9.

Refuse chutes and storage

5.47/5.50   Refuse storage chambers, refuse chutes and refuse hoppers should be sited and constructed to BS 5906. Refuse chutes and rooms provided for the storage of refuse should:

(*a*)   Be separated from other parts of the building by fire-resisting construction;

(*b*)   Not be located within protected stairways or protected lobbies.

Rooms containing refuse chutes or provided for the storage of refuse should be approached either directly from the open air or by way of a protected lobby provided with not less than 0.2 m² or permanent ventilation. Access to refuse storage chambers should not be sited adjacent to escape routes or final exits or near to windows of dwellings.

B 2   INTERNAL FIRE SPREAD (LININGS)

There are only minor amendments to the requirements. The 1985 edition referred to 'surfaces' – this has been changed to 'linings'.
The requirement is as follows:

Requirement	Limits on application
Internal fire spread (linings) B 2(1) To inhibit the spread of fire within the building the internal linings shall: (*a*) Resist the spread of flame over their surfaces; and (*b*) Have, if ignited, a rate of heat release which is reasonable in the circumstances. (2) In this paragraph 'internal linings' means the materials lining any partition, wall, ceiling or other internal structure.	

Readers will note that despite the new structure of the Approved Documents on fire, there is very little change in the guidance to B 2. The classification of materials used in wall and ceiling linings has been simplified and changes have been made to the section on thermoplastic materials.

Performance

This is merely a repeat of the requirement with an explanation that the spread of flame should be limited so as to contain the contribution that the fabric of the building makes to fire growth. This, of course, depends on where the lining is located.

Introduction

Fire spread and lining materials
0.41/0.43   Although not likely to be the materials first ignited, materials for walls and ceilings can significantly affect the spread of fire. Linings in circulation spaces require more consideration as rapid spread may be likely to prevent escape. Materials should have a low surface spread of flame characteristic and/or should produce a low rate of heat release.
The provisions do not apply to floor or stair surfaces or fittings because they are not significantly involved in a fire until it is well developed, so they do not play an important part in the early stages of fire in fire spread.
There is further guidance on the control of flame spread:
B 3, Section 9: surfaces exposed in concealed spaces above a fire-protecting suspended ceiling;
B 3, Section 10: enclosures to above-ground drainage system pipes;
B 4, Section 14: internal surfaces of rooflights in connection with the performance of roof coverings;
B 4, Sections 12–14 deal with external flame spread.

Furniture and fittings
0.44   Furniture and fittings can have a major effect on fire spread but it is not possible to control them through Building Regulations. They may, however, be controlled in some buildings such as those subject to licensing arrangements.
0.45   BS 476: Parts 6 and 7 are the basis for tests for the various classifications, and details of these are in Appendix A, paragraphs A9–A15, and also in Table A8. Classification of thermoplastic material is also given in Appendix A.

Section 6   Wall and ceiling linings

6.1

Table to 6.1   Classification of wall and ceiling linings

Small rooms
Residential buildings >4 m²   Class 3
Non-residential buildings >30 m²
Other rooms   Class 1
Circulation spaces
Within dwellings   Class 1
Other circulation spaces   Class 0
(including common areas of flats and maisonettes)

Definition of walls and ceilings

6.2/6.3   For the purpose of the performance of linings it is necessary to define what a wall and a ceiling includes:

Wall	*Not a wall*
Surface of glazing	Glazing in doors
Parts of a ceiling at more than 70° to the horizontal	Doors and door frames
	Window frames
	Frames in which glazing is fitted
	Architraves and cover moulds
	Picture rails, skirtings and similar narrow members
	Fireplace surrounds
	Mantleshelves
	Fitted furniture
Ceiling	*Not a ceiling*
Surface of glazing	Glazing in doors
Part of a wall at 70° or less to the horizontal	Window frames
	Rooflight frames
	Frames in which glazing is fitted
	Architraves and cover moulds
	Picture rails and similar narrow members

Variations and special provisions

Walls

6.4   Parts of walls in rooms may be of a lower class of surface spread of flame but not lower than Class 3. The limits are:
In a residential building: 20 m²
In a non-residential building: 60 m²
provided the total area of those parts in any one room does not exceed half the floor area of the room. Examples are shown in diagram [2.22].

Fire-protected suspended ceilings

6.5   Suspended ceilings which are fire-protected ceilings, ie those which contribute to the fire resistance of a floor assembly, should:
(*a*)   Satisfy the Table to 6.1 and
(*b*)   If the floor is to have a fire resistance of more than 60 minutes be constructed of materials of limited combustibility. (This is a Type D ceiling – Table A3 in Appendix A.)

Fire-resisting ceilings

6.6   By using a fire-resisting ceiling below a cavity, the need for cavity barriers can be reduced. Such a ceiling should have a Class 0 surface.
(B 3, Section 9 refers – also diagram [2.42] in B 3.)

6.4 **[2.22]** *Special provisions –*
area of Class 3 linings.

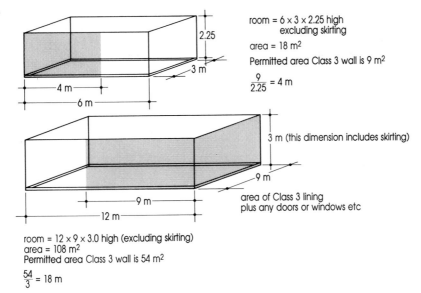

room = 6 × 3 × 2.25 high
        excluding skirting

area = 18 m²

Permitted area Class 3 wall is 9 m²

$\frac{9}{2.25} = 4$ m

3 m (this dimension includes skirting)

9 m

area of Class 3 lining
plus any doors or windows etc

room = 12 × 9 × 3.0 high (excluding skirting)
area = 108 m²
Permitted area Class 3 wall is 54 m²

$\frac{54}{3} = 18$ m

Rooflights
6.7   These should be of the classification in the Table to 6.1.
Plastic rooflights with at least a Class 3 rating can be used in any situation provided they comply with the Table to 6.13 and with the Table to 14.5 in Section 14.

Thermoplastic materials

General
6.8   Those thermoplastic materials which cannot meet Class 0, 1 or 3 standard can still be used in rooflights and lighting diffusers in suspended ceilings. They must, however, comply with the following guidance. Flexible thermoplastic material can also be used in panels to form a suspended ceiling under the provisions which follow.
Details about thermoplastic materials are set out in Appendix A, paragraphs A16–A19, but generally a thermoplastic material is one which softens at below 200°C.
Three classifications are used:
TP(a) rigid; as its name implies, a rigid sheet
TP(a) flexible; not more than 1 mm thick
TP(b) rigid; rigid sheets less than 3 mm thick which do not qualify under the TP(a) rigid test.

Windows and rooflights
6.9/6.10   TP(a) can be used to glaze windows to rooms but not to circulation spaces. Internal glazing should be to the Table to 6.1 (a wall does not include a door), and
TP(a) rigid or TP(b) can be used as the lower surface of rooflights to rooms and circulation spaces – but not protected stairways – provided it complies with the Table to 6.13 and the Table to 14.5.

Lighting diffusers

6.11/6.13   This provision only deals with lighting diffusers which form part of a ceiling. It is not concerned with diffusers which are attached to the soffit of, or suspended beneath, a ceiling (see diagram [2.23]). Lighting diffusers can be translucent or open-structured, may be part of a luminaire or used below rooflights or other light sources.

6.11 **[2.23]** *Lighting diffusers.*

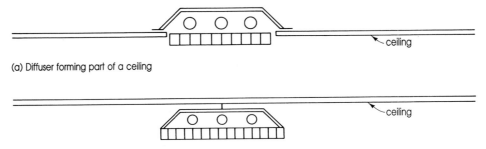

(a) Diffuser forming part of a ceiling

ceiling

ceiling

(b) Diffuser in fitting attached below and not forming part of the ceiling

Unless they have been found to be satisfactory by test as part of a ceiling assembly, thermoplastic lighting diffusers should not be used in fire-protecting or fire-resisting ceilings. Ceilings to rooms and circulation spaces, other than protected stairways, may incorporate thermoplastic lighting diffusers.

The upper surfaces of the thermoplastic panels can be ignored and the provisions of the Tables to 6.1 and 6.11 should be met.

Table to 6.13   Limitations applied to thermoplastic rooflights and diffusers in suspended ceiling and Class 3 plastic rooflights

Mimimum classification of lower surface	*Use of space below the diffusers or rooflight*	*Max. area of each diffuser panel or rooflight[1]*	*Max. total area of diffuser panels and rooflights as 1/2 of floor area of the space in which the ceiling is located*	*Min. separation distance between diffuser panels or rooflights[1]*
TP(a)	Any except protected stairway	No limit[2]	No limit	No limit
Class 3[3] or TP(b)	Rooms Circulation spaces except protected stairways	5 m² 5 m²	50 m² 15 m²	3 m 3 m

NOTES
[1] Smaller panels can be grouped together provided that the overall size of the group and the space between one group and any others satisfies the dimensions shown in the diagram to 18.4.
[2] Lighting diffusers of TP(a) flexible rating should be restricted to panels of not more than 5 m² each (see paragraph 6.14).
[3] There are no limitations on Class 3 materials in small rooms.

Suspended or stretched-skin ceiling

6.14   Panels of TP(a) flexible materials may be used as a ceiling of a room provided that:
(*a*)   The ceiling is not a fire-resisting ceiling;
(*b*)   Each panel does not exceed 5 m² and is supported on all its sides (see diagram [2.24]).

6.14 **[2.24]** *Lighting diffusers Type TP(b) – layout.*

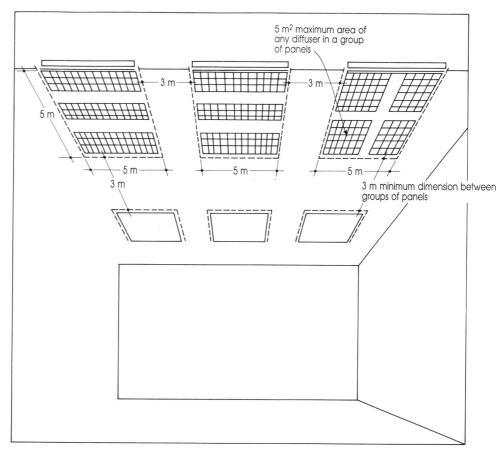

5 m² maximum area of any diffuser in a group of panels

3 m minimum dimension between groups of panels

– – – – – 5 m maximum dimension of diffuser panels

restrictions on layout apply also to Class 3 plastic rooflights and type TP (b) rooflights

B 3   INTERNAL FIRE SPREAD (STRUCTURE)

There are some changes in the wording of the requirement but none of substance. The limits on application of B 3(3) only apply to material alterations to any prison.
The requirement is as follows:

Requirement	Limits on application
Internal fire spread (structure) B 3(1) The building shall be designed and constructed so that, in the event of fire, its stability will be maintained for a reasonable period. (2) A wall common to two or more buildings shall be designed and constructed so that it resists the spread of fire between those buildings. For the purposes of this sub-paragraph, a house in a terrace and a semi-detached house are each to be treated as a separate building. (3) To inhibit the spread of fire within the building, it shall be sub-divided with fire-resisting construction to an extent appropriate to the size and intended use of the building. (4) The building shall be designed and constructed so that the unseen spread of fire and smoke within concealed spaces in its structure or fabric is inhibited.	Requirement B 3(3) does not apply to material alterations to any prison provided under Section 33 of the Prisons Act 1952.

There are many changes from the corresponding provisions in the 1985 edition of AD B 2/3/4. These include:

1   Reductions in some of the higher periods of fire resistance.
2   Introductions of specifications for alternative periods of fire resistance in some situations where a sprinkler system is provided.
3   A new basis for the provision of compartment walls and compartment floors.
4   Deletion of some of the provisions regarding non-combustible construction.
5   Deletion of the term 'protecting structure' (relevant provisions are dealt with as another form of compartmentation);
6   Simplified provisions for junctions between fire-separating walls and roofs.
7   A new basis for the provision of cavity barriers.
8   Provisions for car parks as a use separate from that of storage buildings.

Performance

The guidance begins with a statement on the performance to be achieved. This is the requirement expressed in another way.

Introduction

0.46   This sets out the contents of the various sections. These are:
Section 7 – Loadbearing elements of structure
Section 8 – Sub-division of a building into compartments
Section 9 – Concealed spaces (cavities)
Section 10 – Protection of openings and fire stopping
Section 11 – Special provisions for car parks and shopping complexes

Fire resistance

0.47   Fire resistance is a measure of the ability of an element of construction to withstand the effects of fire in one or more of the following ways. These are resistance to:
(*a*)   Collapse – loadbearing elements only (stability)
(*b*)   Fire penetration – fire-separating elements (integrity)
(*c*)   Transfer of excessive heat – fire-separating elements (insulation)
Loadbearing elements are termed 'elements of structure' and are defined in Appendix E. They are main structural elements such as structural frames and floors and loadbearing walls.

Compartment walls and external walls which may be either loadbearing or non-loadbearing are also elements of structure.

Roofs, curtain walls and some external walls are not considered as loadbearing for the purposes of (*a*) above. A roof acting as a floor would, however, be an element of structure. Loadbearing elements may or may not have a fire-separating function and fire-separating elements may or may not be loadbearing.

0.48   Provisions in other ADs on the use of fire-resisting construction are:

B 1 To protect means of escape

B 4 External walls

B 5 Firefighting shafts

Section 7   Loadbearing elements of structure

Introduction

7.1   The purposes in providing a structure with fire resistance are:

(*a*)   To minimise the risk to occupants. In large buildings some may have to remain while evacuation proceeds;

(*b*)   To reduce the risk to firefighters who may be engaged in search and/or rescue operations;

(*c*)   To reduce danger to persons in the vicinity of the building from the effects of collapse in fire.

Standard of fire resistance

7.2   The minimum periods of fire resistance of elements of structure are set out in Appendix A, Table A1.

Application of fire-resistance standards

7.3   Where an element of structure supports or gives stability to another element of structure, the supporting element should have no less fire resistance than the element it supports.

Elements of structure which are common to more than one building or compartment should be constructed to the greater standard of the relevant provisions. These and other special provisions are set out in Appendix A and particularly in the notes to Table A2.

Exclusions from the provisions for elements of structure

7.4   The following are not regarded as elements of structure for fire-resistance purposes:

(*a*)   A structure which supports a roof unless

(*i*)   The roof acts as a floor such as for vehicle parking or as a means of escape;

(*ii*)   The structure is essential for the stability of an external wall which needs to have fire resistance;

(*b*)   The lowest floor of a building;

(*c*)   A platform floor – this is defined in Appendix E as a floor supported by a structural floor with an intervening cavity for housing services.

Additional provisions

7.5/7.6   Loadbearing walls may have additional functions and reference should be made as follows where such a wall is:

Protecting means of escape	AD B 1, Sections 1–5
A compartment wall	AD B 3, Section 8
A wall between a house and a domestic garage	AD B 3, Section 8 (para. 8.12)
An external wall	AD B 4, Sections 12 and 13
Enclosing a firefighting shaft	AD B 5, Section 17
If a floor is also a compartment floor	AD B 3, Section 8

Floors in domestic loft conversions

7.7   This provision was one of the 'varying the provisions' guidance in the 1985 edition. There is now a size limitation.

Normally a three-storey house should have floors with a 30-minute standard of fire resistance, but when converting a two-storey house to three or more storeys, the existing floor, provided it has a modified 30-minute standard, is conditionally acceptable.

A 'modified 30-minute standard' means 30 minutes for loadbearing capacity and 15 minutes each for stability and insulation (see Appendix A, Table A1).

The conditions are:

(*a*)   Only one new storey is being added;

(*b*)   The new storey contains not more than two additional rooms;

(*c*)   The total floor area of the new storey is not more than 50 m²;

(*d*)   The existing floor separates only rooms (not circulation spaces) provided that

(*e*)   The provisions of AD B1 Section 1 are met.

Raised storage areas	**7.8, 7.10/7.11** This is another of the 'varying the provisions' with similar wording to the 1985 AD.

Raised free-standing floors, possibly supported by racking, are frequently installed in single-storey industrial buildings. Whether these count as galleries (less than half the main floor area) or as additional floors, they would normally require the fire resistance specified for elements of structure.

In favourable circumstances a lesser period, or even an unclad steel structure, might be considered. There would have to be a low number of persons employed, one tier only, no members of the public, a layout to enable anyone on the floor to be easily aware of a fire below and good escape routes, ie one stair discharging within 4.5 m of an exit to the building.

A perforated floor, leaving gaps around the perimeter, or a smoke detector system, appropriately sited, could provide adequate early warning. The surface rating of the ceiling below the raised floor might also be lower than normal providing there is no need for an escaping person to escape under it.

If the floor has a dimension (width or length) of more than 10 m, an automatic detection and alarm system should be installed.

7.9   Buildings which only house automated storage systems into which people do not normally go on to the raised tiers may not need fire resistance to ensure the safety of the occupants.

Conversion into flats	**7.12/7.13** Conversion of an existing building or house into flats is a material change of use to which Part B applies, and where timber joists are to be retained it may be difficult to meet the fire-resistance provisions.

If the means of escape complies with Section 2 in B1 and are adequately protected, the elements of structure in houses up to three storeys can have 30 minutes fire resistance.

If there are four or more storeys, the full standard of fire resistance should be provided.

Section 8   Sub-division of a building into compartments

Introduction	**8.1/8.2** To resist the spread of fire, buildings can be sub-divided into compartments, separated by walls and/or floors of fire-resisting construction, ie compartment walls and compartment floors. The objectives are:

(*a*)   To prevent rapid fire spread which could trap occupants;

(*b*)   To reduce the chance of a large fire developing. Large fires are more dangerous to life safety.

The sub-division necessary depends on:

(*a*)   The use of the building and its fire load (severity and evacuation);

(*b*)   The height of the top storey (evacuation and fire service intervention);

(*c*)   Availability of a sprinkler system (growth rate and possible extinction).

Compartmentation in this section is complementary to means of escape provisions in B1 and external fire spread provisions in B4.

Special forms of compartmentation	**8.4** Particular construction provisions apply to:

(*a*)   Walls common to two or more buildings;

(*b*)   Walls dividing buildings into separated parts in which the parts can be considered independently for fire resistance;

(*c*)   Construction protecting houses from attached or integral garages.

Junctions

8.5   There should be continuity at junctions of fire-resisting elements which enclose a compartment and openings from one compartment to another should maintain effective compartmentation.

Protected shafts

8.6   To restrict fire spread between compartments the spaces that connect them (eg stairways and service shafts) need to be protected – hence the term protected shaft. Walls and floors of protected shafts are compartment walls/floors.

Provision of compartmentation

8.7/8.18   Compartment walls and compartment floors should be provided as follows. The lowest floor of a building does not need to be constructed as a compartment floor.

Table to 8.7   Provision of compartment walls and compartment floors

Purpose group	Construction	Compartment wall	Compartment floor
All	Wall common to two or more buildings	●	
	Providing the separation of parts of a building occupied mainly for different purposes from one another (see Appendix D regarding ancillary use)	●	●
	Providing the division of a building into separate occupancies	●	●
1(a) Flats and maisonettes	Any floor (unless within a maisonette, ie between one storey and another within one dwelling)		●
	Any wall separating a flat or maisonette from another part of the same building	●	
	Any wall enclosing a refuse storage chamber	●	
1(b) and (c) Houses	Any wall separating semi-detached or terraced houses (the houses should be considered as separate buildings)	●	
	Wall between an integral garage and house (see diagram [2.25])	●	
2(a) Institutional	All floors		●

	In hospitals the compartment size is restricted:
	     Multi-storey hospitals: 2000 m^2
	     Single-storey hospitals: 3000 m^2
	All walls to divide storeys of health-care buildings into at least two compartments (see AD B1, Section 3)
		●	

2(b) Other residential	All floors		●
3,4,5,6 and 7 Non-residential	Any wall (other than in a single-storey building) to sub-divide a building into size limits in Table to 8.18	●	
	Any floor in the building or separated part if it contains a storey with a floor more than 30 m above ground level		●
	Any floor of the ground storey where the building has a basement		●
	Any basement floor if the building or separated part has a basement more than 10 m below ground level		●
	In a building forming part of a shopping complex – any wall or floor described in Section 5 of BS 5588: Part 10 as needing to be a compartment wall or floor	●	●

8.11 **[2.25]** *Separation between garage and dwelling.*

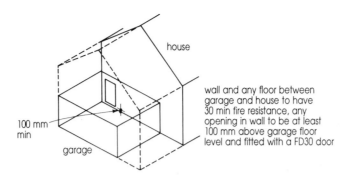

house

wall and any floor between garage and house to have 30 min fire resistance, any opening in wall to be at least 100 mm above garage floor level and fitted with a FD30 door

100 mm min

garage

Table to 8.18 Maximum dimensions of building or compartment (multi-storey non-residential buildings)

Purpose group of building	*Height of floor level of top storey above ground level (m)*	*Floor area of any one storey in the building or compartment (m²)*
Office	No limit	No limit
Assembly and recreation, shop and commercial:		
not sprinklered	No limit	2 000
sprinklered[1]	No limit	4 000
Industrial[3]		
not sprinklered	Not more than 20	7 000
	More than 20	2 000[2]
sprinklered	Not more than 20	14 000
	More than 20	4 000[2]

		Maximum compartment volume (m³)
Storage[3] and other non-residential		
(a) car park for light vehicles	No limit	No limit
(b) any other building or part:		
not sprinklered	No more than 20	20 000
	More than 20	4 000[2]
sprinklered	Not more than 20	40 000
	More than 20	8 000[2]

NOTES
[1] 'Sprinklered' means that the building is fitted throughout with an automatic sprinkler system meeting the relevant recommendations of BS 5306: Part 2, ie the relevant occupancy rating together with the additional requirements for life safety.
[2] This reduced area limit applies only to storeys that are more than 30 m above ground level.
[3] There may be additional limitations on floor area and/or sprinkler provisions in certain industrial and storage uses under other legislation, eg in respect of storage of LPG and certain chemicals.
AUTHOR'S NOTE   In the previous AD the only buildings where the use of sprinklers gave greater compartment size were shops.

Construction of compartment walls and compartment floors

General

8.19   Every compartment wall and compartment floor should:
(*a*)   Form a complete barrier to fire between the compartments they separate; and
(*b*)   Have the fire resistance shown in Appendix A, Table A1.

Compartment walls between buildings

8.20/8.21   Compartment walls which are common to two or more buildings and those used to form a separated part of a building should run the full height of the building in a continuous vertical plane. This does not apply to compartment walls used to divide a building into separate occupancies (see diagram [2.26]).

8.20/8.21 **[2.26]** *Compartment walls.*

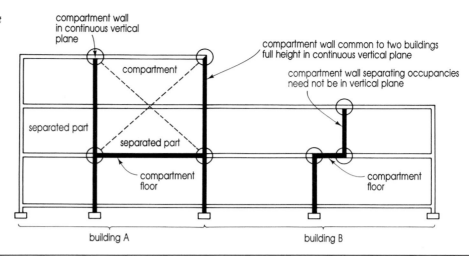

Junctions with other walls

8.22   Where a compartment wall or compartment floor meets another compartment or external wall, the junction should resist fire penetration for the same period as the wall or floor.

Junction with roof

8.23

(*a*)   *Building or compartment – any height, any use*

Roof covering over the distance 'X' in diagram [2.27(a)] to be designation AA, AB or AC on deck of material of limited combustibility.

Roof covering and deck could be a composite structure, eg profiled steel cladding.

Resilient fire-stopping carried up to underside of roof covering.

If roof supporting members pass through the wall, fire protection on the underside of these members for a distance of 1.5 m on either side of the wall may be needed to avoid distortion at the junction.

(*b*)   *Dwelling house and building or compartment in residential (not institutional) office or assembly use and not more than 15 m high*

Roof covering to be AA, AB or AC for at least distance 'X' in diagram [2.27(b)].

[2.27] *Junction of compartment wall with roof.*

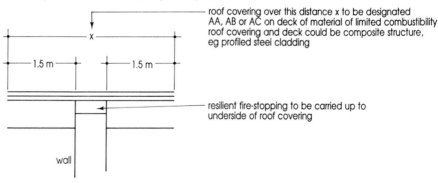

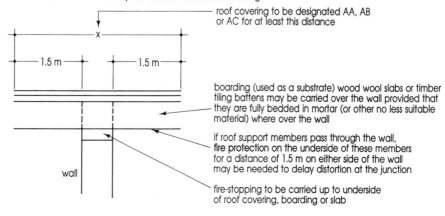

Boarding (used as a substrate), wood wool slabs or timber tiling battens may be carried over the wall provided they are fully bedded in mortar (or other no less suitable material) where they are over the wall.

Fire-stopping to be carried up to underside of roof covering, boarding or slab.

8.26 As an alternative to (*a*) or (*b*) the compartment wall may be extended up through the roof for at least 375 mm above the top surface of the adjoining roof covering.

Compartment construction in hospitals	**8.27** Compartment walls and compartment floors in hospitals designed to the Firecode (see paragraph 0.34), if they have a fire resistance of 60 minutes or more, should be constructed of materials of limited combustibility.
Openings between compartments	**8.28** Openings in compartment walls separating buildings or occupancies. These should be limited to openings for: (*a*) A door needed for means of escape (this should have the same fire resistance as the wall – see Appendix B and Table B1); and (*b*) The passage of a pipe (see AD B 3, Section 10).
Openings in other compartment walls or compartment floors	**8.29** Other than those described in paragraph 8.28, openings should be limited to those for: (*a*) Doors having the appropriate fire resistance – see Appendix B and Table B1; (*b*) The passage of pipes, ventilation ducts, chimneys, appliance ventilation ducts or ducts encasing flue pipes – see AD B 3, Section 10; (*c*) Refuse chutes of non-combustible construction; (*d*) Protected shafts – see paragraph 8.30.
Protected shafts	**8.30** Any stairway or shaft which passes directly from one compartment to another should be enclosed in a protected shaft. For protected shafts that are protected stairways see AD B 1, Sections 1–5. If the stairway also serves as a firefighting stairway see AD B 5, Sections 15–18.
Uses for protected shafts	**8.31** Protected shafts should only be used for stairs, lifts, escalators, chutes, ducts and pipes. Sanitary accommodation may be included in protected shafts.
Construction of protected shafts	**8.32** This should: (*a*) Form a complete barrier to fire between the different compartments; (*b*) Have appropriate fire resistance; (except for glazed screens – see paragraph 8.33 below); (*c*) Satisfy the provisions of paragraphs 8.35 and 8.37. See diagram [2.28].

8.32 **[2.28]** *Protected shafts.*

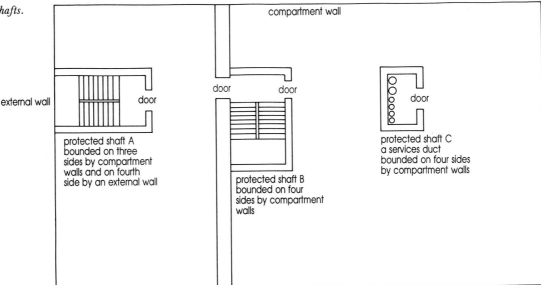

plan
the shaft structure (including any openings) should meet
the relevant provisions

Glazed screens to protected shafts

8.33/8.34   Where a protected shaft contains a stair other than a firefighting stair and is entered from a corridor or lobby, the part between the shaft and the corridor or lobby may incorporate glass if the principles in diagram [2.29] are met. The glass should provide 30 minutes fire resistance in terms of integrity only.

If the principles in diagram [2.29] are not met, see Appendix A, Table A4 regarding limits on uninsulating glazing.

8.33 **[2.29]** *Glazed screen separating protected shaft from lobby or corridor.*

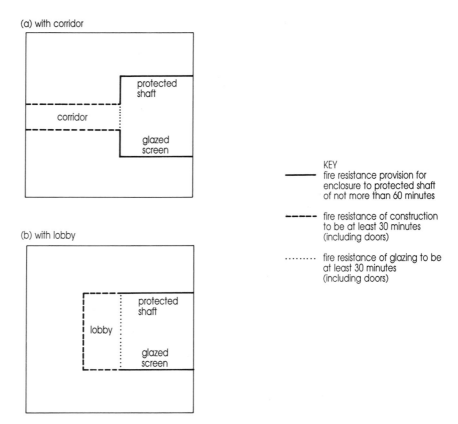

(a) with corridor

protected shaft

corridor

glazed screen

KEY
— fire resistance provision for enclosure to protected shaft of not more than 60 minutes

----- fire resistance of construction to be at least 30 minutes (including doors)

········ fire resistance of glazing to be at least 30 minutes (including doors)

(b) with lobby

protected shaft

lobby

glazed screen

Pipes for oil or gas in protected shafts

8.35/8.36   No pipe conveying oil and no ventilating duct should be within a protected shaft which contains a stair and/or a lift. (Ducts for the purpose of smoke pressurisation and oil pipes in the lift mechanism are excluded.)

Pipes containing natural gas in such a shaft should be of screwed steel or all-welded steel construction in accordance with the Gas Safety Regulations (SI 1972, No.1178) and the Gas Safety (Installation and Use) Regulations, 1984 (as amended 1990). A protected shaft which contains piped flammable gas should have adequate ventilation openings at high and low level.

Openings in protected shafts

8.37   Generally, an external wall of a protected shaft does not need fire resistance but BS 5588: Part 5: Section 2 makes some recommendations for fire resistance of such walls. The guidance in Section 17, paragraph 17.11 has been taken from the BS.

The enclosure of a protected shaft should only have the following openings:

(*a*)   Where part of the enclosure to the shaft is in a wall common to two or more buildings:

(*i*)   A door for means of escape purposes (see Appendix B);

(*ii*)   For the passage of a pipe (see B 3, Section 10);

(*b*)   Other parts of the enclosure (except external walls) should have openings only for:

(*i*)   Fire-resisting doors (see Appendix B).

(*ii*)   Pipes (see B 3, Section 10);

(*iii*)   Inlets and outlets for any ventilation duct (see B 3, Section 10);

(*iv*)   If the shaft contains a lift, the passage of lift cables.

If the machine room is at the bottom of the shaft, the openings should be as small as practicable (diagram [2.30]).

8.37 **[2.30]** *Diagrams illustrating openings etc in protected shafts:*

a *shaft containing vent duct and other items;*
b *lift shaft;*
c *stairway.*

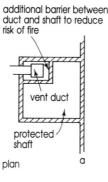

additional barrier between duct and shaft to reduce risk of fire

vent duct

protected shaft

plan

a

NOTE Fire-resisting doors to comply with Appendix B. If in flats, other residential, assembly or office building and above ground they must provide 30 minutes fire resistance. In other cases they must provide half the resistance of the containing wall and never less than 30 minutes. For lift doors see Appendix B.

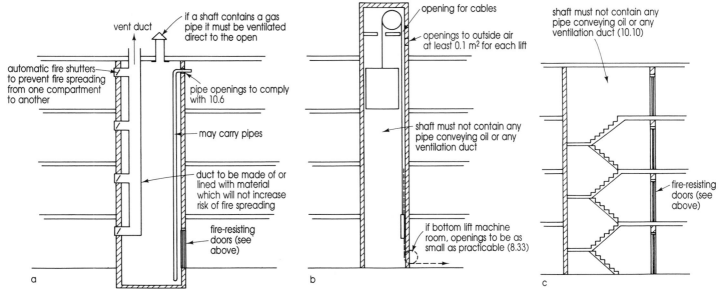

vent duct

if a shaft contains a gas pipe it must be ventilated direct to the open

automatic fire shutters to prevent fire spreading from one compartment to another

pipe openings to comply with 10.6

may carry pipes

duct to be made of or lined with material which will not increase risk of fire spreading

fire-resisting doors (see above)

a

opening for cables

openings to outside air at least 0.1 m² for each lift

shaft must not contain any pipe conveying oil or any ventilation duct

if bottom lift machine room, openings to be as small as practicable (8.33)

b

shaft must not contain any pipe conveying oil or any ventilation duct (10.10)

fire-resisting doors (see above)

c

Section 9   Concealed spaces (cavities)

Introduction

9.1   Cavities in the construction of a building provide a ready route for smoke and flame spread, particularly those voids above other spaces such as in a roof space or over a suspended ceiling. Provisions include the sub-division of large cavities and placing barriers in cavities which could otherwise form a pathway for fire.

Cavities include those formed in 'rain screen' external wall construction.

AD B4, paragraph 12.5, mentions the provisions to be made for the flame spread characteristics of 'rain screen' construction and overcladding.

9.2/9.3   Diagram [2.31] shows that cavity barriers should be built in at the intersection of fire-resisting construction and elements containing a concealed space.

9.2 **[2.31]** *Cavity barriers in abutting elements*

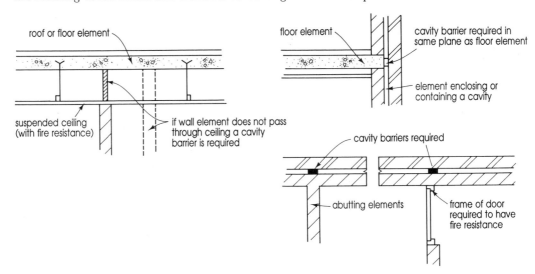

roof or floor element

suspended ceiling (with fire resistance)

if wall element does not pass through ceiling a cavity barrier is required

floor element

cavity barrier required in same plane as floor element

element enclosing or containing a cavity

cavity barriers required

abutting elements

frame of door required to have fire resistance

Table to 9.2

Where barriers are to be provided (diagrams [2.33]–[2.41])	*Purpose group where provision applies*
1. Junction between external cavity wall* and compartment wall that separates buildings. Diagram [2.33].	All purpose groups 1,2,3,4,5,6 and 7
2. Above enclosures to a protected stairway in a house of three or more storeys.[1] Diagram [2.34].	House of three or more storeys (1b and 1c) (see Note 1)
3. Junction between external cavity wall* and every compartment floor and compartment wall. Diagram [2.35].	All purpose groups except dwelling houses (1a,2,3,4,5,6 and 7)
4. Junction between a cavity wall* and every compartment floor, compartment wall or other wall or assembly which forms a fire-resisting barrier. Diagram [2.36].	All purpose groups except dwelling houses (1a,2,3,4,5,6 and 7)
5. In a protected escape route above fire-resisting construction not carried full storey height or to the underside of the roof.[1] Diagram [2.37].	All purpose groups except dwelling houses (1a,2,3,4,5,6 and 7)
6. Above bedroom partitions not carried to full storey height and or, in the case of the top storey, to underside of roof covering.[1] Diagram [2.38].	Other Residential and Institutional: purpose group 3 only
7. Above any corridor enclsoures which are not carried full storey height or (in the top storey) to the underside of the roof covering where the corridor (which is not a protected corridor)should be sub-divided to prevent fire or smoke affecting two alternative routes simultaneously (see para. 3.21 and diagram [2.39]).[2]	All purpose groups except dwelling houses and flats (1a,b,c)
8. To sub-divide any cavity (including any roof space) so that the distance between cavity barriers does not exceed the dimensions in the Table to 9.10. Diagram [2.40].	All purpose groups except dwelling houses and flats (1a,b,c)
9. Within the void behind the external face of rain screen cladding at every floor level, and on the line of compartment walls abutting the external wall of buildings which have a floor more than 20 m above ground level. Diagram [2.41].	Flats and maisonettes and other residential and institutional (purpose groups 1a and 2)

NOTES
* Referred to in items 1,3 and 4 is a cavity wall not complying with diagram [2.32].
[1] These provisions do not apply where the cavity is enclosed on the lower side by a fire-resisting ceiling (diagram [2.42]) which extends throughout the building, compartment or separated part.
[2] Does not apply where the storey is sub-divided by fire-resisting construction carried to full storey height and passing through the line of sub-division of the corridor or where the cavity is enclosed on the lower level as in Note 1.

9.4 **[2.32]** *Exceptions relating to cavities in certain walls.*

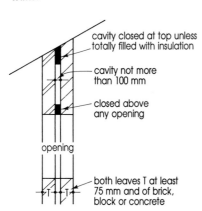

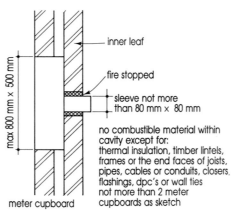

Table to 9.2 **[2.33]** *Item 1.*

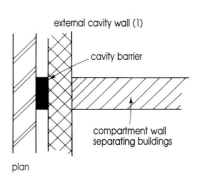

Table to 9.2 **[2.34]** *Item 2.*

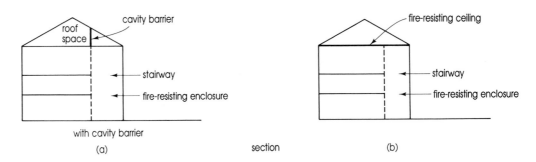

Table to 9.2 **[2.35]** *Item 3.*

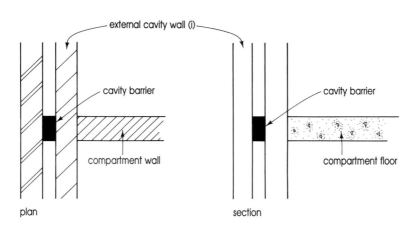

Table to 9.2 **[2.36]** *Item 4.*

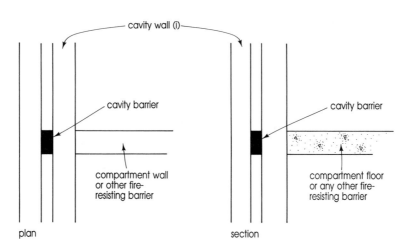

Table to 9.2 **[2.37]** *Item 5.*

Table to 9.2 **[2.38]** *Item 6.*

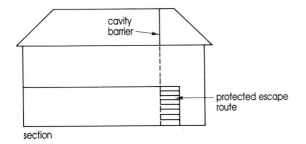

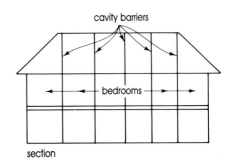

Table to 9.2 **[2.39]** *Item 7.*

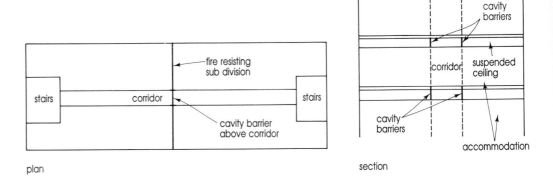

plan   section

Table to 9.2 **[2.40]** *Item 8.*

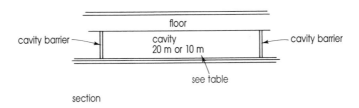

section

Table to 9.2 **[2.41]** *Item 9.*

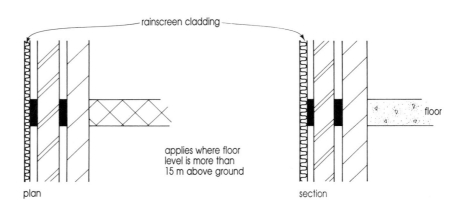

plan   section

9.4   Cavity walls which are excluded from the provisions for cavity barriers are as shown in diagram [2.32]. These are referred to in the Table to 9.2 in items, 1, 3 and 4.

In a house of three or more storeys there are two alternatives which can be used above the enclosures to a protected stairway (diagram [2.34]).

9.5   Compartment walls should be carried up full storey height to a compartment floor or to the roof. Cavity barriers generally have lower fire-resistance standards than those for compartment walls, so it is not appropriate to use cavity barriers where full compartmentation is necessary.

Construction and fixings for cavity barriers

9.6   Every cavity barrier should have a fire resistance of at least 30 minutes (see Appendix A, Table A1, item 16). Exceptionally, a cavity barrier in a stud wall or partition may be formed of:

(*a*)   Steel at least 0.5 mm thick;

(*b*)   Timber at least 38 mm thick;

(*c*)   Polythene-sleeved mineral wool or mineral wool slab. These must be under compression when installed;

(*d*)   Calcium silicate, cement-based or gypsum-based boards at least 12.5 mm thick.

9.7   Any construction provided for any other purpose can be used to form a cavity barrier if it meets the required provisions.

9.8   Cavity barriers should be tightly fitted to rigid construction and mechanically fixed wherever possible. Where not possible (eg at a junction with slates, tiles, corrugated sheeting etc) the junction should be fire-stopped (see Section 10).

9.9   They must also be fixed so that performance will not be made ineffective by:

(*a*)   Movement due to subsidence, shrinkage or thermal changes and movement of the external envelope due to wind;

(*b*)   Collapse in fire of any services penetrating them;

(*c*)   Failure in fire of fixings;

(*d*)   Failure in fire of any abutting construction.

An example is quoted of a suspended ceiling continued over a fire resisting partition with a fire barrier above the line of the partition, when premature failure of the cavity barrier could result from a collapse of the ceiling, but not if the ceiling also had a 30-minute fire resistance.

Maximum dimensions of concealed spaces

9.10   Concealed spaces in non-residential buildings should be sub-divided as shown in the table. There are, however, certain exceptions to these provisions as shown in paragraphs 9.11–9.13.

NOTE   This table is a simplification of that in the 1985 AD and relates only to purpose groups 3–7.

Table to 9.10   Maximum dimensions of cavities in non-residential buildings

Location of cavity	Class of surface exposed in cavity (excluding surface of any pipe, cable or conduit or insulation to any pipe)	Maximum dimension in any direction (m)
Between a roof and a ceiling	Any	20
Any other cavity	Class 1	20
	Class other than Classes 0 or 1	10

9.11   The maximum dimensions in the Table to 9.10 do not apply to any cavity which is:

(*a*)   In a wall which needs to be fire resisting only because it is loadbearing (ie it is not a fire barrier);

(*b*)   In a masonry or concrete external wall shown in diagram [2.32];

(*c*)   In a floor or roof space where the cavity is enclosed on the lower side by a fire-resisting ceiling as in diagram [2.34(b)] provided this ceiling extends throughout the building or compartment subject to a 30 m limit on the extent of the cavity;

(*d*)   Below a floor next to the ground or oversite concrete if:

　　(*i*)   the cavity is less than 1 m in height;

　　(*ii*)   is not normally accessible by persons.

If there are openings in the floor so that combustible material can accumulate in the cavity, then cavity barriers should be provided together with access for cleaning (diagram [2.43]);

(*e*)   Formed behind the external skin in rain-screen external wall construction, by overcladding an existing masonry or concrete external wall or an existing concrete roof. The cavity should not contain combustible insulation and the construction should be as item 9 in the Table to 9.2;

(*f*)   Between double-skinned corrugated or profiled insulated roof and wall sheeting if the sheeting is a material of limited combustibility and both surfaces of the insulation layer have a surface spread of flame of at least Class 0 or Class 1 – Appendix A, Table A7 (diagram [2.44]).

9.11 **[2.42]** *Fire-resisting ceiling below a concealed space. The ceiling should:*
(a) Have at least 30 minutes fire resistance;
(b) Be imperforate except for opening described in paragraph 3.14;
(c) Extend throughout the building or compartment;
(d) Not be demountable.

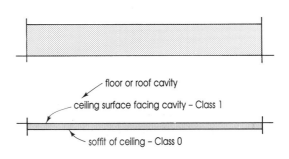

floor or roof cavity

ceiling surface facing cavity – Class 1

soffit of ceiling – Class 0

9.11 **[2.43]** *Cavity in floors next to the ground.*

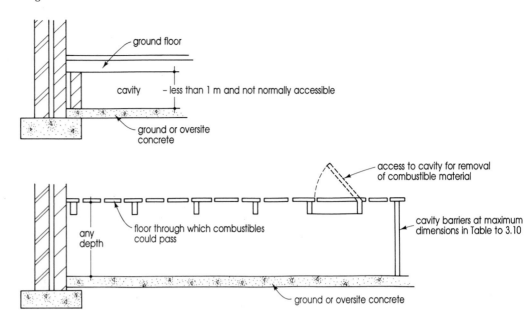

9.11 **[2.44]** *Cavity barriers in double-skinned insulated wall and roof sheeting.*

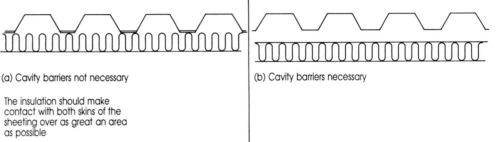

(a) Cavity barriers not necessary

The insulation should make contact with both skins of the sheeting over as great an area as possible

(b) Cavity barriers necessary

9.12 Where a room under a cavity exceeds the 20 m or 10 m dimension in the Table to 9.10, cavity barriers need only be provided on the line of the enclosing walls or partitions. In these cases the cavity barriers should not be more than 40 m apart.

In diagram [2.45] cavity barriers would be required over the walls between Room A and Rooms B and C and between Room B and Rooms C, D and E. Although Room B is more than 40 m long, no further barriers would be necessary.

9.13 Where the concealed space is over an undivided area which exceeds 40 m (in both directions on plan) there is no limit to the size of the cavity provided the details shown on diagram [2.46] are incorporated.

9.12 **[2.45]** *Cavity barriers – large rooms.*

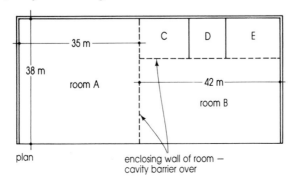

plan

enclosing wall of room — cavity barrier over

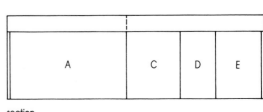

section

9.13 **[2.46]** *Large areas.*

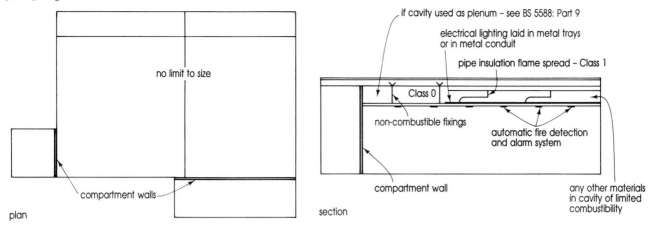

plan   section

no limit to size

compartment walls

if cavity used as plenum – see BS 5588: Part 9

electrical lighting laid in metal trays or in metal conduit

pipe insulation flame spread – Class 1

Class 0

non-combustible fixings

automatic fire detection and alarm system

compartment wall

any other materials in cavity of limited combustibility

Openings in cavity barriers

9.14   The only openings in a cavity barrier should be for:

(*a*)   Doors with 30 minutes fire resistance – FD 30 (Appendix B, Table B1, item 8(a);

(*b*)   The passage of pipes which meet the provisions of B 3, Section 10;

(*c*)   The passage of cables or conduits containing one or more cables;

(*d*)   Openings fitted with an automatic fire shutter;

(*e*)   Ducts fitted with an automatic fire shutter where they pass through the cavity barrier. This does not apply if the ducts are fire resisting.

Section 10   Protection of openings and fire-stopping

Introduction

10.1/10.4   If an element has requirements for fire resistance in terms of integrity and insulation, its effectiveness will be impaired if joints, imperfections in fit or openings to allow services to pass through are not adequately protected by sealing or fire-stopping.

Provisions for fire doors and their openings are given in Appendix B. The measures should delay the passage of fire and will generally retard smoke spread. The test specified in Appendix A for integrity does not stipulate criteria for the passage of smoke.

Openings for pipes

10.5   Three alternatives are given for sealing or fire-stopping pipes which pass through a compartment wall or compartment floor (unless the pipe is in a protected shaft) or through a cavity barrier (diagram [2.47]).

10.5/10.8 **[2.47]** *Pipes in general penetrating walls separating houses, compartment walls and floors, and protected shafts.*

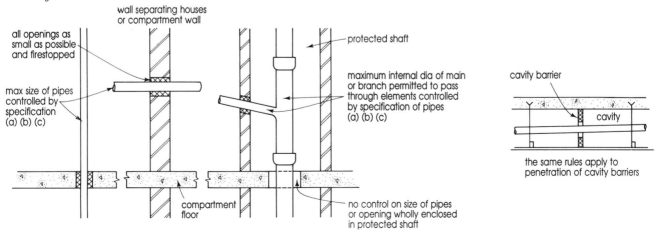

wall separating houses or compartment wall

all openings as small as possible and firestopped

max size of pipes controlled by specification (a) (b) (c)

protected shaft

maximum internal dia of main or branch permitted to pass through elements controlled by specification of pipes (a) (b) (c)

cavity barrier

cavity

the same rules apply to penetration of cavity barriers

compartment floor

no control on size of pipes or opening wholly enclosed in protected shaft

Alternative A – Proprietary seals (any pipe diameter)
10.6   A proprietary sealing system which has been shown by test to maintain the fire resistance of the element.

Alternative B – Pipes with restricted diameter
10.7/10.8   If a proprietary system is not used, fire-stopping may be employed. The opening should be as small as possible and the nominal internal diameter of the pipe should not be more than shown in the Table to 10.7.

Table to 10.7   Maximum nominal diameter of pipes passing through a compartment wall/floor

Situation	Pipe material and maximum nominal internal diameter (mm)		
	Non-combustible material[1] (a)	Lead, aluminium or aluminium alloy, PVC,[2] fibre cement (b)	Any other material (c)
1. Structure (but not a wall separating buildings) enclosing a protected shaft which is not a stairway or lift shaft.	160	110	40
2. Wall separating dwelling houses, or compartment wall or compartment floor between flats.	160	160 (stack pipe)[3] 110 (branch pipe)[3]	40
3. Any other situation	160	40	40

NOTES
[1] A non-combustible material (such as cast iron or steel) which if exposed to a temperature of 800°C will not soften or fracture to the extent that flame or hot gas will pass through the wall of the pipe.
[2] PVC pipes complying with BS 4514: 1983: PVC pipes complying with BS 5255: 1989.
[3] Pipes forming part of an above-ground drainage system and enclosed as shown in diagram [2.49].

10.8   There are concessions for pipes which form part of an above-ground drainage system. These are also illustrated by diagram [2.48].

10.18 **[2.48]** *Pipes in casings forming part of above-ground drainage system in houses, flats or maisonettes.*

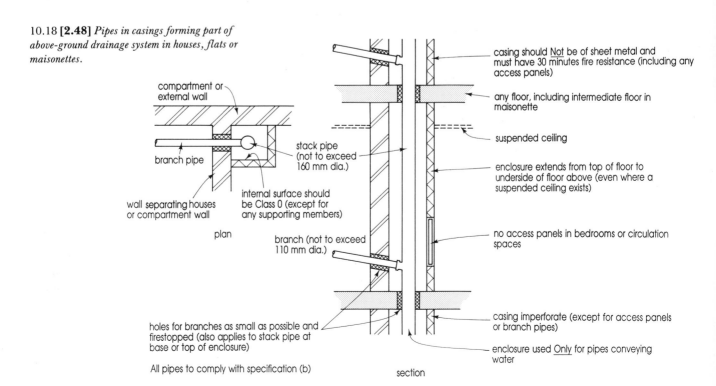

compartment or external wall

branch pipe

wall separating houses or compartment wall

internal surface should be Class 0 (except for any supporting members)

plan

stack pipe (not to exceed 160 mm dia.)

branch (not to exceed 110 mm dia.)

holes for branches as small as possible and firestopped (also applies to stack pipe at base or top of enclosure)

All pipes to comply with specification (b)

section

casing should Not be of sheet metal and must have 30 minutes fire resistance (including any access panels)

any floor, including intermediate floor in maisonette

suspended ceiling

enclosure extends from top of floor to underside of floor above (even where a suspended ceiling exists)

no access panels in bedrooms or circulation spaces

casing imperforate (except for access panels or branch pipes)

enclosure used Only for pipes conveying water

10.9 **[2.49]** *Sleeving of pipes.*

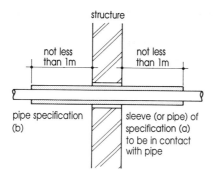

Alternative C – Sleeving

10.9   A pipe with a maximum internal diameter of 160 mm of lead, aluminium, aluminium alloy, fibre cement or PVC may be used with a sleeving of non-combustible pipe (diagram [2.49]).

Ventilating ducts

10.10   Alternative ways in which the integrity of compartments may be maintained where ventilation and air conditioning ducts penetrate fire-separating elements are set out in BS 5588: Part 9: 1989. It is acceptable if the recommendations are followed in respect of air-handling ducts which pass from one compartment to another.

Flues etc

10.11   The walls of a flue, duct containing flues or appliance ventilation duct which pass through a compartment wall or compartment floor should have a fire resistance of at least half that of the wall or floor.

Fire-stopping

10.12   In addition to any other provisions elsewhere for fire-stopping:
(*a*)   Joints between elements which serve as a barrier to the passage of fire should be fire-stopped;
(*b*)   All openings for pipes, ducts, conduits or cables passing through fire barrier elements should be:
      (*i*)   As few as possible;
      (*ii*)   As small as practicable;
      (*iii*)   Fire-stopped (in the case of a pipe or duct in a way which allows thermal movement).

10.13   To prevent displacement, materials used for fire-stopping should be reinforced or supported by materials of limited combustibility wherever the unsupported span exceeds 100 mm and in any case where non-rigid materials are used, unless they have been shown by test to be satisfactory without.

10.14   Proprietary fire-stopping and sealing systems which have been shown by test to maintain the fire resistance of the wall or other element are acceptable. Other suitable fire-stopping materials are:
Cement mortar;
Gypsum-based plaster;
Cement- or gypsum-based vermiculite/perlite mixes;
Glass, crushed rock, blast furnace slag or ceramic-based products with or without resin binders;
Intumescent mastics.

Section 11   Special provisions for car parks and shopping complexes

Introduction

11.1   This is a new section dealing with additional considerations which need to be given to the design and construction of car parks and shopping centres.

Car parks

General principles

11.2   Buildings or parts of buildings used as car parks are not like other buildings in some respects, and some departures from the usual provisions concerning firespread can be made. The fire load is not very high and, of course, well defined. Fire is unlikely to occur between one vehicle and another where the car park is well ventilated and fire is unlikely to spread from one storey to another.

As ventilation is the most important factor, there are different provisions for open-sided car parks and those which are not.

Provisions common to all car park buildings

11.3

1   The relevant provisions of ADs B 1 and B 5.

2   All materials used in the construction of the building, compartment or separated part should be non-combustible, except for:

(*a*)   Any surface finish applied:

(*i*)   To the floor or roof;

(*ii*)   Within any adjoining building, compartment or separated part of the structure which encloses the car park, if the finish accords with the relevant provisions of ADs B 2 and B 4;

(*b*)   Any fire door; and

(*c*)   Any attendant's kiosk not more than 15 m² in area.

Open-sided car parks

11.4   To be regarded as an open-sided car park for the purposes of fire resistance in Appendix A, Table A2 and as a small building or compartment for space separation in AD B 4 (Table to 13.20), it should comply with the following:

(*a*)   The general provisions of 11.3 above;

(*b*)   There should be no basement storeys;

(*c*)   Each storey should be naturally ventilated by:

(*i*)   Permanent openings at each car parking level;

(*ii*)   The aggregate vent area should be not less than 5% of the floor area at that level;

(*iii*)   Half the ventilation should be in two opposing walls;

(*d*)   If there is any other use within the building, the car park should be a separated part.

Car parks which are not open-sided

11.5   If a car park does not have the standard of ventilation set out in 11.4 it cannot be regarded as being open-sided. The provisions of 11.3 should be complied with and some ventilation will be needed whether it is natural or mechanical.

Appendix A, Table A2, sets out higher periods of fire resistance for these car parks.

Natural ventilation

11.6   Where car parks which are not open-sided have natural ventilation:

(*a*)   Each storey should have permanent openings at each level.

(*b*)   The aggregate vent area should be not less than 2.5% of the floor area at that level.

(*c*)   Half the vents should be in opposing walls.

Alternatively, smoke vents at ceiling level can be used. These should have an area of not less than 2.5% of the floor area and be arranged to give a through draught.

Mechanical ventilation

11.7 In most basement car parks and enclosed car parks the minimum standard of natural ventilation shown in 11.6 may not be obtainable. In such cases mechanical ventilation system should be provided. The system should:

(*a*)   Be independent of any other ventilating system;

(*b*)   Be designed to operate at the rate of:

    (*i*)   Six air changes per hour for normal petrol vapour extraction;

    (*ii*)   Ten air changes per hour in a fire condition;

(*c*)   Be designed to run in two parts, each part capable of extracting 50% of the rates shown in (*b*) above, each part to operate singly or simultaneously;

(*d*)   Have an independent power supply to each part which would operate in the event of a main failure;

(*e*)   Have extract points arranged so that 50% are at high level and 50% at low level;

(*f*)   Have fans rated to run at 300°C for at least 60 minutes; the ductwork and fixings should be constructed of materials having a melting point of not less than 800°C.

Shopping complexes

11.8 The provisions in the ADs may not be appropriate when considering the design of shopping complexes.

11.9 Alternative measures to the provisions of the ADs can be found in BS 5588: Part 10: 1991 *Shopping complexes* (particularly Sections 5 and 6) and the relevant recommendations should be followed.

B 4   EXTERNAL FIRE SPREAD

The requirement is as follows:

Requirement	Limits on application
B 4 External fire spread (1) The external walls of the building shall resist the spread of fire over the walls and from one building to another, having regard to the height, use and position of the building. (2) The roof of the building shall resist the spread of fire over the roof and from one building to another having regard to the use and position of the building.	

NOTE The only change from the 1985 requirement is the omission of the reference to adequacy.

Performance

The requirement will be met if:

(*a*)   External walls have low rates of spread of flame and in some cases low rates of heat release to restrict the risk of ignition from an external source and the spread of flame over their surfaces;

(*b*)   Unprotected areas in the side of a building are limited to reduce the radiation that can pass through the wall;

(*c*)   Roofs are constructed to reduce the risk of spread of fire from an external source.

Introduction

External walls

0.49/0.51 Section 12 deals with the fire resistance of external walls and Section 13 with limiting the extent of unprotected areas.

Roofs

0.52 Section 14 deals with reducing the risk of fire spread over roofs.

Section 12 Construction of external walls

Introduction

12.1/12.2   This section makes provisions for the external walls of a building to have sufficient fire resistance to prevent fire spread across the relevant boundary. If a wall is 1 m or more from the relevant boundary a reduced standard is acceptable, but those walls less than 1 m from the relevant boundary and high buildings and assembly buildings are subject to restrictions on combustibility.

Fire resistance standard

12.3   External walls should have the fire resistance given in Appendix A, Table A1 unless they form an unprotected area (see Section 13).

Portal frames

12.4   Where a portal-framed building is near a relevant boundary the external wall near the boundary cannot all be unprotected area, although under AD B 3 there may be no provision for fire resistance of the structure. A portal frame generally acts as a single element because of the moment-restricting connections used, particularly in the column rafter joints. The rafter members of the frame as well as the column members may need to be fire protected where the external wall cannot be wholly protected.

It is feasible to design the foundation and the connection of the portal frame to the foundation so that it transmits the overturning moment caused by the collapse in a fire of unprotected rafters, purlins and roof cladding so as to allow the external wall to perform its structural function. The design methods are set out in *Fire and steel construction, the behaviour of steel portal frames in boundary conditions* (second edition 1990). This is available from the Steel Construction Institute, Silwood Park, Ascot, Berks SL5 7QN.

Portal frames of reinforced concrete can support walls requiring a similar degree of fire resistance without specific provision at the base to resist overturning.

External surfaces

12.5/12.6   External walls should comply with the provisions of diagram [2.50].

The surface of the outer cladding which faces the cavity in 'rain-screen' construction should also meet these provisions.

The extent of combustible material is subject to Section 13 of this AD.

12.5 **[2.50]** *External surfaces of walls in relation to distance from the relevant boundary.*

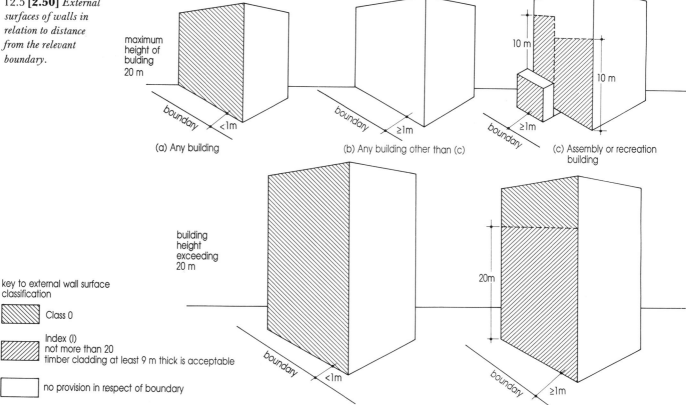

maximum height of bulding 20 m

(a) Any building

(b) Any building other than (c)

(c) Assembly or recreation building

building height exceeding 20 m

10 m

10 m

20m

key to external wall surface classification

Class 0

Index (I) not more than 20 timber cladding at least 9 m thick is acceptable

no provision in respect of boundary

External wall construction **12.7** The use of combustible thermal insulation as an overcladding or in ventilated cavities may present a risk to health and safety in tall buildings even though the provisions in Diagram [2.50] have been met.

In a building with a storey at more than 20 m above ground level, any insulation used should be a material of limited combustibility.

Advice on the use of thermal insulation material can be found in BRE report BR 135, 1988 – Fire performance of external thermal insulation for walls of multi-storey buildings.

Section 13 Space separation

Introduction **13.1** The provisions of this section, which are based on several assumptions, limit the extent of openings and other unprotected areas in the sides of a building so that external fire spread from one building to another will give a reasonable standard of fire safety.

13.2 The assumptions are related to:

(*a*) *Size of fire*. This will depend on compartmentation; a fire may involve a whole compartment but will not spread to other compartments.

(*b*) *Intensity of fire*. This depends on the use of the building (ie purpose group) but this can be moderated by a sprinkler system.

(*c*) *Life risk*. Residential, Assembly and Recreation purpose groups represent a greater life risk. The spread of fire between buildings in other purpose groups on the same site is of low risk and can be discounted.

(*d*) *Buildings on adjoining site*. It is assumed that on the other side of the boundary there is a building of the same elevation and at the same distance from the boundary as the building being considered.

(*e*) *Radiation*. Radiation which may pass through a fire-resistant external wall is discounted.

13.3 It may be advantageous to construct smaller compartments to reduce the separation distance or to enable more unprotected areas to be included without reducing the separation distance.

Boundaries *Relevant and notional boundary*

13.4/13.6 Where the side of a building is on the boundary, that is the 'relevant boundary'. Otherwise it is the actual boundary of the land either parallel to, or making an angle of not more than 80° with the face of the building in question. Note that a boundary can be relevant to more than one face. Where land abuts a road, waterway or railway the relevant boundary is taken as the centre of these. The points are illustrated in diagram [2.51].

13.4 **[2.51]** *Boundary*.

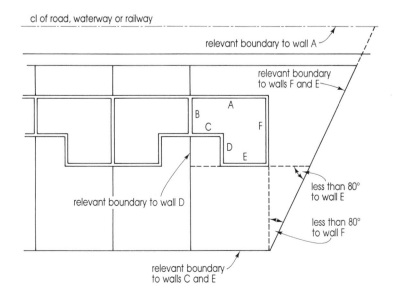

Buildings erected on land which they share in common (ie there is no actual boundary between them) and if one of them is in either one of the residential groups or the assembly group must be assumed to have a notional boundary between them placed as defined in diagram [2.52]. When set, the notional boundary is regarded as the relevant boundary for the second building. Although not mentioned in this section a roof must be treated as a wall in certain circumstances which are illustrated in diagram [2.53]. This information has been transferred into the list of definitions in Appendix E.

13.5 **[2.52]** *Notional boundary.*   13.6 **[2.53]** *Roofs treated as walls.*

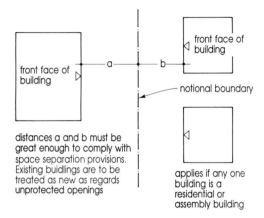

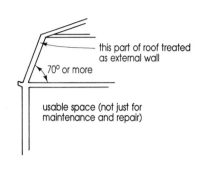

Unprotected areas

13.7/13.9   The definition of unprotected area is in Appendix E and is as shown in diagram [2.54]. Any part of an external wall which has less fire resistance than the appropriate amount given in Appendix A, Table A1 is considered to be an unprotected area.

13.7 **[2.54]** *Definition of unprotected areas.*

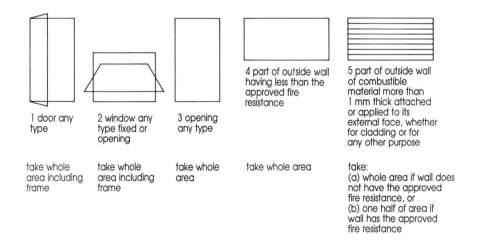

Exclusions

Any part of an external wall of a stairway in a protected shaft (see diagram [2.13]).

NOTE   See provisions in B1 and B5 regarding the relationship of external walls of protected stairways to unprotected areas of other parts of the same building.

13.10   Small unprotected areas which may be disregarded for separation distance purposes are shown in diagram [2.55].

Canopies

13.11   Canopy structures which may not be exempt within Class VI of Schedule 2 provided they are at least 1 m from the boundary need not comply with the space-separation provisions. A high degree of ventilation and heat dissipation is achieved by the open-sided construction and the provisions in this section are considered unduly onerous. They would, however, still be subject to the limitations on the use of plastic rooflights in the Table to 14.5.

13.10 **[2.55]** *Unprotected areas which may be*
disregarded for separation distances.

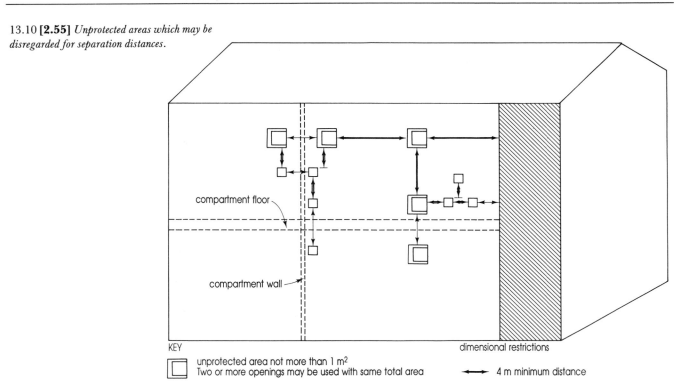

KEY

☐ unprotected area not more than 1 m² Two or more openings may be used with same total area

☐ unprotected area not more than 0.1 m²

▨ external wall of stairway forming a protected shaft. This may also be disregarded when assessing total unprotected area

dimensional restrictions

←→ 4 m minimum distance

←→ 1.5 m minimum distance

←→ no restriction

Large uncompartmented buildings

13.12   Parts of the external wall of large uncompartmented buildings which are more than 30 m from mean ground level may be disregarded in the assessment of unprotected area (diagram [2.56]).

13.12 **[2.56]** *Unprotected areas in tall buildings*
(uncompartmented).

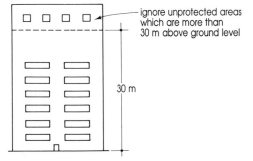

ignore unprotected areas which are more than 30 m above ground level

30 m

External walls within 1 m of the relevant boundary at any point

13.13   The only unprotected areas should be those shown in diagram [2.55] and the rest of the wall should be fire resisting.

External walls 1 m or more from the relevant boundary

13.14   The extent of unprotected area should not exceed that given by one of the calculation methods referred to in paragraph 13.15 with the rest of the wall being fire-resisting.

Methods for calculating acceptable unprotected area

13.15   Two methods are included in the AD. Method 1 is based and similar to Method 1 in the 1985 edition (diagram [2.57]). Method 2 has not been used in previous ADs or regulations. The enclosing rectangle and aggregate notional area methods previously set out in Appendix J of the 1985 AD can be found in the BRE Report *External fire Spread, building separation and boundary distances* (BRE, 1991). These methods may be used instead of Methods 1 and 2. As they were used quite extensively they are reproduced for the convenience of readers.

13.18 **[2.57]** *Calculation of permitted unprotected*
area in buildings of limited size in houses, flats and
other residential buildings: Method 1.
Total extent of unprotected area permitted in side
facing boundary.

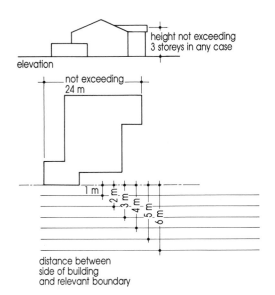

minimum distance between side of building and relevant boundary	maximum total of unprotected areas (m²)
1 m	5.6
2 m	12
3 m	18
4 m	24
5 m	30
6 m	no limit

any parts of the side of the
building in excess of the
maximum unprotected area
should be fire-resisting

Basis for calculating unprotected areas

13.16   The aim is to ensure that a building is separated from the boundary by at least half the distance at which the total thermal radiation intensity received from all unprotected areas in the wall would be 12.6 kW/m² (in still air) assuming the radiation intensity at each unprotected area is:

(*a*)   84 kW/m² – Residential, office or assembly and recreation purpose groups (ie PGs 1, 2, 3 and 5);

(*b*)   168 kW/m² – Shop and commercial, industrial, storage and other non-residential purpose groups (PGs 4, 6 and 7).

Sprinkler systems

13.17   Subject to there being a minimum distance of 1 m, the boundary distance may be half that of an unsprinklered building if a sprinkler system is installed. The system should meet the relevant recommendations of BS 5306: Part 2, ie the relevant occupancy rating together with the additional requirements for life safety.

This new provision has been introduced because it is reasonable to assume that sprinklers will reduce the intensity and extent of any fire which may occur.

Method 1: Small residential

13.18   The method can only be used for a building to be used as a house, flats or other residential purposes (not institutional).

The building must not exceed three storeys (not counting basements) or 24 m in length (see note below). The rules determining the extent of unprotected areas are illustrated in diagram [2.57].

Method 2: Other buildings or compartments

13.19   This method can be used for any building or compartment intended for any use and not less than 1 m from any point on the boundary.

The following rules should be read with the table:

(*a*)   The building should not exceed 10 m in height except for open-sided car parks in purpose group 7(b);

(*b*)   The provisions for space separation will be met if the distance of the side of the building from the relevant boundary and the extent of unprotected area are within the limits given in the table;

(*c*)   Any parts of the side of the building in excess of the maximum unprotected area should be fire-resisting.

Table to 13.19

Minimum distance between side of building and relevant boundary (m)		*Maximum total percentage of unprotected area*
	Purpose groups	
Residential, office, assembly and recreation	*Shop and commerical, industrial, storage and other non-residential*	
(1)	(2)	(3)
Not applicable	1	4
1	2	8
2.5	5	20
5	10	40
7.5	15	60
10	20	80
12.5	25	100

NOTES
(a) Intermediate values may be obtained by interpolation.
(b) Where automatic sprinklers are fitted to BS 5306: Part 2, the values in columns (1) and (2) may be halved subject to a minimum distance of 1 m.
(c) Open-sided car parks (PG 7(b)).
The distances set out in Column 1 may be used instead of Column 2.

Other methods for calculating space-separation distances

Enclosing rectangle
This is a method in which distances are established from a set of tables related to the dimensions of a rectangle enclosing all the openings in the whole face, separated part or compartment. Two sets of figures are given, one for shop, industrial and other non-residential uses and one for all other groups. The former are the more onerous. The plane of reference is to take in more than one face of a building. All of this is illustrated in diagrams [2.58] and [2.59].
A rectangle is constructed on the plane of references so as to enclose the outer limits of all the unprotected areas on that side of the building or compartment. The *enclosing rectangle* is the one next above this size, in both height and width, in the tables provided. These give heights from 3 to 27 m in 3 metre steps and widths from 3 m up to no limit.
Diagram [2.58] illustrates how the rectangle is constructed and four examples of the result on a small elevation.

Unprotected percentage
This is established by taking the aggregate area of all the unprotected areas (see diagram [2.59]) as a percentage of the area of the enclosing rectangle.

The tables

These give distances from the boundary for various combinations of height and width of enclosing rectangles and unprotected percentages from 20 per cent to 100 per cent by steps of 10 per cent. These distances represent the minimum distance between the plane of reference and the boundary, and will decide how near any particular side of the building can be to the relevant boundary. Alternatively, if the distance is fixed, they will decide how much unprotected area can be permitted.
There are two sets of figures, those in parentheses being for residential, office or assembly buildings and the others for the remainder (shop, industrial and other non-residential).

Comment
It may be seen that even if the whole face of a building is an unprotected area the unprotected percentage will never be 100 per cent unless by coincidence the actual rectangle enclosing the outer limits of all unprotected areas is the exact height and width of one of the rectangles listed in the tables. According to how these dimensions work out, the percentage may vary from just under 40 per cent to 100 per cent in the circumstances mentioned above. As an example take a building with a fully glazed face 30.1 m long × 3.1 m high.

13.20 **[2.58]** *Enclosing rectangle method. The interpretation of 'planes of reference' around a building. To find the nearest position that a boundary can be to a building, a series of planes of reference can be drawn around it. The projection of the unprotected areas upon each of these planes of reference and the calculation of the percentage of unprotected areas within the enclosing rectangles will give the minimum distances permitted between the relevant boundary and the planes of reference. If these minimum distances are superimposed upon one plan of the building a zone around the building is produced upon which a boundary cannot encroach.*

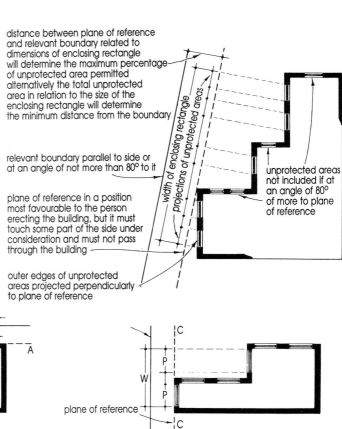

distance between plane of reference and relevant boundary related to dimensions of enclosing rectangle will determine the maximum percentage of unprotected area permitted alternatively the total unprotected area in relation to the size of the enclosing rectangle will determine the minimum distance from the boundary

relevant boundary parallel to side or at an angle of not more than 80° to it

plane of reference in a position most favourable to the person erecting the building, but it must touch some part of the side under consideration and must not pass through the building

outer edges of unprotected areas projected perpendicularly to plane of reference

unprotected areas not included if at an angle of 80° of more to plane of reference

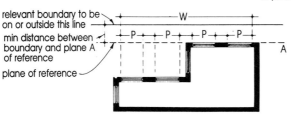

relevant boundary to be on or outside this line

min distance between boundary and plane A of reference

plane of reference

front boundary

side boundary

closest limit of relevant boundary

plane of reference

corner boundary

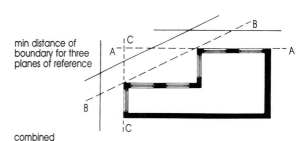

min distance of boundary for three planes of reference

combined

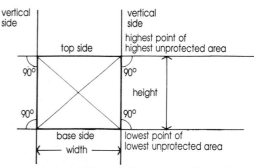

vertical side | vertical side

top side

highest point of highest unprotected area

height

base side

lowest point of lowest unprotected area

width

horizontal distance between outermost lines of unprotected areas as projected on to the plane of reference on plan

[2.59] *Examples of 'enclosing rectangles' and*
'unprotected percentage'.
NOTE TW and TH = the next greatest width and
height dimensional in the tables to W and H.

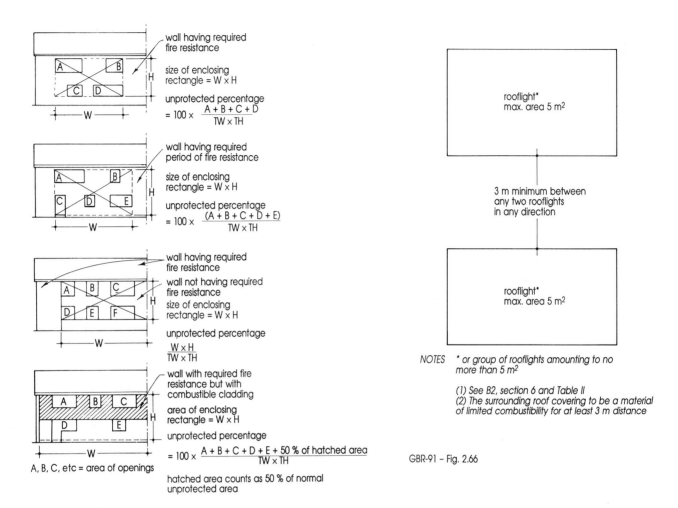

GBR-91 – Fig. 2.66

Unprotected area	$= 30.1 \times 3.1$	$= 93.31$
Next largest rectangle 40×6		$= 240.00$
Unprotected percentage		$= 38.8\%$

Another example 60.1 × 9.1 m high all glazed comes out at 56.9 per cent. Also, what is not explained is how to calculate the area of an enclosing rectangle with a width of 'no limit' (the last item in each table). This is, of course, not possible (the mathematical answer is infinity m², which would make the unprotected percentage zero), so that the only recourse is presumably to take the *actual length* in conjunction with the appropriate height in the table. The distances given by the tables are in 0.5 m intervals and have obviously been rounded off from an exact figure produced by a mathematical formula. Furthermore, they are visually just a large block of figures which can give no immediate impression of the relationships involved. It has therefore been thought worthwhile to present them graphically, one graph for each height of rectangle in each of the two categories of use. From the graphs, the relationship between the rectangle widths, unprotected percentage and distance from the boundary is immediately apparent.

The graphs are also a convenient tool for use during the design stages of a building, to determine the overall general situation where interrelated parameters are being considered. If the situation is critical it will be necessary to check with the tables themselves and if it is then still very close it may be advisable to check using the aggregate notional area method below. As the tables are in very close steps only the alternative width figures (3, 9, 15 etc) are shown to avoid congestion. However, interpolation is quite in order (see diagrams [2.60]–[2.61]).

[2.60] *Graphic representation of table for buildings or compartments in residential, office or assembly groups (NL = no limit).*

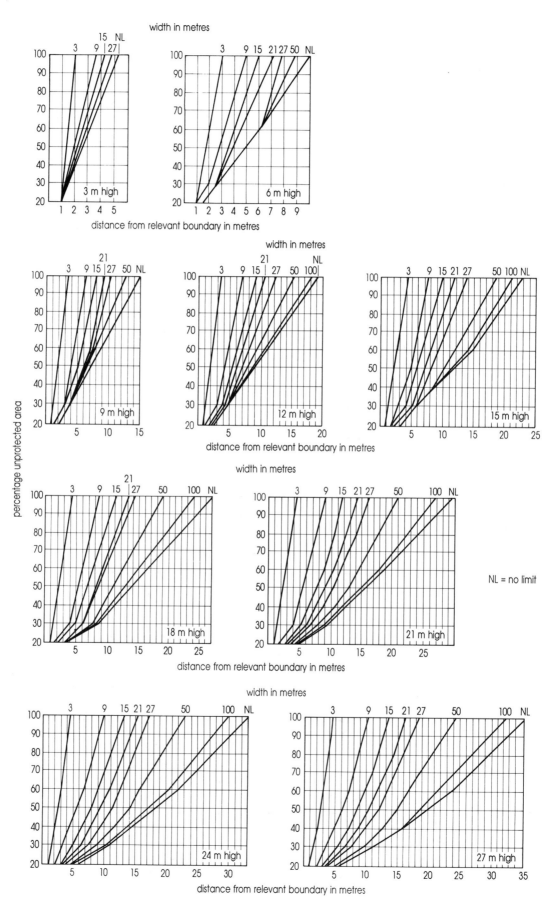

[2.61] *Graphic representation of table for buildings and compartments in shop, industrial and other non-residential groups.*

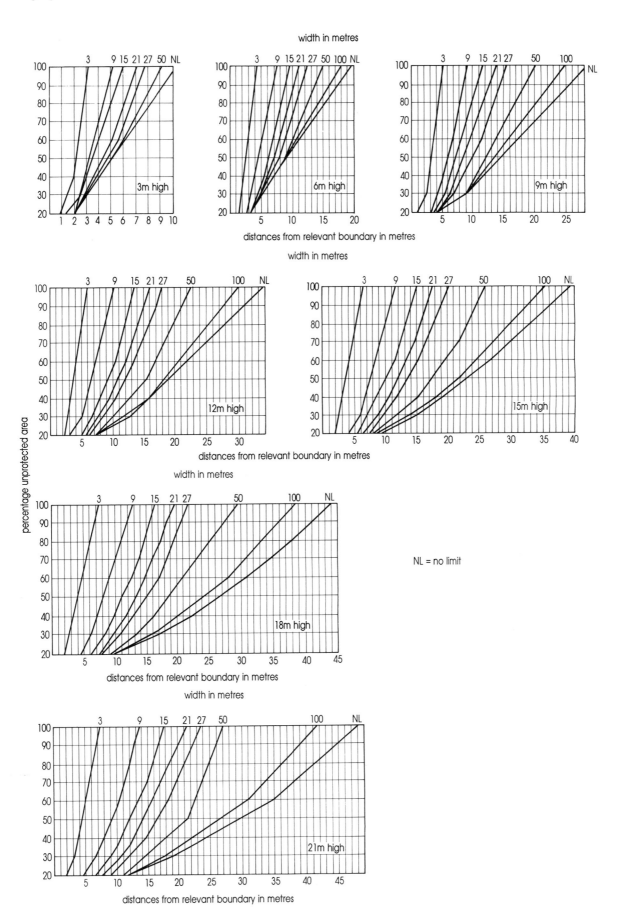

[2.61] *(continued)*.

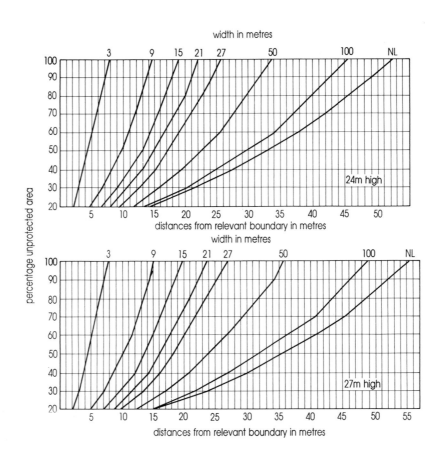

If the above procedure produces an adverse answer the designer is left with three alternatives:
1   Reduce the total unprotected area.
2   Increase the distance from the boundary.
3   Reduce the size of the enclosing rectangle by compartmentation.
As 1 and 2 may not be acceptable, it may be necessary to resort to compartmentation (which may also have other advantages, such as a reduction in the minimum fire-resistance period. A diagram illustrating how this can work is reproduced here as [2.62].

Aggregate notional area method

This method may be used for any building or compartment more than 1 m from the boundary. It should produce a more precise result than the enclosing rectangle method, especially if the building or boundary is irregularly shaped, but it is more time consuming. This Guide gives a general, informative description of the procedure.

Aggregate notional area
The Regulations are concerned with the possible effect of a fire at any point on a boundary. This grows less as the distance between increases. Thus for each point on the boundary an 'aggregate notional area' is calculated, by taking the sum of each unprotected area multiplied by a factor based on the distance from the boundary. The factors to be used are illustrated in diagram [2.63].
The total of these notional areas must fall within a fixed figure which is:
210 m²   For residential, office and assembly buildings.
 90 m²   For shops, industrial and other non-residential groups.

Vertical datum/Datum line/Base line
As it would be impossible to check an infinity of points on a boundary the method requires a series of points to be selected at not more than 3 m intervals on which an imaginary vertical line is set. Each of these is known as a 'vertical datum'. Considering one at a time, a 'datum line' is drawn from the point to the nearest point on the building and a 'base line' is drawn through the vertical datum at right angles to the datum line. This becomes the base for a series of semicircles with radii coorresponding to the distances at which the factors change: the largest of these is 50 m (diagram 1 [2.64]).

[2.62] *Enclosing rectangles (effect of compartmentation on distance from boundary). Compartmentation of a building has a considerable effect on the distance which its sides (or external walls) may be from the relevant boundary. This is shown and explained in the following figures, which assume a residential, assembly or office use.*

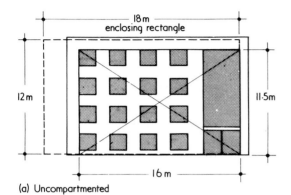

(a) Uncompartmented

1. *Assume rectangle (enclosing unprotected areas) = 11.5 × 16 m*
2. *From table, enclosing rectangle = 12 m × 18 m = 216 m²*
3. *Assume unprotected areas (shaded) = 105 m²*
4. *Unprotected percentage (unprotected areas as percentage of enclosing rectangle) = 105 m² as percentage of 216 m² = 48.6% : use 50% column in table*
5. *From table, distance from boundary = 6 m (minimum)*

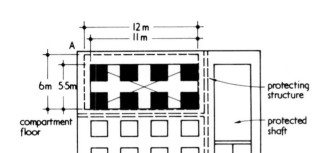

(b) Compartmented
(assume compartmentation as shown)

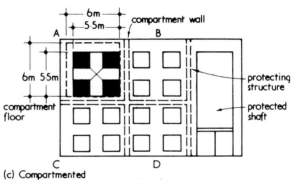

(c) Compartmented
(assume compartmentation as shown)

(a) As the entrance and stairways are now isolated the area becomes a protected shaft and the glazed area does not now count as part of the unprotected area.
(b) The remainder of the building is divided by the compartment floor into compartments A and B. In this example the compartments have the same unprotected area. But where there are two (or more) compartments with different unprotected areas, take the compartment with the greatest unprotected area.

1. *Assume rectangle = 5.5 m × 11 m*
2. *From table, enclosing rectangle = 6 m × 12 m = 72 m²*
3. *Assume unprotected areas = 26 m²*
4. *Unprotected percentage = 26 m² as percentage of 72 m² = 36% : use 40% column in table*
5. *From table, distance from boundary = 3 m (minimum).*

With the inclusion of a compartment wall, the building is now divided into compartments A, B, C and D, each having the same unprotected area for the purpose of this example.

1. *Assume rectangle = 5.5 m × 5.5 m*
2. *From table, enclosing rectangle = 6 m × 6 m = 36 m²*
3. *Assume unprotected areas = 13 m²*
4. *Unprotected percentage = 36% use 40% column in table*
5. *From table, distance from boundary = 2 m (minimum)*

NOTE   In the above diagram the relevant boundary is assumed as parallel with the wall face, and the plane of reference to coincide with the wall face. But this will not always be so.

Diagram 1 **[2.63]** *Application of 'aggregate notional area' method.*

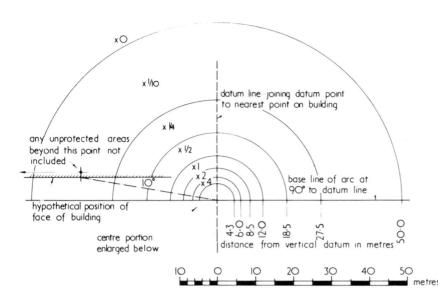

NOTE Measurements taken at any point on the boundary must not produce, for any side of a building or compartment, unprotected areas the aggregate of which, when multiplied by the relevant factors, exceeds $210\,m^2$ for purpose groups residential, office, assembly or $90\,m^2$ for purpose groups shop, industrial, other non-residential.

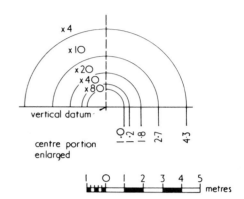

Diagram 2 **[2.64]** *Multiplication factors at specified distances from vertical datum.*

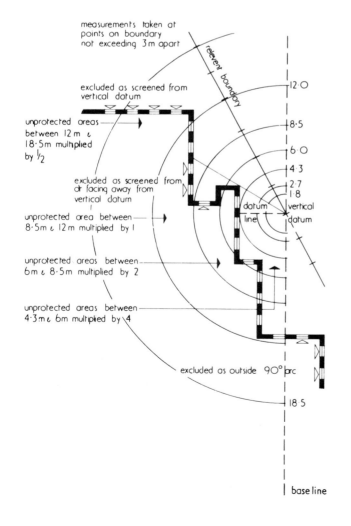

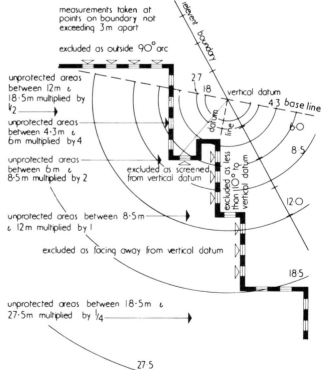

measurements taken at any points on the boundary must not produce, for any side of a building or compartment unprotected areas the aggregate of which when multiplied by the relevant factors exeeds $210\,m^2$ for Purpose Groups residential, office, assembly or $90\,m^2$ for Purpose Groups shop, industrial, other non-residential

Excluded areas

Unprotected areas outside these limits have no effect on the calculation. Windows screened from direct view from the datum (except by other unprotected areas) are excluded as also are any areas which are beyond the limits of the baseline or semicircle or which face away from the datum or are at an angle of less than 10° to it. Diagram 2 [2.64] illustrates the principles.

Procedure

To facilite the checking of a full series of vertical data at 3 m intervals it will be useful to make a protractor of plastic film or tracing paper based on Diagram 1 and to the same scale as the drawing.

Where a building has an irregular outline it may well be necessary to check a series of points. There will, however, also be bases where the critical datum is obvious, such as a plain facade standing on, or parallel to, the boundary and less than 100 m long, in which case the datum must be in line with the centre of the building (assuming evenly spaced glazing). The effect in such a case of varying distances from the boundary on the permitted unprotected area is illustrated in diagram [2.65].

There are many such buildings in urban areas placed on the site boundary where the relevant boundary is the centre of the road or street. If this is not very wide the Regulation may well be restrictive, especially if shop windows are required. In such cases compartmentation could be the only solution.

Diagram 3 **[2.65]** *Effect of distance on continuously glazed building parallel to boundary in shop, industrial or other non-residential buildings.*
NOTE   The shaded bands represent continuous glazing. The total permitted depth is calculated by dividing the maximum aggregate of unprotected areas of 90 m² by the lengths of glazing multiplied by the appropriate factors (ie 8.99, 21.92 etc).

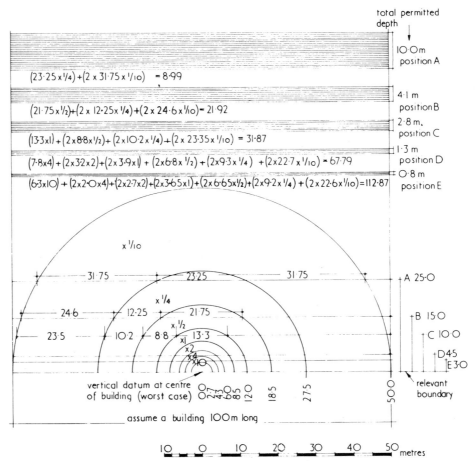

Section 14   Roof coverings

Introduction

14.1/14.2   This section limits the use near a boundary of certain roof coverings which will not give adequate protection should fire spread over them. It does not relate to the roof structure, only to constructions of roof coverings, usually one or more layers of material.

Other sections of Part B have provisions regarding roofs. These are:

B 1: Means of escape – AD B 1 has provisions for roofs that are part of means of escape.

B 2: Internal fire spread – linings. AD B 2 contains provisions for internal surfaces of rooflights.

B 3: Internal fire spread – structure. AD B 3, Section 7 covers roofs used as a floor. Section 8 covers roof passing over the top of a compartment wall.

Classification of performance

14.3   The performance of roof coverings is designated by reference to BS 476: Part 3: 1958. This is described in Appendix A together with the notional performance of some common roof coverings. See Table A5 of the Appendix and notes on BS 476: Part 3.

Rooflights are similarly controlled – see method of classification of thermoplastic rooflights in Appendix A.

Separation distances

14.4   The separation distance is the minimum distance from the roof (or part) to the relevant boundary. The wall separating a pair of semi-detached houses may be disregarded for this purpose, but the boundaries between houses in a terrace may not. The table sets out separation distances according to the type of roof covering and the size and use of the building.

There are no restrictions on the use of roof coverings designated AA, AB or AC.

Table to 14.4   Limitations on roof coverings

Designation of covering of roof or part of roof	Minimum distance from any point on relevant boundary			
	Less than 6 m	At least 6 m	At least 12 m	At least 12 m
AA, AB or AC	√	√	√	√
BA, BB or BC	×	√	√	√
CA, BC or CC	×	√[1]	√[2]	√
AB, BD or CD	×	√[1]	√[2]	√[2]
DA, DB, DC or DD	×	×	×	√[1]
Thatch or wood shingles if performance under BS 476: Part 3 cannot be established	×	√[1]	√[2]	√[2]

NOTES

√   acceptable

×   not acceptable

√[1] Not acceptable on any of the following buildings:

(a) Houses in terraces of three or more houses;

(b) Industrial, storage or other non-residential purpose group buildings of any size;

(c) Any other buildings with a cubic capacity of more than 1500 m³ and only acceptable on other buildings if part of the roof is no more than 3 m² in area and is at least 1.5 m from any similar part, with the roof between the parts covered with a material of limited combustibility.

√[2] Not acceptable on any of the buildings listed under (a), (b) or (c) above.

NOTE   This Table has been simplified and can be used for all purpose groups. Separation distance considerations do not apply to the roofs of a pair of semi-detached houses.

Plastics rooflights

14.5/14.6   The Table to 14.5 sets out the limitations on the use of plastics rooflights (see diagram [2.66]).

14.5 **[2.66]** *Size and spacing of plastics rooflights.*
Lower surface Class 3 or TP(b).

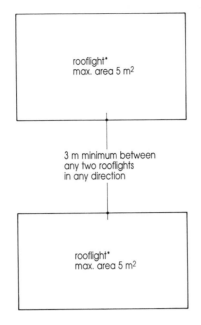

3 m minimum between
any two rooflights
in any direction

rooflight*
max. area 5 m²

rooflight*
max. area 5 m²

NOTES   * or group of rooflights amounting to no
           more than 5 m²

           (1) See B2, section 6 and Table II
           (2) The surrounding roof covering to be a material
               of limited combustibility for at least 3 m distance

Table to 14.5   Plastic rooflights: limitations on use and boundary distance

Minimum classification on lower surface[1]	Space which rooflight can serve	Minimum distance from any point on relevant boundary to rooflight with an external surface classification[2] of		
		TP(a)	AD, BD, CA, CB, CC, CD or TP(b)	DA, DB, DC, DD
1. TP(a) rigid	Any space except a protected stairway	6 m[3]	6 m[5]	20 m
2. Class 3 or TP(b)	(a) Balcony, verandah, carport, covered way or loading bay, which has at least one longer side wholly or permanently open		6 m	6 m 20 m
	(b) Detached swimming pool			
	(c) Conservatory, garage or outbuilding, with a maximum floor area of 40 m²			
	(d) Circulation space[4] (except a protected stairway)	6 m[5]	6 m[5]	20 m[5]
	(e) Room[4]			

NOTES
na Not applicable
[1] See also the guidance to B 2.
[2] The classification of external roof surfaces is explained in Appendix A.
[3] No limit in the case of any space described in 2(a), (b) and (c).
[4] Single-skin rooflight only, in the case of non-thermoplastic material.
[5] The rooflight should also meet the provisions of diagram [2.66].
Polycarbonate and PVC rooflights which achieve a Class 1 rating by test (see paragraph 14.5) may be regarded as having an AA designation.
None of the above designations are suitable for protected stairways – see paragraph 6.12.

Glass in rooflights   **14.7**   Unwired glass at least 4 mm thick used in rooflights can be regarded as having an AA
classification.

B 5   ACCESS AND FACILITIES FOR THE FIRE SERVICE

This is a new requirement.
The requirement is as follows:

Requirement	Limits on application

Access and facilities for the fire service
B 5(1)   The building shall be designed and constructed so as to provide facilities to assist firefighters in the protection of life.
(2)   Provision shall be made within the site of the building to enable fire appliances to gain access to the building.

This requirement was originally proposed to be included in the Building Regulations as long ago as 1969, but apparently it was not possible to do so at that time.

There are many Local Acts in England and Wales which have similar provisions to those in this requirement. The opportunity has now been taken to relate Local Act provisions during the Stage Two review of national Building Regulations and designers may find that there may be differences in requirements.

Most of the Local Act provisions concerning access and facilities for the fire service state that no requirement shall be made concerning means of access unless notice of the Local Act provision is endorsed on or accompanies the planning permission. This, of course, does not apply to the requirements of B 5.

Performance

This sets out a brief resumé of the provisions of the four sections in the AD. The performance will be met if there is sufficient access:
To enable fire appliances to be brought near the building
Into and in the building for firefighters to effect rescue and fight fire
and the building has internal fire mains etc to assist firefighters and is provided with adequate basement ventilation for removal of heat and smoke.

Introduction

0.53/0.54   The size of the building will determine the facilities needed. In deep basements and tall buildings, firefighters will normally work inside the building and here special access facilities will be required together with fire mains. Fire appliances will need access to entry points near the fire mains.

In other buildings, the existing means of escape facilities together with the ability to work from ladders and appliances outside the building will usually be adequate. Vehicle access will be needed to some part of the perimeter, depending on the size of the building.

Access to basement fires is usually difficult for firefighters and basement smoke venting can assist considerably by improving visibility and reducing temperatures so that search, rescue and firefighting operations are more effectively carried out.

Section 15   Fire mains

Introduction

15.1   Rising fire mains serve floors above the ground or access level. Access level is the level at which the fire service gain access and is not necessarily at ground level (for instance, in a podium design).
Falling mains serve levels below-ground or access level.
Fire mains are pipes installed in a building and equipped with valves etc so that the fire service may connect hoses for water to fight fire within it.

'Dry' mains are normally empty and are supplied through a hose from a fire service pump appliance.

'Wet' mains are kept full of water and supplied from storage tanks and pumps in the building but should be constructed so as to allow replenishment of water from a pump appliance in an emergency.

Provision of fire mains

15.2/15.6 Buildings which have:

Firefighting shafts should have fire mains in those shafts.

A floor more than 60 m above ground or access level should have wet rising mains.

Floors less than 60 m may have either 'wet' or 'dry' rising mains.

There should be one fire main in every firefighting shaft and an outlet should be sited in each firefighting lobby which gives access to accommodation from a firefighting shaft.

Further guidance on the design and construction of fire mains is in Sections 2 and 3 of BS 5306: Part 1.

Section 16 Vehicle access

Introduction

16.1 The vehicle access provisions only apply to buildings without fire mains, ie those buildings which do not have firefighting shafts. Access is needed to enable vehicles carrying high-reach turntable ladders and hydraulic platforms to get near to the building and to enable pumping appliances to supply water and equipment for firefighting and rescue. The higher the building, the greater are the access provisions needed. Vehicle access routes and hardstandings should be as set out in paragraphs 16.8–16.10 and the Table to 16.8.

Buildings not fitted with fire mains

16.2/16.4 It should be noted that Building Regulations cannot make requirements for work to be done outside the site of the works shown on plans which are deposited or a building notice served. Access provisions therefore can only be applied within the site.

Access for vehicles to small buildings (ie those up to 2000 m² in floor area with a top storey less than 9 m above ground level) should be provided to within 45 m of the building or to 15% of the perimeter whichever is the less onerous. The actual point of a building to which the distance should be measured is to any point on the projected plan area (described as the 'footprint': see diagram [2.6]. 'Perimeter' is also described in this diagram).

Any elevation to which vehicle access is provided in accordance with the Table to 16.3 should have a 750 mm wide door giving access to the inside of the building.

Table to 16.3   Fire service vehicular access to buildings not fitted with fire mains

Area of building (m²)[1]	Height of floor of top storey above ground (m)[2]	Provide vehicle access to:	Type of appliance
Up to 7000	Up to 9	See paragraph 16.2	Pump
	Over 9	15% of perimeter	High-reach
7 000–280 000	Up to 9	15% of perimeter	Pump
	Over 9	50% of perimeter	High-reach
28 000–56 000	Up to 9	50% of perimeter	Pump
	Over 9	50% of perimeter	High-reach
56 000–85 000	Up to 9	75% of perimeter	Pump
	Over 9	75% of perimeter	High-reach
Over 85 000	Up to 9	100% of perimeter	Pump
	Over 9	100% of perimeter	High-reach

NOTES

[1] The aggregate of all floors in the building

[2] In the case of purpose groups (7(a) (storage) buildings, height is meant to mean roof level. See methods of measurement in Appendix C.

16.2 **[2.67]** *Building footprint and perimeter.*

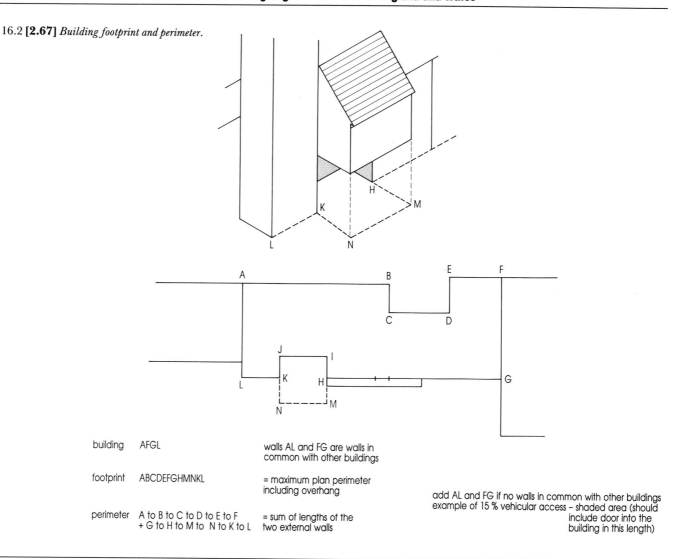

building   AFGL   walls AL and FG are walls in
                                              common with other buildings

footprint   ABCDEFGHMNKL   = maximum plan perimeter
                                              including overhang
                                                                              add AL and FG if no walls in common with other buildings
                                                                              example of 15 % vehicular access – shaded area (should
perimeter   A to B to C to D to E to F   = sum of lengths of the   include door into the
            + G to H to M to N to K to L   two external walls   building in this length)

Buildings fitted with fire mains

16.5/16.7   Buildings which have firefighting shafts should be fitted with fire mains. Where there are fire mains access should be provided for a pumping appliance in the case of dry mains to within 18 m of each fire main inlet point with the inlet visible from the appliance, and in the case of wet mains to within 18 m and within sight of a suitable entrance giving access to the main and in sight of the inlet for the emergency replenishment of the suction tank for the main.

Design of access routes and hardstandings

16.8/16.10   The standards for vehicle access routes are shown in the Table to 16.8. The route can be a road or other route, and manhole covers should be of the strength required for the route.

Cables, branches of trees and other overhead obstructions should be taken into account as these could interfere with the setting up of ladders, etc and a turning circle or hammerhead should be provided for any dead-end access route more than 20 m in length (see diagram [2.68]).

The minimum width of the road between kerbs should be 3.7 m and the minimum width of gateways 3.1 m. The other specifications are shown in the Table.

Table to 16.8   Vehicle access route specification

Appliance	Turning circle between:		Minimum clearance height (m)	Carrying capacity (tonnes)
	kerbs (m)	walls (m)		
Pump	16.8	19.2	3.7	12.5
High-reach	26.0	29.0	4.0	17.0

The notes to the Table state that because some fire authorities have vehicles of different size and weight the building control authority in consultation with the fire authority may use dimensions other than those in the Table.

As the weight of high-reach appliances is distributed over a number of axles it is considered that a route designed to carry 12.5 tonnes should not cause damage. Bridges, however, should have the full 17-tonne capacity.

16.8 **[2.68]** *Examples of high-reach fire appliance access to buildings.*

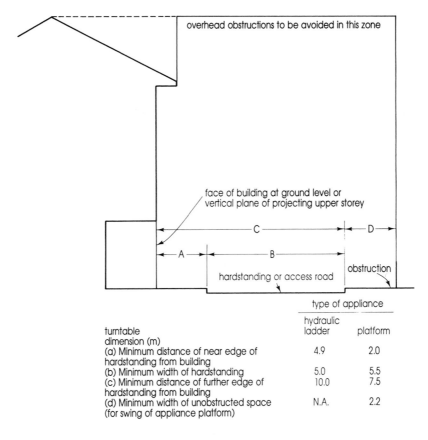

turntable dimension (m)	type of appliance	
	hydraulic ladder	platform
(a) Minimum distance of near edge of hardstanding from building	4.9	2.0
(b) Minimum width of hardstanding	5.0	5.5
(c) Minimum distance of further edge of hardstanding from building	10.0	7.5
(d) Minimum width of unobstructed space (for swing of appliance platform)	N.A.	2.2

NOTE:
hardstanding for high-reach appliances should be as level as possible and should not exceed a gradient of 1 in 12

Section 17 Access to buildings for firefighting personnel

Introduction

17.1   Fire service personnel access to low-rise buildings which have no deep basements will usually be met by use of the normal means of escape and by the provisions for vehicle access given in Section 16. In other buildings the problems of reaching the fire and working inside the building near the fire will require additional facilities such as firefighting lifts, stairs and lobbies, combined within a protected shaft – a firefighting shaft.

Guidance on the construction of protected shafts is given in Section 8.

Provision of firefighting shafts

17.2/17.5

Table to 17.2   Firefighting shafts and firefighting lifts (see diagram [2.69])

Height of storey above ground or access level (m)	Depth of basement storey below ground or access level (m)	Firefighting shaft(s)	Firefighting lift(s)
1. More than 20		Yes	Yes
2.	More than 10	Yes	Yes
3. More than 7.5 and storey area more than 600 m² (other than open-sided car parks – (see 11.4))		Yes	–
	Two or more basement storeys each more than 900 m² Any depth up to 10 m	Yes	–

Shafts which are required to serve upper storeys need not also serve any basement if the basement does not qualify for such provision. Similarly, shafts which are required to serve basements need not serve upper storeys unless the upper storeys qualify.

17.6   For shopping complexes see Section 3 of BS 5588: Part 10.

17.2 **[2.69]** *Provisions of firefighting shafts.*

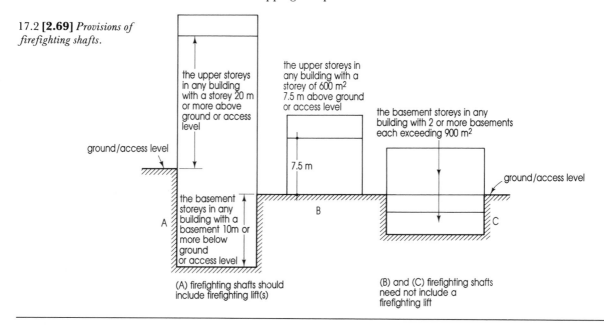

Number and location of firefighting shafts

17.7   If the building is fitted with an automatic sprinkler system to BS 5306: Part 2 the number should be as the Table to 17.7. If the building is not fitted with sprinklers there should be at least one for every 900 m² or part of the floor area of the largest floor more than 20 m above ground level (or 7.5 m in the case of item 2 in the Table to 17.2). The same criterion should also be used where basements require such shafts.

Table to 17.7   Minimum number of firefighting shafts in buildings fitted with sprinklers

Largest qualifying floor area	Minimum number of firefighting shafts
Less than 900	1
900–2000	2
Over 2000	2 plus 1 for every additional 1500 m² or part

17.8   Every part of every storey should be no more than 60 m from the entrance to a firefighting lobby measured on the route where a hose may be laid. If the layout is not known at the design stage this distance should not exceed 40 m.

Design and construction of firefighting shafts

17.9/17.11 Firefighting stairways and firefighting lifts should be approached from the accommodation through a firefighting lobby (see diagram [2.70]). Firefighting shafts should be:

(*a*)   Equipped with fire mains with outlet connections and valves in every firefighting lobby (except at access level);

(*b*)   Designed and installed in accordance with BS 5588: Part 5 regarding:

   (*i*)   planning and construction – Section 2;

   (*ii*)   firefighting lift installation – Section 3; and

   (*iii*) electrical services – Section 4.

17.3 **[2.70]** *Components of a firefighting shaft.*

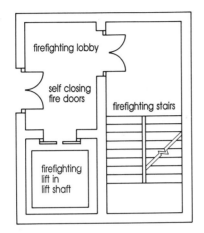

NOTES
(1) Outlets from a fire main should be located in the firefighting lobby except at access level
(2) A firefighting lift is required if the building has a floor 20 m or more above, or 10 m or more below ground or access level
(3) This diagram is only to illustrate the basic components and is not meant to represent the only acceptable layout. Ventilation measures have not been shown, refer to BS 5588: Part 5

Section 18 Venting of heat and smoke from basements

Introduction

18.1/18.2 There can be a need to remove smoke and heat from basements as products of combustion from basement fires tend to escape through stairways and can thus make access very difficult for fire service personnel. Venting of heat and smoke through outlets can improve visibility and reduce temperatures so that search-and-rescue activities become less difficult. Smoke vents can also be used by the fire service to let cooler air into basements (see diagram [2.71]).

18.2 **[2.71]** *Fire-resisting construction for smoke outlet shafts.*

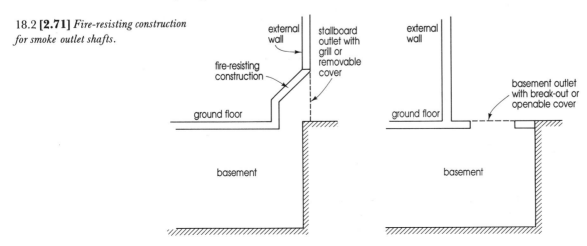

Provision of smoke outlets

18.3/18.5 Although each basement space should have one or more smoke outlets, this may not always be possible, especially if the plan is deep and the amount of external wall is restricted. In such cases spaces on the perimeter should be vented and allowance should be made for other spaces to be indirectly vented by firefighters opening connecting doors. If, however, a basement is compartmented each compartment should be separately vented.

Smoke outlets connected directly to the open air should be provided from every basement storey except for:

(*a*)   A basement in a single family dwelling (PG1(b) or 1(c)); or

(*b*)   (*i*)   A floor area of not more than 200 m²; and

        (*ii*)   A floor not more than 3 m below the adjacent ground level;

(*c*)   Strongrooms.

Natural smoke outlets

18.6/18.11 Outlets should have a combined clear cross-sectional area not less than 2.5% of the floor area which they serve. If an outlet terminates in a place which is not readily accessible, it should be kept unobstructed and be covered only with a non-combustible grille or louvre. If an outlet terminates in an accessible place it may be covered by a pavement light, stallboard or panel which can be broken out or opened. The position of these covered outlets should be indicated.

Separate outlets should be provided from places of special fire risk and no outlet should be positioned where it would prevent the use of any escape route from the building.

Mechanical smoke extract

18.12/18.13 If a basement is provided with a sprinkler system to BS 5306: Part 2, a system of mechanical ventilation may be installed as an alternative to natural venting. Sprinklers need not be installed in storeys other than the basement storey unless they are required for other reasons. The extract system should:

(*a*)   Give at least 10 air changes per hour;

(*b*)   Be capable of handling gas temperatures of 400°C for not less than one hour;

(*c*)   Come into operation automatically on activation of either the sprinkler system or an automatic fire detection system (conforming to at least the L3 standard of BS 5839: Part 1).

Construction of outlet ducts or shafts

18.14/18.15 These should be enclosed by non-combustible fire-resisting construction which should include any bulkheads. Where they are from different basement storeys or different parts of the same basement storey, they should also be separated by a non-combustible fire-resisting construction.

Basement car parks

18.16 The provisions for ventilation of basement car parks in Section 11 of this AD will satisfy the smoke-venting needs from any basement which is used as a car park.

Appendix A   Performance of materials and structures

This describes in detail how the provisions for various elements, which are set out in Approved Documents B1–B5, can be met. It deals with a number of aspects of the fire performance of materials and construction with supporting tables as follows:

A1/2   General

A3/4/5   Fire resistance

Table A1   Specific provisions of tests for fire resistance

Table A2   Minimum periods of fire resistance

Table A3   Limitations on fire protecting suspended ceilings

Table A4   Limitations on use of uninsulated glazed elements

A6   Roofs

Table A5   Designation of roof coverings

A7   Non-combustible materials

Table A6   Use of non-combustible materials

A8   Materials of limited combustibility

Table A7   Use of materials of limited combustibility

Table A8   Performance ratings of some materials and products
A 9/15   Internal linings
A 16/19   Thermoplastic materials
A 20   Fire test methods
Guidance on increasing the fire resistance of existing timber floors is given in BRE Digest 208 (BRE, 1988)

General

A 1   The performance of an element, product or material can be demonstrated by:
(*a*)   Being shown by test to be capable;
(*b*)   Having been assessed as meeting the performance (by suitably qualified fire safety engineers or laboratories approved by an appropriate body, such as NAMAS, BRE etc);
(*c*)   Conforming with one of the notional performance constructions in the tables in this Appendix;
(*d*)   Conforming with an appropriate specification in Part II of the BRE report *Guidelines for the construction of fire-resisting structural elements* (BRE, 1988).

A 2   Building Regulations deal with fire safety in buildings as a whole and are thus aimed at limiting fire hazard. Standard fire tests do not normally measure fire hazard, they just assess the response of a material or product etc to one or more aspects of fire behaviour. They are only one of the factors to be taken into account, and other factors are set out in this Appendix.

Fire resistance

A 3/A 4   Standards of fire resistance are based on assumptions about the severity of fires and the consequences of failure of an element. Fire severity is an estimate in broad terms from the use of the building (hence purpose groups) and on the assumption that the building contents (the fire load) are the same for buildings in the same use.
The factors which affect the standard of fire resistance which is specified include:
(*a*)   Combustible material – the amount per unit of floor area in various types of building (the fire load density);
(*b*)   Height of the top floor of a building – this affects ease of escape, firefighting operations and the consequences of collapse;
(*c*)   Occupancy – ease of evacuation;
(*d*)   Basements – lack of ventilation may cause heat build-up, affect the duration of fire and complicate firefighting;
(*e*)   Single storey – escape is direct and structural failure may not precede evacuation. The use of buildings can change, so precise estimates of fire severity based on the particular case may be misleading. If such a fire engineering approach is made, consideration should be given to any future changes in the fire load which may occur.

A 5   The performance for elements of structure, doors etc is determined by reference to the methods specified in BS 476: Parts 20 to 23 or to Part 8: 1972 in respect of items tested or assessed before 1 January 1988 in respect of one or more of the following criteria:
(*a*)   Resistance to collapse: *loadbearing capacity* – loadbearing elements.
(*b*)   Resistance to fire penetration: *integrity* – fire-separating elements.
(*c*)   Resistance to transfer of excessive heat: *insulation* – also to fire-separation elements.
NOTE   BS 476: Part 8: 1972 is a large chunk of not readily digestible information but is, nevertheless, reproduced here. It gives the specific provisions of test for each element in terms of the three performance criteria above.
Table A2 gives minimum periods of fire resistance for all purpose groups and care must be taken to read the various modifications set out below it. The notes on the application of the fire-resistance standards should also be studied.

Table A1   Specific provisions of test for fire resistance of elements of structure etc

Part of building	Minimum provisions when tested to the relevant part of BS 476[1] (minutes)			Method of exposure
	Loadbearing capacity[2]	Integrity	Insulation	
1. Structural frame, beam or column	*	N/A	N/A	Exposed faces
2. Loadbearing wall (which is not also a wall described in items 3–20)	*	N/A	N/A	Each side separately
3. Floors:				
(a) In upper storey of two-storey dwelling house (but not over garage)	30	15	15	From underside[3]
(b) Any other floor	*	*	*	
4. Roofs:				
(a) Any part forming an escape route	30	30	30	From underside[3]
(b) Any roof that performs the function of a floor	*	*	*	
5. External walls:				
(a) Any part less than 1 m from any point on the relevant boundary	*	*	*	Each side separately
(b) Any part 1 m or more from the relevant boundary	*	*	15[4]	From inside
6. Compartment wall separating buildings (Section 8, paragraph 8.10)	60 or * whichever is less	60 or * whichever is less	60 or * whichever is less	Each side separately
7. Compartment wall other than 6	*	*	*	Each side separately
8. Protected shaft (including firefighting stair)				
(a) Any glazing described in Section 8, diagram [2.29]	N/A	30	No provision[5]	Each side separately
(b) Any other part between shaft and a protected lobby/corridor described in diagram [2.29]	30	30	30	
(c) Any part not described in (a) or (b)	*	*	*	
9. Enclosure (not forming part of a compartment wall or protected shaft to a:				
(a) Protected stairway	30	30	30[6]	Each side separately
(b) Lift shaft	30	30	30	
(c) Service shaft	30	30	30	
10. Firefighting shafts:				
(a) Construction separating firefighting shaft from rest of building 1	20	120	120	From side remote from shaft
	60	60	60	From shaft side
(b) Construction separating firefighting stairway, firefighting lift shaft and firefighting lobby	60	60	60	Each side separately
11. Enclosure (not a compartment wall or described in item 8) to a:				
(a) Protected lobby	30	30	30	Each side separately
(b) Protected corridor	30	30	30	
12. Subdivision of a corridor	30	30	30[6]	Each side separately
13. Wall separating an attached or integral garage from a dwelling house	30	30	30[6]	From garage side
14. Enclosure in a flat or maisonette to a protected entrance hall or to a protected landing	30	30	30[6]	Each side separately

Table A1 Specific provisions of test for fire resistance of elements of structure etc.

Part of building	Minimum provisions when tested to the relevant part of BS 476[1] (minutes)			Method of exposure
	Loadbearing capacity[2]	Integrity	Insulation	
15. Fire-resistant construction:				
(a) Enclosing communal areas in sheltered housing	30	30	30	Each side
(b) In dwellings not described elsewhere	30	30	30[6]	separately
16. Cavity barrier	N/A	30	15	Each side separately
17. Ceiling described in Section 9, diagrams [2.34] and [2.42]	N/A	30	30	From underside
18. Duct described in Section 9, para 3.14(e)	N/A	30	No provision	From underside
19) Casing round a drainage system described in Section 10, diagram [2.48]	N/A	30	No provision	From underside
20. Flue walls described in Section 10, diagram [2.49]	N/A	*	*	From outside
21. Fire doors	The provisions are shown in Table B1			

NOTES
[1] Part 21 for loadbearing elements: Part 22 for non-loadbearing elements: Part 23 for fire-protected suspended ceilings; Part 24 for ventilation ducts. BS 476: Part 8 test results are acceptable for items assessed before 1 January 1988.
[2] Applied to loadbearing walls only
[3] A suspended ceiling should only be relied on to contribute to the fire resistance of the floor if the ceiling meets the appropriate provisions given in Table A3.
[4] 30 minutes for any part adjacent to external escape routes (no provision for glazed elements in respect of insulation).
[5] Except for any limitations on glazed elements given in Table A4.
[6] See Table A4 for permitted extent of uninsulated glazed elements.
* The period of fire resistance as set out in Table A2.

Application of Table A2

The fire-resistance standards for all purpose groups are now brought together in this table and there are some significant changes from the standards in the 1985 edition. Reference is no longer made to the floor area or cubic capacity of certain buildings, there are different height limitations and the periods of fire resistance have generally been reduced. In some instances anomalies occur because of the height criteria where some periods of fire resistance have increased from those in the previous edition.

The heights used were '7.5 m', '15 m', '28 m' and 'over 28 m' with no differentiation in basement depths. The new heights used are 'not more than 5 m', 'not more than 20 m', 'not more than 30 m' and 'more than 30 m'. Basement depths are 'more than 10 m deep' and 'not more than 10 m deep'.

The four-hour period has disappeared and the greatest period of fire resistance is 120 minutes (in fact all the periods are now expressed in minutes rather than hours).

The use of sprinklers was acceptable only in shops to increase compartment size in the 1985 AD but in this revision, most buildings fitted with a sprinkler system can be constructed with reduced periods of fire resistance.

The general principles of application are:

(a) Where one element gives stability to another, the fire resistance of the supporting element should be no less than the minimum fire resistance of the other element (whether the other element is loadbearing or not). This principle could be varied:

1 Where the supporting structure is in the open air and is not likely to be affected by a fire in the building;

2 The supporting structure is in a different compartment with a fire-separating element with a high fire resistance between the compartments.

(b) Where an element forms part of more than one building or compartment, the element should have the higher standard of the relevant provisions.

Table A2   Minimum periods of fire resistance

Purpose group of building	Minimum period (minutes) for elements of structure in a:					
	Basement storey[a] including floor over		Ground or upper storey			
	Depth (m) of lowest basement		Height (m) of top storey above ground, in building or separated part of building			
	more than 10	not more than 10	not more than 5	not more than 20	not more than 30	more than 30
1. Residential (domestic):						
(a) Flats and maisonettes	90	60	30[b]	60[b]	90[c]	120[c]
(b) and (c) Dwelling houses	Not relevant	30[b]	30[b]	60[g]	Not relevant	Not relevant
2. Residential:						
(a) Institutional[d]	90	60	30[b]	60	90	120[b]
(b) Other residential	90	60	30[b]	60	90	120[b]
3. Office:						
Not sprinklered	90	60	30[a]	60	90	Not permitted
Sprinklered[2]	60	60	30[a]	30[a]	60	120[b]
4. Shop and commercial:						
Not sprinklered	90	60	60	60	90	Not permitted
Sprinklered[2]	60	60	30[a]	60	60	120[b]
5. Assembly and recreation:						
Not sprinklered	90	60	60	60	90	Not permitted
Sprinklered[2]	60	60	30[a]	60[a]	60	120[b]
6. Industrial:						
Not sprinklered	120	90	60	90	120	Not permitted
Sprinklered[2]	90	60	30[b]	60	90	120[b]
7. Storage and other non-residential:						
(a) any building or part not described elsewhere:						
Not sprinklered	120	90	60	90	120	Not permitted
Sprinklered[2]	90	60	30[b]	60	90	120[e]
(b) Car park for light vehicles:						
(i) open-sided park[3]	Not applicable	Not applicable	15[b,f]	15[b,f]	15[b,f]	60
(ii) any other park	90	60	30[b]	60	90	120[e]

Modifications referred to in Table A2

[a] The floor over a basement (or if there is more than one basement, the floor over the topmost basement) should meet the provisions for the ground and upper storeys if that period is higher.

[b] Increased to a minimum of 60 minutes for compartment walls separating buildings.

[c] Reduced to 30 minutes for any floor within a maisonette, but not if the floor contributes to the support of the building.

[d] Hospitals designed in accordance with the NHS Firecode documents should have a minimum 60 minutes standard.

[e] Reduced to 90 minutes for elements not forming part of the structural frame.

[f] Increased to 30 minutes for elements protecting the means of escape.

[g] 30 minutes in the case of three storey dwelling houses, increased to 60 minutes minimum for compartment walls separating buildings.

NOTES

[1] Refer to Table A1 for the specific provisions of test.

[2] 'Sprinklered' means that the building is fitted throughout with an automatic sprinkler system meeting the relevant recommendations of BS 5306: Part 2; ie the relevant occupancy rating together with the additional requirements for life safety.

[3] The car park should comply with the relevant provisions in Approved Document B 3, Section 5.

(*c*)   Where, because of the slope of the ground, one side of a basement is open at ground level, elements of structure could be considered as in an above-ground structure.

(*d*)   Some elements may be excluded from needing fire resistance but fire resistance will be needed if the element:

1   Is part of (or supports) an external wall and AD B 4 has a provision to limit the extent of unprotected area in the wall;

2   Is part of (or supports) a compartment wall (including a wall common to two or more buildings, a wall between a dwelling house and an attached or integral garage); or

3   Supports a gallery.

For the purposes of the application of Table A2, the ground storey of a building which has one or more basement storeys and no upper storeys can be considered as single storey. The fire resistance of the basement should be that appropriate to basements.

(*e*)   Single-storey buildings are subject to the periods under the heading 'not more than 5 m'. If they have basement storeys these are subject to the period appropriate to their depth.

Table A3 sets out criteria regarding suspended ceilings that can contribute to the fire resistance of a floor. This table is the same as in the 1985 edition but with changes to the note concerning supports and fixings. Previously the provision was that supports and fixings for Types B, C and D should be non-combustible.

Table A3   Limitations on fire-protecting suspended ceilings

Height of building or separated part (m)	Type of floor	Provision for fire resistance of floor (minutes)	Description of suspended ceiling
Less than 15	Not compartment	60 or less	Type A, B, C or D
	Compartment	Less than 60 / 60	Type B, C or D
15 or more	Any	60 or less	Type C or D
No limit	Any	More than 60	Type D

NOTES

Ceiling type	Description
A	Surface of ceiling exposed to the cavity should be Class 0 or Class 1.
B	Surface of ceiling exposed to the cavity should be Class 0.
C	Surface of ceiling exposed on the cavity should be Class 0. Ceiling should not contain easily openable access panels.
D	Ceiling should be of a material of limited combustibility and not contain easily openable access panels. Any insulation above the ceiling should be of a material of limited combustibility.

Any access panels provided in fire-protecting suspended ceilings of type C or D should be secured in position by releasing devices or screw fixings, and they should be shown to have been tested in the ceiling assembly in which they are incorporated.

Table A4 sets out limitations on the use of fire-resisting glazed elements. These limitations do not apply to insulated fire-resisting glazed elements.

This is a new table and relates to AD B 1 – Means of escape.

Table A4   Limitations on the use of uninsulated glazed elements on escape routes (These limitations do not apply to glazed elements which satisfy the relevant insulation criterion: see Table A1)

Position of glazed element	Maximum total glazed area in parts of a building with access to:			
	A single stairway		More than one stairway	
	Walls	Door leaf	Walls	Door leaf
1. Single-family dwelling houses: (i) Within the enclosures of a protected stairway or within fire-resisting separation shown in Approved Document B 1, diagram [2.5]	Fixed fanlights only	Unlimited	Fixed fanlights only	Unlimited
(ii) Within a fire-resisting partition described in Approved Document B 1, paragraph 1.8	Unlimited	Unlimited	Unlimited	Unlimited
2. Within the enclosures of a protected entrance hall or protected landing or a flat or maisonette	Fixed fanlights only	Ulimited above 1.1 m from floor	Fixed fanlights only	Unlimited above 1.1 m from floor
3. Between residential/sleeping accommodation and a common escape route (corridor, lobby or stair)	Nil	Nil	Nil	Nil
4. Between a protected stairway[1] and: (i) The accommodation; or (ii) A corridor which is not a protected corridor Other than in item 3 above	Nil	25% of door area	Unlimited above 1.1 m[2]	50% of door area
5. Between: (i) A protected stairway and a protected lobby or protected corridor; or (ii) Accommodation and a protected lobby Other than in item 3 above.	Unlimited above 1.1 m from floor	Unlimited above 0.1 m from floor	Unlimited above 0.1 m from floor	Unlimited above 0.1 m from floor
6. Between the accommodation and a protected corridor forming a dead end, other than in item 3 above.	Unlimited above 1.1 m from floor	Unlimited above 0.1 m from floor	Unlimited above 1.1 m from floor	Unlimited above 0.1 m from floor
7. Between accommodation and any other corridor; or subdividing corridors other than in item 3 above.	Not applicable	Not applicable	Unlimited above 0.1 m from floor	Unlimited above 0.1 m from floor

NOTES
[1] If the *protected stairway* is also a *protected shaft* (Section 8, paragraphs 8.33 and 8.34) or a *firefighting stairway* (Section 17, paragraph 17.11) there may be further restrictions on the uses of glazed elements.
[2] Measured vertically from the landing floor level or the stair pitch line.

Roofs   **A 6**   Performance in terms of resistance of roofs to external fire exposure is determined by the test procedure specified in BS 476: Part 3: 1958. This is not the latest version, but the current version, published in 1975, is undergoing revision, and it appears that this is the reason it has not so far been adopted. The test is designed to check the performance of the roof from the outside only.

Roofs or parts of roofs, if used as an escape route or if performing the function of a floor, may need to be fire resisting. Approved Documents B 1 and B 3 cover these circumstances. A note on BS 476: Part 3 is included below.

BS 476: Part 3: 1958 and 1975

In the 1958 standard two groups of letters, A to D, are used to express the results. The first letter represents penetration resistance and the second resistance to surface spread of flame. They are measured in separate tests.

The test is performed by applying a moving flame for 1 minute over a specified size of sample which is being subjected to radiant heat from a furnace designed to represent the exposure of a roof 7.5 m above ground to a fire in a building 13.5 m away, having a facade 15 m × 15 m with 50 per cent window opening. The test lasts 60 minutes following a 1 minute preliminary ignition test.

The designations are as follows:

First letter: penetration time

A   Not less than 1 hour.

B   Not less than 30 minutes.

C   Less than 30 minutes.

D   During the preliminary flame test.

Second letter: spread of flame

A   None.

B   Not more than 21 in (533.4 mm).

C   More than 21 in (533.4 mm).

D   Continues to burn for five minutes after withdrawal of test flame, or spreads more than 15 in (381 mm) during the preliminary test.

These designations are not used in the 1975 edition and both criteria are determined by one test. The results are expressed by the letter X if the sample fails the preliminary ignition test, or P if it passes, followed by a number indicating the time before penetration occurred, eg P60 means it did not occur in less than an hour. The extent of surface ignition (previously called spread of flame) is given in actual figures in the report, but no codified classification system is used.

The results are the mean of three samples and the equipment is arranged to simulate the slope of the roof on which the construction will be used. The sample may include a rooflight for which test results can also be given.

Notional designations

Table A5 supplies notional designations for some generic roof coverings.

Table A5   Notional designations of roof coverings

Part i: Pitched roofs covered with slates or tiles

Covering material	Supporting structure	Designation
1. Natural slates 2. Fibre reinforced cement slates 3. Clay tiles 4. Concrete tiles	1. Timber rafters with or without underfelt, sarking, boarding, woodwool slabs, compressed straw slabs, plywood, wood chipboard, or fibre insulating board	AA
5. Bitumen felt strips slates Type 2E, with Type 2B underlayer bitumen felt	3. Timber rafters and boarding, plywood, woodwool slabs, wood chipboard, or fibre insulating board	BB
6. Strip slates of bitumen felt, class 1 or 2	2. Timber rafters and boarding, plywood, woodwool slabs, compressed straw slabs, wood chipboard, or fibre insulating board	CC

NOTE
Any reference in this table to bitumen felt of a specified type is a reference to bitumen felt as so designated in BS 747: 1977.

Part ii: Pitched roofs covered with self-supporting sheet

Roof covering material	Construction	Supporting structure	Designation
1. Profiled sheet of galvanised steel, aluminium, fibre reinforced cement, or pre-painted (coil coated) steel or aluminium with a pvc or pvf2 coating	1. Single skin without underlay, or with underlay of plasterboard, fibre insulating board, woodwool slab	Structure of timber, steel or concrete	AA
2. Profiled sheet of galvanised steel, aluminium, fibre reinforced cement, or pre-painted (coil coated) steel or aluminium with a pvc or pvf2 coating	2. Double skin without interlayer, or with interlayer of resin-bonded glass fibre, mineral wool slab, polystyrene, or polyurethane.	Structure of timber, steel or concrete	AA

Part iii: Flat roofs covered with bitumen felt

A flat roof comprising bitumen felt should (irrespective of the felt specification) be deemed to be of designation AA if the felt is laid on a deck constructed of any of the materials prescribed in the Table in part iv, and has a surface finish of:

(a) Bitumen-bedded stone chippings covering the whole surface to a depth of at least 12.5 m,
(b) Bitumen-bedded tiles of a non-combustible material,
(c) Sand and cement screed, or
(d) Macadam.

Part iv: Pitched roofs covered with bitumen felt

Number of layers	Type of upper layer	Type of underlayer	Deck of 6 mm plywood, 12.4 mm wood chipboard, 16 mm (finished) T&G or 19 mm (finished) plain edged timber boarding	Deck of compressed straw slab	Deck of screeded woodwool slab	Profiled fibre reinforced cement or steel deck (single or double skin) with or without fibre insulating board overlay	Profiled aluminium deck (single or double skin) with or without fibre insulating board overlay	Concrete or clay pot slab (in situ or pre-cast)
Two or three layers built up in accordance with CP 144: Part 3: 1970	Type 1E	Type 1B minimum mass 13kg/10m²	CC	AC	AC	AC	AC	AB
	Type 2E	Type 1B minimum mass 13kg/10m²	BB	AB	AB	AB	AB	AB
	Type 2E	Type 2B	AB	AB	AB	AB	AB	AB
	Type 3E	Type 3B or 3G	BC	AC	AB	AB	AB	AB

NOTE
Any reference in this table to bitumen felt of a specified type is a reference to bitumen felt as so designated in BS 747: 1977.

Part v: Pitched or flat roofs covered with fully supported material

Covering material	Supporting structure	Designation

1. Aluminium sheet
2. Copper sheet
3. Zinc sheet
4. Lead sheet
5. Mastic asphalt
6. Vitreous enamelled steel
7. Lead/tin alloy coated steel sheet
8. Zinc/aluminium alloy coated steel sheet
9. Pre-painted (coil coated) steel sheet
    including liquid-applied pvc coatings
	1. Timber joists and:
	    tongued and grooved boarding, or
	    plain edged boarding
		AA*

	2. Steel or timber joists with deck of:
	    woodwool slabs, compressed straw
	    slab, wool chipboard, fibre insulating
	    board, or 9.5 mm plywood
		AA

	3. Concrete or clay pot slab (in situ or
	    pre-cast) or non-combustible deck of
	    steel, aluminium, or fibre cement (with
	    or without insulation)
		AA

NOTE

* Lead sheet supported by timber joists and plain edged boarding may give a BA designation.

Illustrations of some roof coverings are shown in diagrams [2.72] to [2.74].

A6 **[2.72]** *Part I: pitched roofs covered with slates or tiles.*

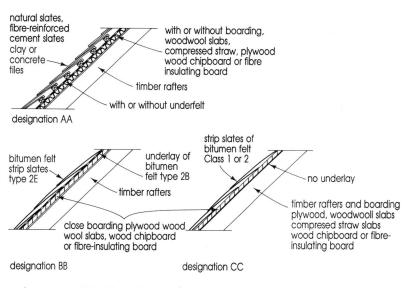

natural slates, fibre-reinforced cement slates clay or concrete tiles

with or without boarding, woodwool slabs, compressed straw, plywood wood chipboard or fibre insulating board

timber rafters

with or without underfelt

designation AA

bitumen felt strip slates type 2E

underlay of bitumen felt type 2B

timber rafters

close boarding plywood wood wool slabs, wood chipboard or fibre-insulating board

designation BB

strip slates of bitumen felt Class 1 or 2

no underlay

timber rafters and boarding plywood, woodwooll slabs compresed straw slabs wood chipboard or fibre-insulating board

designation CC

performance could be affected by insulation on the underside of the roof

A6 **[2.73]** *Part II: pitched roofs covered with self-supporting sheets.*

corrugated sheets of galvanised steel, aluminimum, fibre-reinforced cement or prepainted (coil coated) steel or aluminimum with a pvc or pvf$_2$ coating

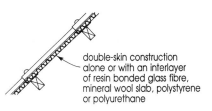

double-skin construction alone or with an interlayer of resin bonded glass fibre, mineral wool slab, polystyrene or polyurethane

main structure of steel timber or concrete

designation AA

A6 **[2.74]** *Part V: pitched or flat roofs covered with fully supported material.*

aluminimum, copper, zinc or lead sheets, vitreous enamelled steel or mastic asphalt

boards t and g or plain edge on timber joists

designation AA (except for lead on plain edge boards which is BA)

steel or timber joist, wood wool slab, compressed straw, chipboard (wood or flax), fibreboard, 9.5 mm plywood designation AA

aluminium, copper zinc, lead or mastic asphalt

r.c. slab, hollow pot, or p.c. concrete

designation AA

non-combustible metal or deck

designation AA

with or without insulation

Note on BS 747: 1977 Specification for roofing felts

The Types specified in the table include 1E, 2E, 3E in conjunction with underlayers 1B, 2B, 3B or 3G.

The numbers 1, 2, 3, 4 indicate the base material as follows:

1 Mineral fibre, 2 Asbestos fibre, 3 Glass fibre, 4 Sheathing felt.

The letters indicate the type and hence the use as follows:

B   Fine granule faced both sides

E   Fine granule faced one side, mineral granules other side

F   Reinforced with hessian

G/H   Venting base layers.

Type B are normal underlayers including a top layer to be faced with chippings.

Type E are for finishing layers on sloping roofs.

Type F are for sarking and vapour barriers below insulation

Types G/H are for bottom layers on roofs where partial bonding is required for ventilation.

Types 4A and B (not mentioned in the table) are dimensionally stable for underlayers below mastic asphalt and sarking below sheet metal roofs.

A 7   Non-combustible materials are defined in Table A6 either as listed products or in terms of performance when tested to BS 476: Part 4: 1970 or Part 11: 1982. Where there is a provision for non-combustibility only these materials may be used. They may also be used for the specific applications in Table A6.

Non-combustible materials may also be used where there is a provision for materials of limited combustibility (see AD A 8).

Table A6   Use of non-combustible materials

Use	*Non-combustible materials*
1. *AD B 1, paragraph 5.22:* Ladders referred in that paragraph	Any material which when tested to BS 476: Part 11 does not flame and there is no rise in
2. *AD B 3, paragraph 8.28:* Refuse chutes	temperature on either the centre (specimen) or furnace thermocouples.
3. *AD B 3, paragraph 9.13:* Suspended ceilings and their supports where this provision is for these to be constructed of non-combustible materials.	Totally inorganic materials such as concrete, fired clay, ceramics, metals, plaster and masonry containing not more than 1% by weight or volume of organic material (use in
4. *AD B 3, Table to 10.7:* Pipes meeting these provisions	buildings of combustible metals such as magnesium/aluminium alloys should be
5. *AD B 3, diagram [2.49]:* Flue walls	assessed in each individual case). Concrete bricks or blocks meeting BS 6073:
6. *AD B 3, paragraph 11.3:* Construction forming car parks	Part 1: 1981. Products classified as non-combustible under BS 476: Part 4: 1970.

Materials of limited combustibility

A 8   This is a relatively new term which came into the Regulations for the first time in 1985. It is based on the use of BS 476: Part 11: 1982, which in effect assesses the amount of combustible material within a largely non-combustible product, and is really a more sophisticated version of BS 476: Part 4: 1970, which was, and still is, used for defining the term non-combustible.

The materials of limited combustibility are defined in Table A7 and also include composite products such as plasterboard. Where these materials are exposed as linings they should also have the flame spread rating which is appropriate.

A note on BS 476: Parts 4 and 11 follows.

BS 476: Part 4: 1970 Non-combustibility tests

The test is made by heating a sample in a furnace and materials classified as non-combustible are those which make little or no thermal contribution to the furnace and do not produce a flame (parameters are specified). Three samples are tested. The test can be applied to coated materials.

The sample is tested over a period of 20 minutes in a furnace temperature of 750°C (±10).

BS 476: Part 11: 1982 Assessing the heat emission from building materials

This is the first of a new series for evaluating the behaviour of building materials in a fire. It gives a way of expressing results, but does not specify acceptance criteria, which depend upon the intended conditions of use (the Approved Document states the criteria required). It is designed for assessing simple materials, natural or artificially mixed, but not for combinations such as laminates. The test is made on a small cylinder of the material, placed in a cylindrical furnace with provision for measuring the temperature in the centre of the sample. The period of the test is generally until a stable temperature situation has been reached or 120 minutes maximum.

Three criteria are reported which are the mean of five tested specimens:

1   The total of periods of sustained flaming (exceeding 5 seconds each).
2   The rise in furnace temperature (as a result of heat contributed by the sample).
3   The rise in the temperature in the sample.

Limitations on these figures are used for classifying notional non-combustibility in Appendix A.

Table A7

Use	*Materials of limited combustibility*
1. Stairs where there is no provision in Section 5, paragraph 5.19 for them to be constructed of materials of limited combustibility.	(a) Any non-combustible material listed in Table A6
2. Materials above a suspended ceiling meeting the provisions in Section 9, paragraph 9.13.	(b) Any material of density 300 kg/m³ or more which, when tested to BS 476: Part 11, does not flame and the rise in temperature on the furnace thermocouple is not more than 20°C
3. Reinforcement/support for fire-stopping referred to in Section 10, paragraph 10.13.	(c) Any material with a non-combustible core at least 8 mm thick having combustible facings (on one or both sides) not more than 0.5 mm thick. (Where a flame spread rating is specified, these materials must also meet the appropriate test requirements)
4. Roof coverings meeting the provisions: (a) In Section 9, paragraph 9.11, or (b) In Section 14, Table to 14.4 or (c) In Section 14, diagram [2.66]	
5. Roof deck meeting the provisions of Section 8, diagram [2.27].	
6. Class 0 materials meeting the provisions of Appendix A, paragraph A12(a).	
7. Ceiling tiles or panels of any fire-protecting suspended ceiling (Type D) in Table A3.	
8. Compartment walls and compartment floors in hospitals referred to in Section 8, paragraph 8.27.	
9. Insulation material in external wall construction referred to in Section 12, paragraph 12.7.	
10. Insulation above any fire-protecting suspended ceiling (Type D) in Table A3.	Any of the materials (a), (b), (c), above or (d) Any material of density less than 300 kg/m³ which, when tested to BS 476: Part 11, does not flame for more than 10 seconds and the rise in temperature on the centre (specimen) thermocouple is not more than 35°C and on the furnace thermocouple is not more than 25°C

Internal linings

A 9/A 12   The incidence of flame spread over the surfaces of walls and ceilings is controlled by providing for the lining materials to meet certain performance levels through testing. BS 476: Part 6: 1981 or 1989 sets out a method whereby products can be tested and given 'fire propagation' indices according to their performance. The index of performance (I) relates to the overall test performance and sub-index of performance (i_1) is derived from the first 3 minutes of test.

Linings which can be tested under BS 476: Part 7 for 'surface spread of flame' performance are classified as Class 1, 2, 3 or 4 but the highest performance classification for lining materials is Class 0.

This is not a classification identified in a British Standard test but it can be achieved if a material or the surface of a composite product is either:

(*a*)   Composed throughout of materials of limited combustibility; or

(*b*)   A Class 1 material having –
    A fire-propagation index (I) of not more than 12, and
    A sub-index (i_1) of not more than 6.

Materials which ignite easily have a high rate of heat release and/or those which reduce the time to flashover are not likely to meet these indices of performance.

A 13/A 14   Composite products which are defined as materials of limited combustibility should also comply with the appropriate test requirement specified in ADs B 2, B 3 and B 4.

Table A8 lists the notional performance ratings under BS 476: Parts 6 and 7 tests of some widely used products.

Table A8 Typical performance ratings of some generic materials and products

Rating	*Material or product*
Class 0	1. Any non-combustible material or material of limited combustibility. (Composite products listed in Table A7 must meet the test requirements given in paragraph A12(b)) 2. Brickwork, blockwork, concrete and ceramic tiles 3. Plasterboard (painted or not, or with a PVC facing not more than 0.5 mm thick) with or without an air gap or fibrous or cellular insulating material behind 4. Woodwool cement slabs 5. Mineral fibre tiles or sheets with cement or resin binding
Class 3	6. Timber or plywood with a density more than 400 kg/m^3, painted or unpainted 7. Wood particle board or hardboard, either treated or painted 8. Standard gloss reinforced polyesters

NOTES
(a) Materials and products listed under Class 0 also meet Class 1.
(b) Timber products listed under Class 3 can be brought up to Class 1 with appropriate proprietary treatments.
(c) The following materials and products may achieve the ratings listed below. However, as the properties of different products with the same generic description vary, the ratings of these materials/products should be substantiated by test evidence.

Class 0: aluminium-faced fibre insulating board, flame-retardant decorative laminates on a calcium silicate board, thick polycarbonate sheet, phenolic sheet and UPVC;
Class 1: phenolic or melamine laminates on a calcium silicate substrate and flame-retardant decorative laminates on a combustible substrate.

A 15   Test results are often given in the manufacturers' or trade association literature. These should be carefully checked to ensure that they are suitable, as small differences in thickness, substrate, fixings, adhesive, etc could significantly affect the rating.

Thermoplastic materials

A 16   A thermoplastic material is any synthetic polymeric material which has a softening point below 200°C when tested. The test method is in BS 2782: Part 1: Method 120A: 1976.

A 17   In isolation, a thermoplastic material cannot be assumed to protect a substrate when used as a lining to a wall or ceiling. The surface rating of both products must meet the required classification, but if the thermoplastic material is fully bonded to a non-thermoplastic substrate only the surface rating of the composite needs to comply.

A 18   The guidance in Approved Documents B 2 and B 4 describes concessions which are made for thermoplastic materials which may not comply with the appropriate criteria when used as windows, rooflights and lighting diffusers within suspended ceilings.

A 19   For the purposes of Approved Documents B 2 and B 4 thermoplastic materials should be used according to their classification 0–3 under BS 476: Parts 6 and 7. Alternatively, if they have a rating they may be classified TP(a) rigid, TP(a) flexible or TP(b) as described below.

TP(a) rigid
1   Rigid solid pvc sheet
2   Solid polycarbonate sheet at least 3 mm thick
3   Multi-skinned rigid sheet – unplasticised pvc or polycarbonate Class 1 rating – tested to BS 476: Part 7: 1971 or 1987
4   Any other rigid thermoplastic product which reaches a specific standard when tested to BS 2782: 1970(1974): Method 508a*

TP(a) flexible
Not more than 1 mm thick – flexible. Complies with Type C requirements of BS 5438: Test 2: 1989*

TP(b)
1   Rigid polycarbonate sheet products less than 3 mm thick
2   Multiple-skin polycarbonate sheet products which do not qualify as TP(a) when tested
or
3   Other products when tested reach a specific standard*

Fire test methods   **A 20**   PD 6520: 1988, a BSI publication, gives a guide to the various test methods in BS 476 and BS 2782. BS 6336: 1982 is a guide to the development and presentation of fire tests and their use in hazard assessment.

Appendix B Fire doors

In the 1985 edition the fire resistance of fire doors was included in the main table in the Appendix relating to fire resistance of elements of structure. In the new Approved Document there is a separate Appendix and Table.

B 1   This explains that all fire doors should have the performance as shown in Table B1 and that the table identifies doors by their performance under test to BS 476: Part 22.

FD 30, for instance, means that the door has 30 minutes fire resistance in terms of integrity, and a suffix (S) is added for doors where restricted smoke leakage at ambient temperatures is needed.

The method of test is exposure from each side of the door separately, except for lift doors, where the test is from the landing side only.

B 2   All fire doors should be fitted with an automatic self-closing device except fire doors to cupboards and to service ducts, which are normally kept locked shut.

B 3   There are occasions where self-closing devices can be a hindrance in the use of a building, so self-closing fire doors may be held open by:
(*i*)   A door closure delay device, or
(*ii*)   An automatic release system but only if the door can be closed manually and is not to:
            The only escape stair serving a building or part, or
            An escape stair serving a building in any Residential purpose group, or
            A firefighting stair, or
(*iii*)   A fusible link, subject to B 4.

B 4   A fusible link cannot be used on a means of escape doorway unless it complies with the details shown in diagram [2.75].

* The Approved Document contains the fine detail of the test results to be achieved but these are not repeated here.

B 5   Hinges generally should be made from materials having a melting point of not less than 800°C or, if of other material, have been shown to be satisfactory when tested as part of a door assembly.

B 6   Hardware used on fire doors can affect the performance of a door in fire.

Reference is made to a *Code of practice for hardware essential to the optimum performance of fire resisting timber doorsets* published by the Association of Builders' Hardware Merchants in 1983.

B 7   All fire doors should be marked with the appropriate fire safety sign as to whether the door is:

to be kept closed when not in use

to be kept locked when not in use

held open by an automatic release mechanism.

The signs should comply with BS 5499: Part 1 and should be fixed to the outsides of fire doors to cupboards and service ducts and to both sides of all other fire doors.

B 8   Fire safety signs are not necessary on:

doors within dwelling houses

doors to and within flats and maisonettes

doors to bedrooms in 'Other residential' premises and lift entrance doors.

B 9   It will be necessary to establish the minimum period of fire resistance to which the performance of some doors is linked by referring to Tables A1 and A2. The limits of uninsulated glazing are set out in Table A4.

B4 **[2.75]**

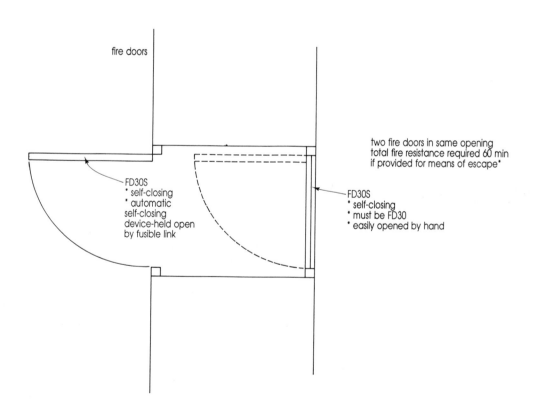

Table B1   Provisions for fire doors

Position of door	*Minimum fire resistance of door in terms of integrity (minutes)*[1]
1. In a compartment wall separating buildings	As for the wall in which door is fitted, but a minimum of 60
2. In a compartment wall: (a) If it separates a flat or maisonette from a space in common use	FD 30S
(b) Enclosing a protected shaft forming a stairway situated wholly or partly above the adjoining ground in a building used for flats, other residential, assembly and recreation, or office purposes	FD 30S
(c) Enclosing a protected shaft forming a stairway not described in (b) above	Half the period of fire resistance of the wall in which it is fitted but 30 minimum and with suffix S
(d) Not described in (a), (b) or (c) above	As for the wall it is fitted in, but add S if the door used for progressive horizontal evacuation under Approved Document B 1
3. In a compartment floor	As for the floor in which it is fitted
4. Forming part of the enclosures of: (a) A protected stairway (except where described in item 9)	FD 30S
(b) A lift shaft or	FD 30
(c) A service shaft	FD 30
which does not form a protected shaft in 2(c) above	
5. Forming part of the enclosures of: (a) A protected lobby approach (or protected corridor) to a stairway	FD 30S
(b) Any other protected corridor	FD 20S
6. Affording access to an external escape route	FD 30
7. Sub-dividing: (a) Corridors connecting alternative exits	FD 20S
(b) Dead-end portions of corridors from the remainder of the corridor	FD 20S
8. Any door: (a) Within a cavity barrier	FD 30
(b) Between a dwelling house and a garage	FD 30
(c) Forming part of the enclosure to a communal area in sheltered housing	FD 30S
9. Any door: (a) Forming part of the enclosures to a protected stairway in a single-family dwelling house	FD 20
(b) Forming part of the enclosure to a protected entrance hall or protected landing in a flat or maisonette	FD 20
(c) Within any other fire-resisting construction in a dwelling not described elsewhere in this table	FD 20

NOTES

Unless pressurisation techniques complying with BS 5588: Part 4 are used, these doors should also have a leakage rate not exceeding $3\,m^3/m/h$ (head and jambs only) when tested at 25 Pa under BS 476: Section 31.1.

[1] To BS 476: Part 22 (or BS 476: Part 8 subject to paragraph A5).

Appendix C Methods of measurement

C 1   Some form of measurement is an integral part of many of the provisions of this document. The rules as to how these are to be made are illustrated in diagrams [2.76]–[2.79].

C1 **[2.76]** *Rules for measurement.*

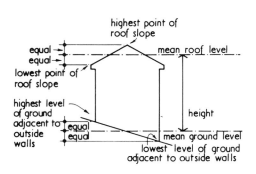

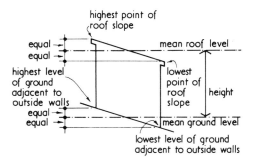

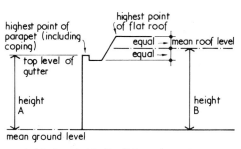

use height A or height B whichever is greatest

C1 **[2.77]** *Rules for measuring volume.*

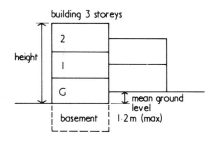

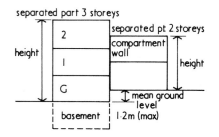

To count the number of storeys in a building, or in a separated part of a building, count only at the position which gives the greatest number and exclude any basement storeys.

Number of storeys and height of building or separated part.

NOTE   In assembly buildings, a gallery is included as a storey, but not if it is a loading gallery, fly gallery, stage grid, lighting bridge or any gallery provided for similar purposes, or for maintenance or repair. In other purpose group buildings, galleries are not counted as storeys.

C1 **[2.78]** *Height of top storey (height of storeys measured from level of ground on lowest side of building).*

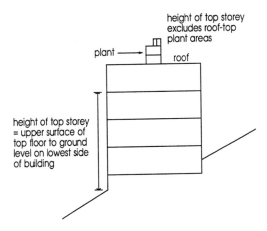

C1 **[2.79]** *Rules for measurement.*

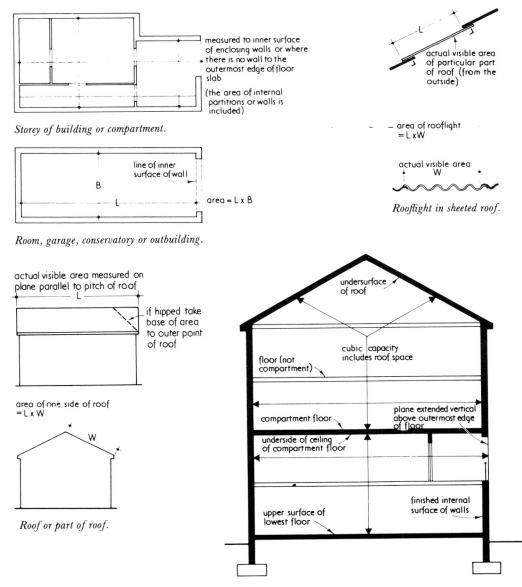

Storey of building or compartment.

Room, garage, conservatory or outbuilding.

Roof or part of roof.

Rooflight in sheeted roof.

Rules for measuring volume.

Appendix D Purpose groups

There is now a separate Appendix for purpose groups, so instead of being at the beginning of the document where it was most useful, unfortunately it has been banished to the end.

The provisions depend, inter alia, on the use to which the building is to be put. In the 1985 Regulations there were nine purpose groups, but the number has been extended to 11 and the groups are now numbered, which makes for easier reference.

Residential group 1 is entitled 'residential (domestic)' and now has three classes:

1(a) – Flats and maisonettes

1(b) – Dwelling houses with a floor more than 4.5 m above ground level

1(c) – Other dwelling houses

Residential group 2 (2(a) and 2(b)) is renamed 'institutional' and 'other residential'.

The shop group (group 4) is now called 'shop and commercial'.

(Group 5) is now 'assembly and recreation' and 'other non-residential'.

(Group 7) is 'storage and other non-residential'.

The storage class has a separate purpose group for car parks.

There have also been some changes in the descriptions of the uses. Sometimes a building or compartment may have more than one use and it may be appropriate to treat each use as a separate purpose group.

These situations are:

(*a*)   Where the ancillary use is a flat or maisonette;

(*b*)   Where the ancillary use is of an area that is more than one fifth of the total floor area of the building or compartment; or

(*c*)   Where the storage area in a building of purpose group 4 (shop or commercial) amounts to more than one third of the total floor area of the building or compartment.

In other cases there may be two main uses of a building which are entirely independent and are not ancillary to each other. In such instances each of the uses should be considered as belonging to its own purpose group.

In some large buildings there may be a mix of many uses, and here the risk which one part of the complex may have on another should be considered.

Special measures may be necessary to reduce any such risk.

Table D1   Classification of purpose groups

Title	Group	Purpose for which the building or compartment of a building is intended to be used
Residential[1] (domestic)	1(a)	Flat or maisonette
	1(b)	Dwelling house which contains a habitable storey with a floor level which is more than 4.5 m above ground level
	1(c)	Dwelling house which does not contain a habitable storey with a floor level which is more than 4.5 m above ground level
Residential (institutional)	2(a)	Hospital, nursing home, home for old people or for children, school or other similar establishment used as living accommodation or for the treatment, care or maintenance of people suffering from illness or mental or physical disability or handicap, place of detention, where such people sleep on the premises
(Other)	2(b)	Hotel, boarding house, residential college, hall of residence, hostel, and any other residential purpose not described above
Office	3	Offices or premises used for the purpose of administration, clerical work (including writing, book keeping, sorting papers, filing, typing, duplicating, machine calculating, drawing and the editorial preparation of matter for publication, police and fire service work), handling money (including banking and building society work), and communications (including postal, telegraph and radio communications) or radio, television, film, audio or video recording, or performance (not open to the public and their control
Shop and commercial	4	Shops or premises used for a retail or wholesale trade or business (including the sale to members of the public of food or drink for immediate consumption and retail sales by auction, self-selection and over-the-counter wholesale trading, the business of lending books or periodicals for gain and the business of a barber or hairdresser) and premises to which the public is invited to deliver or to collect goods in connection with their hire, repair or other treatment, or (except in the case of repair of motor vehicles) where they themselves may carry out such repairs or other treatments
Assembly and recreation	5	Place of assembly, entertainment or recreation; including bingo halls, broadcasting, recording and film studios open to the public, casinos, dance halls; entertainment-, conference-, exhibition- and leisure-centres; funfairs and amusement arcades; museums and art galleries; non-residential clubs, theatres, cinemas and concert halls; educational establishments, dancing schools, gymnasia, swimming pool buildings, riding schools, skating rinks, sports pavilions, sports stadia; law courts; churches and other buildings for worship, crematoria; libraries open to the public, non-residential day centres, clinics, health centres and surgeries; passenger stations and termini for air, rail, road or sea travel; public toilets; zoos and menageries
Industrial	6	Factories and other premises used for manufacturing, altering, repairing, cleaning, washing, breaking up, adapting or processing any article; generating power or slaughtering livestock
Storage and other non-residential[2]	7(a)	Place for the storage or deposit of goods or materials (other than described under 7(b)). and any building not within any of the purpose groups 1 to 6
	7(b)	Car parks designed to admit and accommodate only cars, motorcycles and passenger or light goods vehicles weighing no more than 2500 kg gross

NOTES

[1] Includes any surgeries, consulting rooms, offices or other accommodation, not exceeding 50 m^2 in total, forming part of a dwelling and used by an occupant of the dwelling in a professional or business capacity.

[2] A detached garage not more than 40 m^2 in area is included in purpose group 1(c); as is a detached open carport of not more than 40 m^2, or a detached building which consists of a garage and open carport where neither the garage nor open carport exceeds 40 m^2 in area.

Appendix E Definitions

Relevant paragraph numbers are shown in parentheses.

Access room　A room which passes the only escape route from an inner room. (1.16, 2.6, 2.11, 3.9)

Accommodation stair　A stair, additional to that or those required for escape purposes, provided for the convenience of occupants. (0.32, 4.25)

Alternative escape routes　Escape routes sufficiently separated by either direction and space, or by fire-resisting construction, to ensure that one is still available should the other be affected by fire.
NOTE　A second stair, balcony or flat roof which enables a person to reach a place free from danger from fire is considered an alternative escape route for the purposes of a dwelling house. (0.28, 0.30, 1.20, 2.18, 3.3, 3.5, 3.8, 3.20, 3.21)

Alternative exit　One of two or more exits, each of which is separate from the other. (2.10, 2.12, 2.13, 2.15, 2.16, 3.28, Table B1)

Appliance ventilation duct　A duct provided to convey combustion air to a gas appliance. (8.28, 10.11)

Atrium (plural: atria)　A vertical space within a building (other than a shaft used solely for stairs, escalators, lifts or services), openly connecting three or more storeys and enclosed at the top by a floor or roof. (5.38)

Automatic release mechanism　A device which will allow a door held open by it to close automatically in the event of each or any one of the following:
(*a*)　　Detection of smoke by automatic apparatus suitable in nature, quality and location;
(*b*)　　Operation of a hand-operated switch fitted in a suitable position;
(*c*)　　Failure of electricity supply to the device, apparatus or switch;
(*d*)　　Operation of the fire alarm system if any. (B3)

Automatic self-closing device　Does not include rising butt hinges unless the door is:
(*a*)　　To (or within) a dwelling;
(*b*)　　Between a dwelling house and its garage; or
(*c*)　　In a cavity barrier.
(B2, B3)

Basement storey　A storey with a floor which at some point is more than 1.2 m below the highest level of ground adjacent to the outside walls. (However, see Appendix A, Table A2, for situations where the storey is considered to be a basement only because of a sloping site.) (Sections 1, 2, 4, 5, 7, 8, 11, 17 and 18)

Boundary　The boundary of the land belonging to the building, or where the land abuts a road, railway, canal or river, the centreline of that road, railway, canal or river. (See diagram [2.51].)

Cavity barrier　A construction provided to close a concealed space against penetration of smoke or flame, or provided to restrict the movement of smoke or flame within such a space. (6.6 and Section 9)

Ceiling　A part of a building which encloses and is exposed overhead in a room, protected shaft or circulation space. (The soffit of a rooflight is included as part of the surface of the ceiling, but not the frame. An upstand below a rooflight would be considered as a wall.) (3.20 and Sections 6 and 9)

Circulation space　A space (including a protected stairway) mainly used as a means of access between a room and an exit from the building or compartment. (0.41, 1.8, 3.12, 6.9)

Class 0　A product performance classification for wall and ceiling linings. The relevant test criteria are set out in Appendix A, paragraph A12. (A7, A8, A12)

Common balcony　A walkway, open to the air on one or more sides, forming part of the escape route from more than one flat or maisonette. (2.10, 2.16)

Common stair An escape stair serving more than one flat or maisonette. (2.18, 2.29–2.34, 2.43)

Compartment (fire) A building or part of a building, comprising one or more rooms, spaces or storeys, constructed to prevent the spread of fire to or from another part of the same building, or an adjoining building. (A roof space above the top storey of a compartment is included in that compartment). (See also Separated part.) (Section 8)

Compartment wall or floor A fire-resisting wall/floor used in the separation of one fire compartment from another. (Constructional provisions are given in Section 8).

Concealed space or cavity A space enclosed by elements of a building (including a suspended ceiling) or contained within an element, but not a room, cupboard, circulation space, protected shaft or space within a flue, chute, duct, pipe or conduit. (Section 9)

Conservatory A single-storey part of a building where the roof and walls are substantially glazed with a transparent or translucent material.

Corridor access A design of a building containing flats in which each dwelling is approached via a common horizontal internal access or circulation space which may include a common entrance hall. (2.16)

Dead end Area from which escape is possible in one direction only. (Sections 2 and 3)

Direct distance The shortest distance from any point within the floor area, measured within the external enclosures of the building, to the nearest storey exit ignoring walls, partitions and fittings, other than the enclosing walls/partitions to protected stairways. (3.5)

Dwelling A unit of residential accommodation occupied (whether or not as a sole or main residence):
(*a*)   By a single person or by people living together as a family; or
(*b*)   By not more than six residents living together as a single household, including a household where care is provided for residents.

Element of structure
(*a*)   A member forming part of the structural frame of a building or any other beam or column;
(*b*)   A loadbearing wall or loadbearing part of a wall;
(*c*)   A floor;
(*d*)   A gallery;
(*e*)   An external wall, and
(*f*)   A compartment wall (including a wall common to two or more buildings). (However, see the guidance to B3, paragraph 7.4, for exclusions from the provisions for elements of structure.) (diagram [2.80])

[2.80] *Elements of structure: the structural elements of a building.*

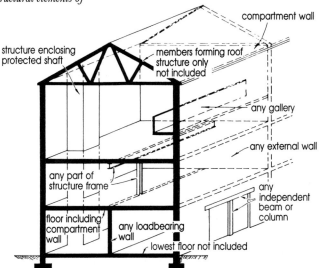

externally non-combustible means consisting of, or faced with, non-combustible material

Emergency lighting   Lighting provided for use when the supply to the normal lighting fails. (5.33)

Escape lighting   That part of the emergency lighting which is provided to ensure that the escape route is illuminated at all material times. (5.33)

Escape route   Route forming that part of the means of escape from any point in a building to a final exit. (Sections 1–5 and 18.11)

Evacuation lift   A lift that may be used for the evacuation of disabled people in a fire.

External wall (or side of a building) includes a part of a roof pitched at an angle of more than 70° to the horizontal, if that part of the roof adjoins a space within the building to which persons have access (but not access only for repair or maintenance).

Final exit   The termination of an escape route from a building giving direct access to a street, passageway, walkway or open space, and sited to ensure the rapid dispersal of persons from the vicinity of a building so that they are no longer in danger from fire and/or smoke. (Sections 1, 2, 4 and 5)

Fire door   A door or shutter, provided for the passage of persons, air or objects, which together with its frame and furniture as installed in a building, is intended (when closed) to resist the passage of fire and/or gaseous products of combustion, and is capable of meeting specified performance criteria to those ends. (It may have one or more leaves, and the term includes a cover or other form of protection to an opening in a fire-resisting wall or floor, or in a structure surrounding a protected shaft.) (10.4, 11.3, App. B)

Fire-resisting (fire resistance)   The ability of a component or construction of a building to satisfy for a stated period of time, some or all of the appropriate criteria specified in the relevant part of BS 476. (7.2, 7.3, 13.2, A3–A5)

Fire stop   A seal provided to close an imperfection of fit or design tolerance between elements or components, to restrict the passage of fire and smoke. (10.2, 10.12–10.14)

Firefighting lift   A lift designed to have additional protection, with controls that enable it to be used under the direct control of the fire service in fighting a fire. (Sections 15–18).

Firefighting lobby   A protected lobby providing access from a firefighting stair to the accommodation area and to any associated firefighting lift. (Section 17)

Firefighting shaft   A protected enclosure containing a firefighting stair, firefighting lobbies and, if provided, a firefighting lift, together with its machine room. (4.25, 8.33, 8.37, Sections 15–18)

Firefighting stair   A protected stair communicating with the accommodation area only through a firefighting lobby. (2.32, 4.3, 4.31, 5.19 and Section 17)

Gallery   A floor, including a raised storage area, which is less than one-half of the area of the space into which it projects. (7.2, 7.8)

Habitable room   A room used, or intended to be used, for dwelling purposes (including for the purposes of Part B, a kitchen, but not a bathroom). (2.1, 2.11, 7.7)

Height   (of a building or storey for the purposes of Part B) Height of a building is measured as shown in Appendix C, diagram C3, and height of the floor of the top storey above ground is measured as shown in Appendix C, diagram C5.

Inner room   Room from which escape is possible only by passing through another room (the access room). (1.16, 2.6, 2.11, 3.9)

Material of limited combustibility   A material performance specification that includes non-combustible materials, and for which the relevant test criteria are set out in Appendix A, paragraph A8.

Means of escape   Structural means whereby (in the event of fire) a safe route or routes is or are provided for persons to travel from any point in a building to a place of safety. (Section B1)

Measurement area, cubic capacity, height of a building and number of storeys, see Appendix C, diagrams [2.76]–[2.79], occupant capacity, travel distance, and width of a doorway, escape route and a stair (see paragraph 0.37).

Non-combustible material   The highest level of reaction to fire performance. The relevant test criteria are set out in Appendix A, paragraph A7.

Notional boundary   A boundary presumed to exist between buildings on the same site (see Section 13, diagram [2.52]). The concept is applied only to buildings in the residential and the assembly and recreation purpose groups.

Open spatial planning   The internal arrangement of a building in which more than one storey or level is contained in one undivided volume, eg split-level floors. For the purposes of this document there is a distinction between open spatial planning and an atrium space.

Perimeter (of building)   The maximum aggregate plan perimeter, found by vertical projection onto a horizontal plane (see Section 16, diagram [2.67]).

Pipe (for the purposes of Section 10) includes pipe fittings and accessories; and excludes a flue pipe and a pipe used for ventilating purposes (other than a ventilating pipe for an above-ground drainage system).

Places of special fire risk   Oil-filled transformer and switchgear rooms, boiler rooms, storage space for fuel or other highly flammable substances, and rooms housing a fixed internal combustion engine. (3.9, 4.27, 5.40, 18.8)

Platform floor (access or raised floor)   A floor supported by a structural floor, but with an intervening concealed space which is intended to house services. (7.4)

Pressurisation   A method of protecting escape routes against the ingress of smoke by maintaining an air pressure difference between the protected area and adjoining accommodation. (2.26, 3.22, 5.45, 8.35)

Protected circuit   An electrical circuit protected against fire. (5.35)

Protected corridor/lobby   A corridor or lobby which is adequately protected from fire in adjoining accommodation by fire-resisting construction. (Sections 2, 3 and 4)

Protected entrance hall/landing   A circulation area consisting of a hall or space in a dwelling, enclosed with fire-resisting construction (other than any part which is an external wall of a building). (2.12, 2.15)

Protected shaft   A shaft which enables persons, air or objects to pass from one compartment to another, and which is enclosed with fire-resisting construction. (Sections 8, 10 and 17)

Protected stairway   A stair discharging through a final exit to a place of safety (including any exit passageway between the foot of the stair and the final exit) that is adequately enclosed with fire-resisting construction. (Sections 1–5)

Purpose group   A classification of a building according to the purpose to which it is intended to be put. See Appendix D, Table DI.

Relevant boundary   The boundary which the side of the building faces (and/or coincides with) and which is parallel, or at an angle of not more than 80°, to the side of the building (see Section 13, diagram [2.51]). A notional boundary can be a relevant boundary.

Rooflight   A domelight, lantern light, skylight, ridge light, glazed barrel vault or other element intended to admit daylight through a roof. (Sections 6 and 14)

Room (for the purposes of B 2)   An enclosed space within a building that is not used solely as a circulation space. (The term includes not only conventional rooms, but also cupboards that are not fittings, and large spaces such as warehouses, and auditoria. The term does not include voids such as ducts, ceiling voids and roof spaces).

Separated part (of a building)   A form of compartmentation in which a part of a building is separated from another part of the same building by a compartment wall. The wall runs the full height of the part, and is in one vertical plane. (See paras 8.4 and 8.21)

Single-storey building   A building consisting of a ground storey only. (A separated part which consists of a ground storey only, with a roof to which access is only provided for repair or maintenance, may be treated as a single storey building.) Basements are not included in counting the number of storeys in a building (see Appendix C).

Storey includes:

(*a*)   Any gallery in an assembly building (purpose group 5); and

(*b*)   Any gallery in any other type of building if its area is more than half that of the space into which it projects; and

(*c*)   A roof, unless it is accessible only for maintenance and repair.

Storey exit   A final exit, or a doorway giving direct access into a protected stairway, firefighting lobby, or external escape route.

NOTE   A door in a compartment wall in a hospital is considered as a storey exit for the purposes of B 1, see paragraph 3.28.

Suspended ceiling (fire-protecting)   A ceiling suspended below a floor, which contributes to the fire resistance of the floor. Appendix A, Table A3, classifies different types of suspended ceiling.

Thermoplastic material   See Appendix A, paragraph A16.

Travel distance (unless otherwise specified, eg as in the case of flats)   The actual distance to be travelled by a person from any point within the floor area to the nearest storey exit, having regard to the layout of walls, partitions and fittings. (Sections 2, 3 and 4)

Unprotected area   In relation to a side or external wall of a building means:

(*a*)   Window, door or other opening; and

(*b*)   Any part of the external wall which has less than the relevant fire resistance set out in Section 12; and

(*c*)   Any part of the external wall which has combustible material more than 1 mm thick attached or applied to its external face, whether for cladding or any other purpose. (Combustible material in this context is any material that is not included in Tables A6 or A7 in Appendix A.)

References

BS 476: *Fire tests on building materials and structures.*

Part 3: 1958 *External fire exposure roof tests.*

Part 4: 1970 (1984) *Non-combustibility test for materials* Amendment 1: AMD 2483, 2: AMD 4390.

Part 6: 1981 *Method of test for fire propagation for products.*

Part 6: 1989 *Method of test for fire propagation for products.*

Part 7: 1971 *Surface spread of flame tests for materials.*

Part 7: 1987 *Method for classification of the surface spread of flame of products* Amendment 1: AMD 6249.

Part 8: 1972 *Test methods and criteria for the fire resistance of elements of building construction* Amendment 1: AMD 1873, 2: AMD 3816, 3: AMD 4822.

Part 11: 1982 *Method for assessing the heat emission from building products.*

Part 20: 1987 *Method for determination of the fire resistance of elements of construction (general principles)* Amendment 1: AMD 6487.

Part 21: 1987 *Methods for determination of the fire resistance of loadbearing elements of construction.*

Part 22: 1987 *Methods for determination of the fire resistance of non-loadbearing elements of construction.*

Part 23: 1987 *Methods for determination of the contribution of components to the fire resistance of a structure.*

Part 24: 1987 *Method for determination of the fire resistance of ventilation ducts.*

Part 31: *Methods for measuring smoke penetration through doorsets and shutter assemblies.*

Section 31.1: 1983 *Measurement under ambient temperature conditions.*

BS 747: 1977: *Specification for roofing felts* Amendment 1: AMD 3775, 2: AMD 4609, 3: AMD 5101.

BS 2782: 1970 *Methods of testing plastics:*

Part 1: *Thermal properties:* Method 120A *Determination of the Vicat softening temperature for thermoplastics.*

Part 5: *Miscellaneous methods:* Method 508A.

BS 4514: 1983 *Specification for unplasticized PVC soil and ventilating pipes, fittings and accessories* Amendment 1: AMD 4517, 2: AMD 5584.

BS 5255: 1989 *Specification for thermoplastics waste pipe and fittings.*

BS 5266: *Emergency lighting.*

Part 1: 1988 *Code of practice for the emergency lighting of premises other than cinemas and certain other specified premises used for entertainment.*

BS 5306: *Fire extinguishing installations and equipment on premises.*
Part 1: 1976 (1988) *Hydrant systems, hose reels and foam inlets* Amendment 1: AMD 4649, 2: AMD 5756.
Part 2: 1990 *Specification for sprinkler systems.*
BS 5395: *Stairs, ladders and walkways.*
Part 2: 1984 *Code of practice for the design of helical and spiral stairs* Amendment 1: AMD 6076.
BS 5438: 1976 *Methods of test for flammability of vertically oriented textile fabrics and fabric assemblies subjected to a small igniting flame:* Test 2: 1989.
BS 5499: *Fire safety signs, notices and graphic symbols.*
Part 1: 1990 *Specification for fire safety signs.*
BS 5588: *Fire precautions in the design, construction and use of buildings.*
Part 1: 1990 *Code of practice for residential buildings.*
Part 2: 1985 *Code of practice for shops* Amendment 1: AMD 5555, 2: AMD 6239, 3: AMD 6478.
Part 3: 1983 *Code of practice for office buildings* Amendment 1: AMD 5556, 2: AMD 5825, 3: AMD 6160.
Part 4: 1978 *Code of practice for smoke control in protected escape routes using pressurization* Amendment 1: AMD 5377.
Part 5: 1991 *Code of practice for firefighting stairs and lifts.*
Part 6: 1991 *Code of practice for assembly buildings.*
Part 8: 1988 *Code of practice for means of escape for disabled people.*
Part 9: 1989 *Code of practice for ventilation and air conditioning ductwork.*
Part 10: 1991 *Code of practice for enclosed shopping complexes.*
BS 5720: 1979 *Code of practice for mechanical ventilation and air conditioning in buildings.*
BS 5839: *Fire detection and alarm systems for buildings.*
Part 1: 1988 *Code of practice for system design, installation and servicing.*
BS 5867 *Specification for fabrics for curtains and drapes.*
Part 2: 1980 *Flammability requirements* Amendment 1: AMD 4319.
BS 5906: 1980 *Code of practice for storage and onsite treatment of solid waste from buildings.*
BS 6073 *Precast concrete masonry units.*
Part 1: 1981 *Specification for precast concrete masonry units* Amendment 1: AMD 3944, 2: AMD 4462.
BS 6336: 1982 *Guide to development and presentation of fire tests and their use in hazard assessment.*
BS 6387: 1983 *Specification for performance requirements for cables required to maintain circuit integrity under fire conditions.*
CP 144: *Roof coverings.*
Part 3: 1970. *Built-up bitumen felt,* Amendment 1: AMD 2527, 2: AMD 5229.
CP 1007: 1955 *Maintained lighting for cinemas.*
PD 6520: 1988 *Guide to fire test methods for building materials and elements of construction.*

Other publications referred to in Approved Document B 1/2/3/4/5

Wake up! Get a smoke alarm. Home Office booklet FB2, HMSO 1988
Design principles for smoke ventilation in enclosed shopping centres. BRE, 1990. (Revision of Smoke control methods in enclosed shopping complexes of one or more storeys. A design summary. (BRE) HMSO, 1979
Draft guide on fire precautions in existing hospitals. Home Office, 1982
Firecode. HTM 81
Fire precautions in new hospitals. (DHSS) HMSO, 1987
Firecode. HTM 88. Guide to fire precautions in NHS housing in the Community for mentally handicapped or mentally ill people (DHSS) HMSO
Firecode. Nucleus fire precautions recommendations (D of H) HMSO, 1989
Building Bulletin 7. Fire and the design of educational buildings. (DES) HMSO, 1988
Joint circular DOE, Home Office and Welsh Office, Memorandum on overcrowding and houses in multiple occupation. Circular 12/86 (DOE), 39/86 (Home Office), 23/86 (Welsh Office) HMSO, 1986
Gas Safety Regulations 1972 (SI 1972, No. 1178)
Gas Safety (Installation and Use) Regulations 1984, as amended 1990 (SI 1984, No. 1358)
Fire Precautions Act 1971. Guide to fire precautions in existing places of work that require a fire certificate: Factories, offices, shops and railways premises. HMSO, 1989
Guide to Safety at Sports Grounds. HMSO
External fire spread: Building separation and boundary distances, BRE 187, 1991
The behaviour of steel portal frames in boundary conditions, 1990 (available from the Steel Construction Institute, Silwood Park, Ascot, Berks, SL5 7QN)

Guidelines for the construction of structural elements. BR 128 BRE, 1988

Increasing the fire resistance of existing timber floors. BRE Digest 208, 1988

Fire test results on building products: fire resistance. FPA, 1983

Rules for the construction and installation of firebreak doors and shutters. LPC, 1988

Fire protection for structural steel in buildings (second edition). ASFPCM, 1988

Chapter 3

Approved Document C Site Preparation and Resistance to Moisture

Introduction

Most of this part deals with the basic need of all buildings – to keep out moisture both from above and below ground. The Approved Document to C 4 is really more of analysis of the principles of weatherproofing a building above ground and resisting moisture from below. Perhaps the opportunity will be taken to remove some of these basic principles from the Approved Document at the next revision.

Contaminants were included in Part C at the 1985 revision and the guidance which is really for experts has been reduced with reference made to publications emanating from the Building Research Establishment. The Appendix to C 2 which enjoyed the unusual status of inclusion in the Approved Document but not being part of the guidance has been omitted.

Changes in ventilation provisions below timber floors include halving the area of ventilation openings whilst at the same time increasing the height of the ventilated space from 125 mm to 150 mm. Ventilation of certain suspended concrete floors is also included. The minimum cavity width where a cavity is partially filled with insulation is stated as 50 mm.

Damp-proof membranes of polyethylene should now be 1200 gauge, where previously 1000 gauge was acceptable. There is also reference to the need to protect insulation from the effects of moisture.

The requirements of Parts C 1, 2 and 3 are as follows:

Requirement	Limits on application
Preparation of site C 1. The ground to be covered by the building shall be reasonably free from vegetable matter.	
Dangerous and offensive substances C 2. Precautions shall be taken to avoid danger to health and safety caused by substances found on or in the ground to be covered by the building.	
Subsoil drainage C 3. Subsoil drainage shall be provided if it is needed to avoid – (*a*) the passage of ground moisture to the interior of the building; (*b*) damage to the fabric of the building	
Resistance to weather and ground moisture C 4. The walls, floors and roof of the building shall resist the passage of moisture to the inside of the building.	

Performance

The performance level for C 1, 2 and 3 repeats the requirement and the level for C 4 will be met by:

(*a*)   a floor next to the ground preventing undue moisture from reaching the upper surface of the floor,

(*b*)   a wall preventing undue moisture from reaching the inside of the building and, if external, adequately resist the penetration of rain and snow to the inside of the building,

(*c*)   a roof resisting the penetration of moisture from rain or snow to the inside,

(*d*)   ensuring all the above are not damaged by moisture from the ground, rain or snow nor carry such moisture to any part which would be damaged by it.

Moisture should be either prevented from getting to materials which would be damaged or by using materials which will not be damaged. No guidance is given in the Approved Document on prevention of damage caused by water vapour on cold surfaces.

See Approved Document L (Conservation of fuel and power), Approved Document F (Ventilation) and the BRE publication *Thermal insulation: avoiding risks*.

Introduction

0.1/0.2   There are five sections.
Section 1 – Site preparation and site drainage
Section 2 – Contaminants
Section 3 – Floors next to the ground
Section 4 – Walls
Section 5 – Cladding for external walls and roofs
0.3   In this document reference to 'moisture damage' means damage serious enough to a material or structure that it would present an imminent danger to health or safety, or reduce the performance of insulation.

Definitions

0.4   'Floor' is the lower surface of any space in a building including finishes laid as part of the permanent construction.

'Wall' is a vertical construction including piers, columns and parapets, and chimneys if they are attached to a building.

Windows, doors or other openings are excluded.

'Moisture' includes water in both liquid and vapour form.

'Contaminant' is any material (including animal or faecal matter) in or on the ground to be covered by the building as well as any substance which is or could become toxic, corrosive, flammable or radioactive and so be a danger to health and safety.

Section 1   Site preparation and site drainage

1.1   Normal sites (not contaminated) need the following provisions.

Organic material
1.2   Turf and vegetable matter must be removed to sufficient depth to prevent future growth;
Note, however, that this does not apply if the building is to be used for:
(*a*)   Storage, where any persons employed are only engaged in taking care of, or the taking in or out of the goods, or
(*b*)   A purpose where such provision would not increase the protection to health and safety of persons employed in the building.
NOTE   These same exceptions apply to many of the provisions of this Part. The same was the case in Part C of the 1976 Regulations, where such cases were known as 'excepted buildings'. As this is a convenient term, which saves repetition, it is also used in this Guide where appropriate.
1.3   Building services below ground (including drainage) must be sufficiently robust or flexible to accommodate the presence of any roots, and joints are to be such that roots cannot penetrate.

Service entries
Where external walls or floors are penetrated by services the entry points should be sealed in accordance with:
Drainage: BSCP 8301: 1985.

Gas: The Gas Safety (Installation and Use) Regulations 1984, SI 1984 No. 1358 Regulation 18, and the Gas Safety Regulations 1972 (SI 1972 No 1178), Regulation 7.
Water: BS 6700: 1985.
Electricity: The Electricity Supply Regulations 1988.
Telephone: British Telecom internal note.

Site drainage

1.4 The following provisions assume that the site is not subject to flooding, or if it is, it has been dealt with.

1.5 If the water table can rise to within about 0.25 m of the lowest floor, or surface water could enter or adversely affect the building the ground should be drained by gravity, or other safeguards instituted (see 1.7).

1.6 If an active subsoil drain is cut, it should be dealt with as shown in diagram [3.1].

1.7 As an alternative to providing subsoil drainage, the building may be designed to prevent the passage of ground moisture to the inside, or to any materials which might be affected by it.

1.6 [**3.1**] *Subsoil drains cut during excavation.*

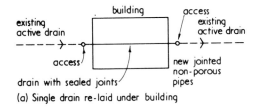

(a) Single drain re-laid under building

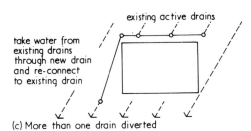

(c) More than one drain diverted

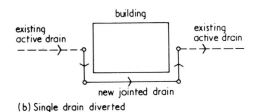

(b) Single drain diverted

Section 2 Contaminants

Solid and liquids from previous uses of land can cause problems of site contamination. Additionally, gases can be a further source of contamination, especially from burial of waste in landfills (see 2.8).

Natural contamination by the radioactive gas, radon, and its decay products occurs in certain parts of the country, principally in Devon and Cornwall.

Signs of contaminants

2.2 Sites which contain contaminants may be identified from planning records or local knowledge of previous uses. Table 1 of the Approved Document gives examples which include chemical works, gasworks, dumps, mines, sewage works and a number of others: see Table for full list.

Where such identification has not been made, there are signs which can reveal the presence of contaminants, such as unusual colours or odours, unnatural vegetation, old drums or containers. Table 2 of the Document lists these and indicates the possible contaminant and appropriate action required. It should be noted that the ground to be covered by the building includes the ground to be covered by its foundations.

2.3 If such signs are present the Environmental Health Officer must be told, and he will confirm or otherwise, the presence of contaminants. The recommended action in Table 2 assumes that the ground will have at least 100 mm of in-situ concrete laid on it after the removal.

Table 2 Possible contaminants and actions

Signs of possible contamination	Possible contaminants	Relevant action
Vegetation (absence, poor or unnatural growth)	Metals Metal compounds* Organic compounds Gases	None Removal
Surface materials (unusual colours) and contours may indicate wastes and residues	Metals Metal compounds* Oily and tarry wastes Asbestos (loose) Other fibres Organic compounds including phenols Combustible material including coal and coke dust Refuse and waste	None Removal, filling or sealing Filling or sealing None Removal or filling Removal or filling Total removal or see guidance
Fumes and odours (may indicate organic chemicals at very low concentrations)	Flammable explosive and asphyxiating gases including methane and carbon dioxide Corrosive liquids Faecal animal and vegetable matter (biologically active)	Removal Removal, filling or sealing Removal or filling
Drums and containers (whether full or empty)	Various	Removal with all contaminated ground

NOTE   Liquid and gaseous contaminants are mobile and the ground covered by the building can be affected by such contaminants from elsewhere. Some guidance on landfill gas and radon is given in this document; other liquids and gases should be referred to a specialist.

*Special cement may be needed for sulphates.

2.4   In Table 2 the following definitions apply:

Removal   The contaminants and any contaminated ground which is to be covered by the building is to be removed to a depth of 1 m below the lowest floor level (or less if the Local Authority agrees). In some cases the Local Authority may require the work to be done by specialists.

Filling   The ground to be covered to a depth of 1 m (less if the Local Authority agrees) with suitable material which will not react adversely with any remaining contaminant. The type of filling and the design of the ground floor are to be considered together.

Sealing   A suitable imperforate barrier between contaminant and building sealed at joints, around edges and service entries. Polythene may not be suitable with liquid contaminants containing solvents.

2.5   Where the removal of large quantities of material is involved remedial measures should be the subject of expert advice. In the most hazardous conditions total removal may be the only answer, but in some cases remedial measures may reduce the risk to acceptable levels.

2.6   Guidance on site investigation can be found in the BS Draft for Development 175: 1988 *Code of practice for the identification of potentially contaminated land* and further information on sites in general is given in BS 5930: 1981 *Code of practice for site investigations*.

Gaseous contaminants   *Radon*

2.7   Radon is a naturally occurring, radioactive colourless and odourless gas formed in small quantities by radioactive decay. It can move through the subsoil and thus into buildings. Exposure to high levels for long periods increases the risk of the development of lung cancer. Radon contamination of sites is more likely to occur in Cornwall or Devon or in parts of Somerset, Northamptonshire or Derbyshire. Where a house or an extension is to be built in these areas precautions against radon may be necessary and the precise areas are reviewed from time to time. Current information can be obtained either from the Local Authority building control officers or from Approved Inspectors.

Guidance on the construction of dwellings in areas susceptible to radon has been published by the Building Research Establishment, entitled *Radon: guidance on protective measures for new dwellings*.

Landfill gas and methane

2.8 Landfill gas is generated by the action of anaerobic micro-organisms on biodegradable material and generally consists of methane and carbon dioxide with small quantities of other gases. It can migrate under pressure through the subsoil and through cracks and fissures into buildings.

Gases similar to landfill gas can also arise naturally and should be treated as for landfills.

Methane is an asphyxiant, will burn and can explode in air. Carbon dioxide is non-flammable but toxic. Many of the other components of landfill gas are flammable and some are also toxic.

2.9 Where the ground to be covered by a building is:

on, or within 250 m of landfill,

suspect for gaseous contamination,

within the likely sphere of influence of a landfill where gas production is possible,

further investigation should be made to determine what, if any, protective measures are necessary.

2.10 Guidance on the construction of buildings near landfill sites has been published by BRE as a Report.

The broad guidelines for dwellings are:

(*a*) Where the level of methane in the ground is unlikely to exceed 1 per cent by volume and the construction of the ground floor of a house is of suspended concrete and ventilated – no further protection is required.

(*b*) Carbon dioxide must be considered and judged independently from methane.

A carbon dioxide concentration of greater than 1½ per cent by volume in the ground indicates a need for measures to be considered to prevent its ingress. A 5 per cent by volume level implies that specific design measures are required.

(*c*) Permanent continuous mechanical ventilation to prevent build-up of gas is not feasible. Passive protection is generally the only viable alternative and is effective only where gas concentrations in the ground are low and likely so to remain.

2.11 In other cases expert advice should be sought.

If necessary this could result in a complete investigation into the nature and source of any hazardous gases and the potential for future gas generation from the site.

The amount of gas in the ground and its pressure relative to the atmosphere should be considered.

If there is a low level of gas or if the volume of gas is very small no remedial measures may be needed.

When found necessary using expert advice, protective measures should be incorporated into the building, including maintenance and monitoring arrangements.

References

2.12

(*a*) Department of Environment (Her Majesty's Inspectorate of Pollution). *The Control of Landfill Gas*, Waste Management Paper No.27 (1989), HMSO.

(*b*) British Standards Institution Draft for Development: *Code of Practice for the identification of potentially contaminated land and its investigation* DD 175/88.

(*c*) Crowhurst, D. 'Measurement of gas emissions from contaminated land. BRE Report 1987. HMSO ISBN 0 85125 246 X.

(*d*) ICRCL 17/78 *Notes on the development and after-use of landfill sites*. 8th edition December 1990 Interdepartmental Committee on the Redevelopment of Contaminated Land.*

(*e*) ICRCL 59/83 *Guidance on the assessment and redevelopment of contaminated land*. 2nd edition July 1987. Interdepartmental Committee on the Redevelopment of Contaminated Land.*

(*f*) Institute of Wastes Management. *Monitoring of Landfill Gas*. Sept. 1989.

(*g*) BS 5930: 1981 *Code of practice for site investigations*.

(*h*) BRE *Radon: guidance on protective measures for new dwellings*. BRE Report. Garston 1991. ISBN 0 85125 511 6.

(*j*) BRE *Construction of new buildings on gas contaminated land*. BRE Report. Garston 1991. ISBN 085125 513 2.

*Obtainable from: Department of Environment Publication Sales unit, Building 1, Victoria Road, South Ruislip, Middlesex HA4 0NZ.

Section 3   Floors next to the ground

3.1   Three types are described:
O   Ground supported floors.
O   Suspended timber floors.
O   Suspended concrete floors.
3.2   They should all:
(*a*)   Resist ground moisture from reaching the upper surface. This does not apply to 'excepted buildings' (see Site preparation 1.2).
(*b*)   Not be damaged by moisture from the ground.

Ground supported floors

3.3   Any ground supported floor will meet the performance if the ground is covered with dense concrete laid on a hardcore bed and a damp-proof membrane is provided. Insulation may be incorporated.

Technical solution

3.4   Unless subject to water pressure (see 3.8) ground supported floors will be adequate if constructed as below:
(*a*)   Concrete 100 mm thick minimum, mix at least 50 kg cement to 0.11 m³ fine aggregate, 0.16 m³ coarse aggregate or mix ST2 – BS 5328. If there is embedded steel the mix should be 50 kg cement to 0.08 m³ fine aggregate and 0.13 m³ coarse aggregate or mix ST4 – BS 5238.
(*b*)   Hardcore bed of clean broken brick or similar inert material free from substances which can damage concrete (including sulphates).
(*c*)   Damp-proof membrane above, below or through the concrete and continuous with, or sealed to damp-proof courses in walls, piers, etc.
3.5   Membranes below concrete to be at least 1200 (300 μm) polyethylene (eg polythene) with sealed joints on a bed of material which will not damage it (this usually means that the hardcore should be blinded with sand or topped with a weak mix to provide a flat surface).
3.6   A membrane above concrete may be as above or 3-coat cold applied bitumen or similar moisture and vapour-resisting material protected by screed or finish unless it is pitchmastic or similar material suitable itself as a floor finish.
3.7   A timber floor finish may be bedded on material which also serves as a damp-proof membrane. Timber fillets below the membrane to be treated with preservative (see BS 1282: 1975 *Guide to wood preservatives*), and diagram [3.2].

3.4 **[3.2]** *Ground supported floors.*   3.7 *Timber finishes on ground supported floors.*

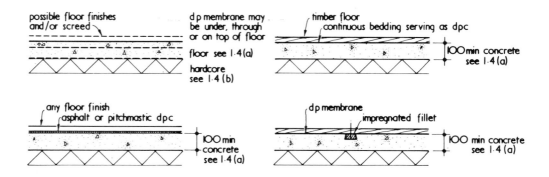

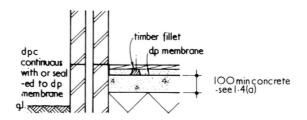

3.8   Alternatively, there are the relevant recommendations of Clause 11 of CP 102: 1973 *Protection of buildings against water from the ground.* BS 8102: 1990 *Code of practice for design and installation of damp proof courses in masonry construction* includes recommendations for floors subject to water pressure (eg in basements).

Suspended timber floors

3.9   These will be adequate if:
(*a*)   The ground is covered to resist moisture and prevent plant growth.
(*b*)   There is a ventilated space between this cover and the timber.
(*c*)   There are dpcs between the timber and any material which can carry ground moisture.
3.10   Unless the floor has a finish which is highly vapour-resistant (in which case see 3.11) it may be as follows:
(*a*)   A ground covering of either:
       (i)   100 mm concrete mix 50 kg/0.13 m^3/0.18 m^3 cement, fine, coarse, aggregate or mix STI: BS 5328, if not reinforced, on hardcore bed as in 3.4(*b*) or
       (ii)   50 mm concrete as above on 1200 gauge minimum polythene with sealed joints on material which will not damage it.

The top of the covering should either be all above the highest adjoining ground level or laid to fall to an outlet at a point above the lowest adjoining level (see diagram [3.3]).
(*b*)   A ventilated air space as shown in diagram [3.4]. If pipes are used to convey ventilation air they must be at least 100 mm diameter. Each external wall should have ventilation openings to give at least the equivalent of 1500 mm^2 free openings for each metre run of wall and there should be a free path between walls (this is roughly the equivalent of one normal air brick every 6 m).
(*c*)   Damp-proof courses of impervious sheet material, engineering brick, slates in cement or other moisture resisting material (see diagram [3.4]).
3.11   Alternatively, the relevant recommendations of Clause 11 of CP 102: 1973 may be followed.

3.10(*a*) [**3.3**] *Positioning of ground covering.*

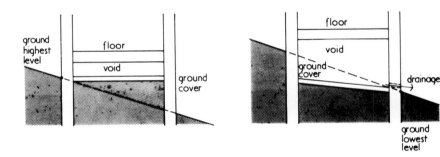

3.10 [**3.4**] *Suspended timber floor – Construction.*

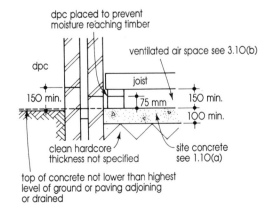

Suspended concrete floors

3.12   In-situ or precast concrete floors will be adequate if they prevent moisture from reaching the upper surface and the reinforcement is protected against moisture.
3.13   Diagram [3.5] illustrates the principles to be followed.
3.14(*a*) If the ground below the floor has been excavated below the level of the surrounding ground and will not be effectively drained a damp-proof membrane should be provided.

3.13 **[3.5]** *Suspended concrete ground floors.*

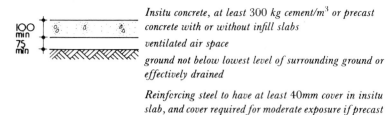

Insitu concrete, at least 300 kg cement/m³ or precast concrete with or without infill slabs

ventilated air space

ground not below lowest level of surrounding ground or effectively drained

Reinforcing steel to have at least 40mm cover in insitu slab, and cover required for moderate exposure if precast

(*b*) Where there may be a risk of accumulation of gas which may lead to an explosion 150 mm clear ventilation space should be provided from the ground to the underside of the floor (or insulation).

(*c*) Where the ventilation referred to in (*b*) is provided the walls should contain ventilation openings as those set out in 3.10(*b*).

NOTE Suspended concrete floors may be constructed without an air space. If so, the construction should be as paragraphs 3.3–3.8.

Section 4 Walls

The layout of this section is somewhat pedantic and repetitive and an explanatory summary is given instead of rigidly following the coding system. Nevertheless, all *relevant* information is included.

4.1/4.4 All walls should meet the performance standards in 0.3 with the usual limitation for 'excepted buildings'.

All walls should have a dpc of bituminous material, engineering bricks, slates in cement of other moisture-resistant material. They should be continuous with any damp-proof membrane in floors. In external walls they should be positioned as shown in diagram [3.6].

4.5 Alternatively, the performance can be met by following the recommendations of Clauses 4 and 5 of BS 8215: 1991. *Code of practice for the design and installation of damp proof courses in masonry construction.* BS 8102: 1990 includes recommendations for walls subject to groundwater pressure, including walls of basements.

4.4 **[3.6]** *Positioning damp-proof courses. NOTE The 150 mm minimum is not essential if a part of the building protects the wall.*

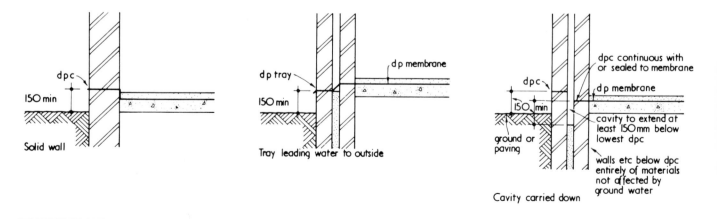

External walls

4.6 These may be either solid or cavity.

Solid walls

4.7/4.8 The effectiveness of solid walls depends on their ability to absorb and hold moisture long enough for it to be dispersed during a dry period before reaching the inner face. This will depend on the type of brick or block and the severity of exposure. A method of classifying exposure conditions has been developed (see note on exposure in BS 5628: Part 3: 1985, or DD 93: 1984 and the BRE publication *Thermal insulation: avoiding risks*). For 'very severe' exposure they should be protected by cladding. They may also be rendered as suggested in the Approved Document for 'severe' (but not 'very severe') conditions if built as follows:

Brickwork at least 328 mm thick or dense aggregate concrete blockwork 250 mm or lightweight aggregate or aerated autoclaved concrete blockwork 215 mm thick. Mortar strength to be compatible with the brick or block used and joints raked back 10 mm.

20 mm rendering in two coats with textured finish, mix 1:1:6 cement, lime, sharp sand, except for dense concrete blocks which should be 1:½:4 proportion.

BS 5262: 1976 has recommendations for a wider range of mixes according to the type of masonry and severity of exposure.

Copings must be provided to exposed tops, and unless the coping is itself impervious (including joints) should be laid on a dpc.

Damp-proof courses should be provided to direct water towards the outer face:

○   Wherever the downward flow will be interrupted, such as by lintels and

○   Under openings, unless sills are impervious (including joints) and

○   Where an internal wall is carried up as an external wall.

NOTE   We are talking here of solid (not cavity) walls.

4.9   A solid external wall may be insulated on the inside or the outside. Where on the inside a cavity should be provided to give a break in the path for moisture and where on the outside should provide resistance to ingress of moisture and ensure that the wall stays relatively dry.

4.10   Alternatively, the recommendations of the following BSS may be followed:

BS 5628: Part 3: 1985 *Structural masonry, materials, design and workmanship.*

BS 5390: 1976 *Stone masonry.*

Cavity external walls

4.11/4.12   These rely on having two leaves separated by a drained air space or any other means of preventing water being carried to the inner leaf (such as impervious insulation). A suitable specification is:

(*a*)   An outer leaf of masonry (brick, block, stone etc).

(*b*)   A cavity 50 mm minimum width, bridged only by wall ties or damp proof trays provided to prevent moisture being carried to the inner leaf.

NOTE   There is no mention of the specific example of jambs to openings and this is of particular importance.

(*c*)   An inner leaf of masonry or frame and lining.

4.13   Alternatively, the recommendations of BS 5628: Part 3: 1985 may be followed.

Cavity insulation

4.14   Insulation may be placed in a cavity under the following conditions:

(*a*)   Rigid material, the subject of, and installed in accordance with, an Agrément certificate.

(*b*)   Urea formaldehyde (UF) foam in accordance with BS 5617: 1985 suitable for walls with masonry or concrete inner and outer leaves, installed in accordance with BS 5618: 1985.

4.12/4.14 [**3.7**] *Insulated external walls: examples.*

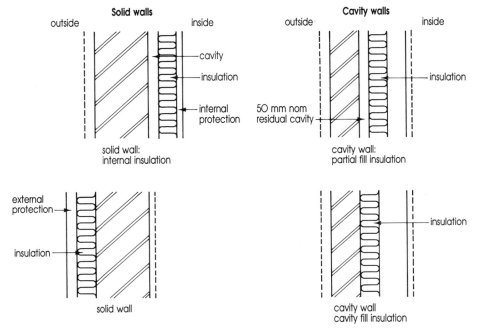

The suitability of the wall should be assessed before starting in accordance with BS 8208: Part 1: 1985, and the installer should hold a certificate of Registration of Assessed Capability from the BSI.

(c)   Other insulating materials should be installed in accordance with BS 6232: Part 1 and Part 2: 1982 (blown man-made mineral fibre in cavity walls with masonry or concrete leaves). Suitability and installation to be as in (b) above.

Alternatively, the insulation should be the subject of, and installed in accordance with the terms of a current Agrément Certificate or ETA.

4.15   The suitability of the wall for filling should be assessed before work is carried out using BS 8208 *Guide to the assessment of suitability of external cavity walls for filling with thermal insulants* Part 1: 1985 *Existing traditional cavity construction.*

Section 5   Cladding for external walls and roofs

5.1/5.5   This can protect a building by either holding off the rain or snow at the face (totally impervious) or by stopping it penetrating beyond the back of the cladding (weather resisting). Cladding will be adequate if it:

(a)   Is impervious and jointless or has sealed joints (in which case allowance must be made for structural and thermal movement) or,

(b)   Has overlapping dry joints and is backed by a material which will divert any water which penetrates back towards the outer face. The latter is the principle behind most framed or lapped cladding systems. Their suitability depends on the severity of exposure, especially to wind-driven rain and snow on the surfaces (such as tile hanging or sheeting). Very special consideration is required on large elevations where the direction of the wind-driven water may frequently be upwards (for example when the United Nations' building in New York was first occupied, water was seen to come spouting into the building through the outlets designed for drainage of the cavity behind the cladding grid).

The weather-resisting part of the wall should not rely on paint or include any coating or surfacing which does not, in itself, provide all the weather resistance. The meaning of this is not entirely clear, but seems to suggest that the wall should not rely on the combined effect of several partially resistant layers.

Claddings can be classified as follows [diagram 3.8].

(a)   Impervious: metal, plastic, glass and bituminous products.

(b)   Weather-resisting: stone, slate, cement products, fired clay and wood products.

(c)   Moisture-resisting: bitumen and plastic products (lapped at the joints if used as sheet material). These materials should be vapour-permeable unless there is an air space immediately behind them [3.8].

5.6   Dry joints between cladding units should be designed either:

(a)   So that rain will not pass through them, or

(b)   If rain does pass through, is directed towards the exposed face without penetration beyond the back of the cladding.

Dry joints may not be suitable. Much depends on design of the joint or cladding and the severity of exposure.

5.7   Each sheet, tile and section of cladding should be securely fixed.

5.8   Insulation can be incorporated into the construction provided it is either protected from moisture or is unaffected by it.

5.9   Alternatively, the recommendations of the following British Standards may be followed:

(a)   Walls and roofs: CP 143 *Sheet roof and wall coverings of troughed and corrugated aluminium* Part 1: 1958.

Zinc: Part 5: 1964.

Galvanised corrugated steel: Part 10: 1973.

Copper: Part 12: 1970.

Aluminium: Part 15: 1973.

Semi-rigid asbestos/bitumen sheet: Part 16: 1974.

Section 5 [**3.8**] *Types of cladding to external walls.*

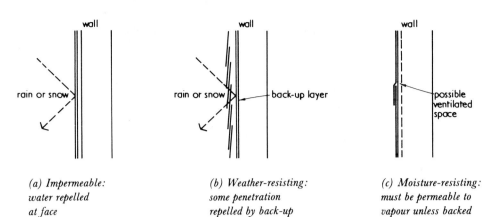

(a) *Impermeable:*
water repelled
at face

(b) *Weather-resisting:*
some penetration
repelled by back-up
material

(c) *Moisture-resisting:*
must be permeable to
vapour unless backed
by a ventilated space

Recommendations for lead are in BS 6915: 1988.
(*b*)   Walls and roofs: BS 5247: Part 14: 1975 *Corrugated asbestos cement.*
(*c*)   Walls and steep roofs: BS 8200: 1985 *Non-loadbearing external vertical enclosures.*
(*d*)   Walls only: CP 297: 1972 *precast concrete cladding.*
(*e*)   Walls only: CP 8298: 1989 *Natural stone cladding.*

For the assistance of readers brief summaries of the more important BS publications referred to in this Approved Document are given below.

CP 102: **1973 Protection of buildings against water from the ground**	Section Two of this CP is concerned with structures below ground level which are subject to hydrostatic pressure. Two types are described: Type A Where a continuous membrane impervious to water and vapour is used, and Type B Which uses only high grade reinforced concrete to exclude water but not necessarily all vapour. It recommends the provision of land drains around such structures wherever possible to reduce water pressure. Under Type A it deals with mastic asphalt and bitumen sheet tanking both internally and externally applied. It should be consulted whenever the structure will be subjected to hydrostatic pressure. Section Three deals with the problem of the capillary rise of moisture in walls and floors in contact with the ground (rising damp). It covers much the same ground as the Approved Document itself but in more detail. Clause 10 concerns the damp-proofing of walls, principally with the materials and workmanship involved in laying dpcs. It stresses the need for continuity between wall dpcs and floor membranes. Clause 11 concerns the damp-proofing of floors. The degree of protection required depends on the nature of the floor finish (pervious or impervious and whether adversely affected by moisture). What is often critical is the adhesive used to fix the flooring. There are two useful tables showing the properties and limitations of waterproof flooring and membranes, and of the various kinds of floor finish. Recommendations are given for mastic asphalt as flooring or membrane and for bitumen sheet, hot pitch or bitumen, cold bitumen and cold tar/pitch/rubber emulsions. There is a section on suspended timber floors which expands on the material in the Approved Document with diagrams.
BS 5628: Part 3: **1985 CP for the use of masonry**	This code of practice supersedes CP 121: Part 1: 1973. It is a veritable encyclopedia of information (100 pages) on all aspects of masonry wall design and construction and its highly detailed approach goes far beyond the consideration normally given by designers or builders to this important subject. It has three principal sections covering materials, design and workmanship. Among its principal design considerations are: O Design and detailing for stability (but not detailed calculations, for which see Part 1). O Movement. O Exclusion of moisture. O Durability.

○   Fire resistance.
○   Thermal properties.
○   Sound reduction.

Virtually all of these are the concern of Building Regulations.

Part C is concerned with the exclusion of moisture and in this respect the BS describes a method of assessing the exposure category based on the local spell index method in DD 93. These indices are based on the amount of driving rain which might be expected to fall on a vertical surface during the worst spell in a period of three years. These run from 98 l/m^3 (very severe) down to 24 l/m^2 (very sheltered): six categories in all. The designer must select which category applies to any particular situation (by reference to DD 93 or local knowledge). The BS then gives tables from which suitable wall types can be chosen; Table 11A for single leaf walls of brick or concrete, rendered or plain, 11B for cavity walls with various finishes and cavities either clear or filled with insulation. The point is made that cavity filling reduces the resistance to penetration (UF foam being worse than other types) and that total resistance to penetration can only be achieved by cladding with metal, plastics, slates, tiles or timber, whether on single leaf or cavity walls.

BS 5390: 1976 CP for stone masonry

This BS covers all aspects of the design and construction of stonework. The information relevant to Part C is contained in Clause 20, exclusion of rain.

Water penetration may occur through the porosity of the stone or mortar or through cracks. The latter are usually the result of using too strong a mortar.

Reference is made to the classification system in CP 121 which has only three categories of exposure, severe, moderate and sheltered. Only walls incorporating a cavity or internal lining are suitable for severe conditions. Solid stone walls are only suitable for sheltered conditions. The thickness, and the detailing at floors, openings, projections and parapets are all very important and the BS gives a great deal of information on these.

BS 5262: 1976 CP for external rendered finishes

This code deals with external renderings on all common backgrounds, whether for protective or purely visual reasons. It contains sections on materials, backgrounds, design, application and repair.

Various mixes are recommended for undercoats and finishing coats to suit differing backgrounds and exposure conditions. The latter are defined on the basis of BRS Digest 127 (later included in CP 121 and now overtaken by DD 93) and two maps are included showing exposure gradings and an annual driving rain index for the British Isles. Resistance to water penetration is best achieved by using several coats with each coat being slightly more porous than the coat below. Two or three coats are normal depending on exposure. The theory is that it is better to have a surface that will absorb some water and subsequently dry out than a completely impervious surface that will almost certainly crack and then prevent drying out of moisture which has penetrated the cracks.

There is helpful advice on detailing with diagrams.

BS 8200: 1985 CP for design of non-loadbearing vertical enclosures of buildings

This BS covers a very wide field indeed. It is intended principally as a general design guide for all non-loadbearing cladding systems, including masonry etc, as well as grid and large panel systems, although it does not deal specifically with any of them. It does cover all the normal design problems eg

○   Thermal, moisture and structural movement.
○   Jointing and sealing.
○   Control of heat, sound and water.

The last item is dealt with in clause 33 which is a very interesting dissertation on how and why water may penetrate construction. The forces which cause this are the kinetic energy of raindrops, capillary action, gravity and pressure differentials.

The principles of watertight construction are explained as requiring three elements:

(a)   The rainscreen to prevent direct penetration.

(b)   An air space ventilated to ensure that the air pressure is equal to that outside, hence rain is not drawn in.

(c)   An air barrier across which is the pressure differential between outside and the interior of the building.

A lot of advice is also given on weathering and run-off, to avoid unsightly appearance as well as moisture penetration.

It should have a place on every architect's bookshelf.

References

C1/2/3

BS 5930: 1981 *Code of practice for site investigation.*

DD 175: 1988 *Code of practice for the identification of potentially contaminated land and its investigation.*

C4

BS 1282: 1975 *Guide to the choice, use and application of wood preservatives.*

BS 5247: *Code of practice for sheet roof and wall coverings:*

Part 14: 1975 *Corrugated asbestos-cement Amendment slips 1: AMD 2821, 2: AMD 3502.*

BS 5262: 1976 *Code of practice for external rendered finishes* Amendment slips 1: AMD 2103, 2: AMD 6246.

BS 5328: *Concrete:*

Part 1: 1990 *Guide to specifying concrete*

Part 2: 1990 *Method for specifying concrete mixes.*

BS 5390: 1976 (1984) *Code of practice for stone masonry* Amendment slip 1: AMD 4272.

BS 5617: 1985 *Specification for urea-formaldehyde (UF) foam systems suitable for thermal insulation of cavity walls with masonry or concrete inner and outer leaves.*

BS 5618: 1985 *Code of practice for thermal insulation of cavity walls (with masonry or concrete inner and outer leaves) by filling with urea-formaldehyde (UF) foam systems.*

BS 5628: *Code of practice for use of masonry:*

BS 6232: *Thermal insulation of cavity walls by filling with blown man-made mineral fibre:*

Part 1: 1982 *Specification for the performance of installation systems* Amendment slip 1: AMD 5428

Part 2: 1982 *Code of practice for installation of blown man-made mineral fibre in cavity walls with masonry and/or concrete leaves.*

BS 6915: 1988 *Specification for design and construction of fully supported lead sheet roof and wall coverings.*

BS 8200: 1985 *Code of practice for design of non-loadbearing external vertical enclosures of buildings.*

BS 8102: 1990 *Code of practice for protection of structures against water from the ground.*

BS 8208: *Guide to assessment of suitability of external cavity walls for filling with thermal insulants:*

Part 1: 1985 *Existing traditional cavity construction.*

BS 8215: 1991 *Code of practice for design and installation of damp-proof courses in masonry construction.*

BS 8298: *Code of practice for design and installation of natural stone cladding and lining.*

CP 102: 1973 *Code of practice for protection of buildings against water from the ground* Amendment slips 1: AMD 1151, 2: AMD 2196, 3: AMD 2470.

CP 143: *Code of practice for sheet roof and wall coverings:*

Part 1: 1958 *Aluminium, corrugated and troughed*

Part 5: 1964 *Zinc*

Part 10: 1973 *Galvanised corrugated steel*

Part 12: 1970 *Copper* Amendment slips 1: AMD 863, 2: AMD 5193

Part 15: 1973 (1986) *Aluminium* Amendment slip 1: AMD 4473

Part 16: 1974 *Semi-rigid asbestos bitumen sheet.*

CP 297: 1972 *Precast concrete cladding (non-loadbearing).*

DD 93: 1984 *Methods for assessing exposure to wind-driven rain.*

Chapter 4

Approved Document D
Toxic Substances

D1   CAVITY INSULATION

This is the shortest of the Approved Documents designed officially to bring the use of UF foam for cavity insulation within the orbit of the Regulations.

The reasons for its inclusion as a separate Part are very difficult to perceive, since the provisions required are already wholly dealt with in the Approved Document to Part C (C 4.4.14). There is therefore no point in repeating them here.

The requirement itself is as follows:

Requirement	Limits on application
Cavity insulation D 1. If insulating material is inserted into a cavity in a cavity wall reasonable precautions shall be taken to prevent the subsequent permeation of any toxic fumes from that material into any part of the building occupied by people.	

The performance level required is that the fumes given off should not penetrate occupied parts of the building to an extent which would give rise to an irritant concentration, and the provisions required to meet this standard are that there should be a continuous barrier which will minimise, as far as practicable, the passage of fumes to occupied parts.

The technical details are as stated in 4.14 of C 4.

These rules apply to both new and existing buildings because under Regulation 3 filling an existing cavity wall is a 'material alteration.'

NOTE The Approved Documenmt does not actually rule out filling cavity walls that do not have a masonry inner leaf, but requires only that there should be a 'continuous barrier' against the passage of fumes. However, the technical solution offered is only concerned with walls having a masonry inner leaf. In Scotland foam cavity fill has been used on timber framed houses in the past, but since April 1985 has been specifically prohibited by the Scottish Building Standards Regulations.

References

The following British Standards and other documents are referred to in the Approved Document.

BS 5617: 1985 *Specification for urea-formaldehyde (UF) foam systems suitable for thermal insulation of cavity walls with masonry or concrete inner and outer leaves.*

BS 5618: 1985 *Code of practice for thermal insulation of cavity walls (with masonry or concrete inner and outer leaves) by filling with ura-formaldehyde (UF) foam systems.*

BS 8208 *Guide to assessment of suitability of external cavity walls for filling with thermal insulants.* Part 1: 1985 *Existing traditional cavity construction.*

Chapter 5

Approved Document E 1/2/3 Airborne and Impact Sound

Layout and changes

Several changes have been made to the 1985 Regulations both in the requirements and in the guidance in the Approved Document.

The requirements have been extended to include material change of use to a dwelling. This is not stated in E 1, E 2 or E 3 but it is activated by the inclusion of sound insulation in the main Regulations (regulation 6(e)).

The limits on application have been deleted from the Schedule 1 requirements but there are some significant aspects which have been reconsidered. These are:

Walls: Now include walls separating a kitchen from another part of the same building.

Floors: Extended to include stairs which form part of the separation between dwellings.

The Approved Document now has six Sections. Sections 1, 2, 3 and 4 relate to new dwellings and Sections 5 and 6 deal with conversion work. Standards have been upgraded for precast concrete floors and walls and a new laboratory test procedure is included as an alternative to ways of demonstrating compliance.

There is an Appendix which gives methods of determining the mass of masonry walls specified in the Document.

Requirement	Limits on application
Airborne sound (walls) E 1 – (1) A wall which (*a*)　　　separates a dwelling from another building or from another dwelling, or (*b*)　　　separates a habitable room or kitchen within a dwelling from another part of the same building which is not used exclusively as part of the dwelling shall resist the transmission of airborne sound.	
Airborne sound (floors and stairs) E 2. A floor or a stair which separates a dwelling from another dwelling, or from another part of the same building which is not used exclusively as part of the dwelling, shall resist the transmission of airborne sound.	
Impact sound (floors and stairs) E 3. A floor or a stair above a dwelling which separates it from another dwelling, or from another part of the same building which is not used exclusively as part of the dwelling shall resist the transmission of impact sound.	

Performance

This states that the requirements will be met if the relevant parts of the dwelling are designed and built in such a way that noise from normal domestic activities in an adjoining dwelling or other building is kept down to a level that will not threaten the health of the occupants of the dwelling and will allow them to sleep, rest and engage in normal domestic activities in satisfactory conditions.

0.1   The introduction to the provisions explains the basic considerations which have to be taken into account when dealing with sound insulation. Sections 1, 2, 3 and 4 give guidance on constructions in relation to new buildings and Sections 5 and 6 relate to conversion work.

0.2   The Approved Document describes three methods to demonstrate compliance:

(1)   By adopting the widely used forms of construction in Sections 1, 2 and 5;

(2)   By using a construction similar to one that has been shown by test to comply (Sections 3 and 6);

(3)   By testing a part of the construction (Sections 4 and 6).

Compliance of completed work can be demonstrated by a field test (Section 6).

Introduction to the provisions

0.3/0.5 There are two types of sound source: (1) airborne, such as speech and musical instruments and (2) impact, such as footsteps, moving of furniture etc.

An airborne source sets up vibrations in the air, which in turn cause the surrounding elements to vibrate. An impact causes the element to vibrate directly. These vibrations are passed on to adjoining elements in contact with them. All these elements cause the air in adjoining spaces to vibrate and thus noise is transferred. To achieve insulation this flow of energy, either direct or indirect (flanking) must be restricted.

Direct transmission

0.6/0.10 The factors affecting airborne sound transmission are as follows:

O   Mass: heavy materials are less easily vibrated. The figures given for mass will be minimum levels.

O   Stiffness or damping: this resists vibration and turns sound energy into heat. Thin walls made from materials of differing mechanical properties may need different mass to achieve the same result. Cavity walls may need at least as much mass as solid walls because of their lowr stiffness.

O   Structural isolation by means of cavities or resilient layers; timber framed walls rely almost entirely on isolation and are much lighter than masonry.

O   The avoidance of airpaths, including those due to shrinkage: porous materials and gaps must be sealed.

O   Avoidance of resonance, the phenomenon which occurs when a membrane vibrates at the same frequency (pitch) as the sound source, which reinforces the source itself (what happens in an organ pipe).

Impact sound transmission is reduced by using a soft covering or an upper layer isolated by a porous spongy material (floating layer) in which case it is important to avoid rigid bridges. Such isolation also assists in reducing airborne sound transmission.

Flanking transmission (diagram [5.1])

0.11/0.13 This happens when there is a path along which sound can travel between elements on opposite sides of a wall or floor. The path may be through solid structure or via an airspace (such as the cavity of an external wall). The structural paths are usually important with solid masonry elements and airspace paths with thin panels (such as studding or ceilings) in which the structural waves do not travel so freely.

Thus the mass of masonry flanking elements is also important unless it is divided into small areas by windows or other openings, in which case vibration will be reduced. Minimum mass may also be needed for thin panels connected by airspaces, such as ceilings below roof spaces. The mass required will be less if the air path is blocked by non porous material.

Conversion work

0.14   Although it is desirable to apply the same level to conversion work as to new work, the improvement of resistance to flanking sound transmission in conversions is often impracticable. The constructions and test procedures suggested for conversion work acknowledge that the sound insulation achieved may not equal that for a new building.

0.13 **[5.1]** *Direct and flanking transmission.*

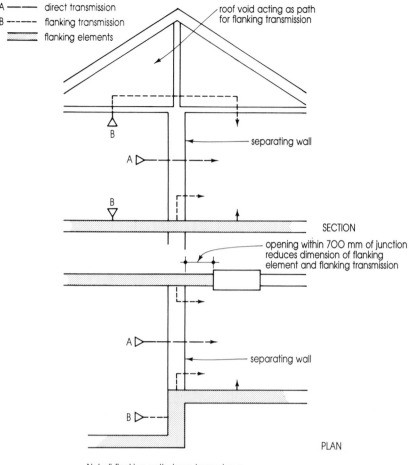

A ——— direct transmission
B ------- flanking transmission
▨▨▨ flanking elements

roof void acting as path
for flanking transmission

separating wall

SECTION

opening within 700 mm of junction
reduces dimension of flanking
element and flanking transmission

separating wall

PLAN

Not all flanking paths have been shown

Special factors
0.15　　The presence of steps or staggers between adjacent dwellings improves the insulation and needs to be considered. Careless detailing or workmanship can easily reduce the insulation.

NEW BUILDING

Section 1　Separating walls for new building

The actual requirement is that 'the wall shall resist the transmission of airborne sound' (diagram [5.2]).

E 1 **[5.2]** *Walls in dwellings which must be sound resisting.*

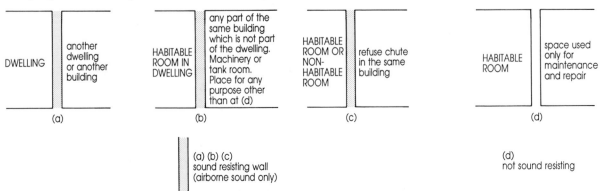

DWELLING	another dwelling or another building						

(a)

HABITABLE ROOM IN DWELLING | any part of the same building which is not part of the dwelling. Machinery or tank room. Place for any purpose other than at (d)

(b)

HABITABLE ROOM OR NON-HABITABLE ROOM | refuse chute in the same building

(c)

HABITABLE ROOM | space used only for maintenance and repair

(d)

(a) (b) (c)
sound resisting wall
(airborne sound only)

(d)
not sound resisting

1.2 **[5.3]** *Types of wall.*

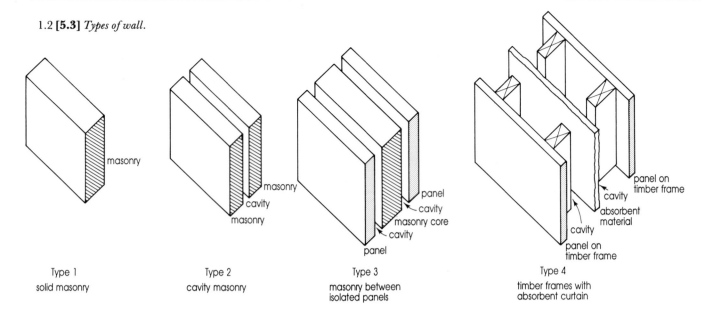

Type 1
solid masonry

Type 2
cavity masonry

Type 3
masonry between
isolated panels

Type 4
timber frames with
absorbent curtain

1.1   Four types of wall are described (diagram [5.3]):

Type 1   Solid masonry: resistance to airborne sound depends mainly on the mass of the wall.

Type 2   Cavity masonry: resistance depends on mass of the leaves and isolation.

Type 3   Masonry core with freestanding panels: resistance depends partly on mass and type of core and partly on isolation and mass of the panels.

Type 4   Timber frame and absorbent curtain: resistance depends on the mass of leaves' isolation and absorption of sound in the airspace between.

1.2   For each type there is a selection of specifications. Attention must be paid to all details of the walls themselves and junctions with other elements. These are diagrammatically illustrated separately for each type, which involves a lot of repetition. In this guide therefore new diagrams are used which illustrate the general principles, many of which are the same for all four types, with additional notes or sketches to define the differences where these occur. All the information is still there, but should the user wish to refer solely to a single type use, the Approved Document itself may be preferred.

Refuse chutes

1.3   There are special rules for these illustrated in diagram [5.4].

1.3 **[5.4]** *Wall separating refuse chute from habitable room and other rooms.*

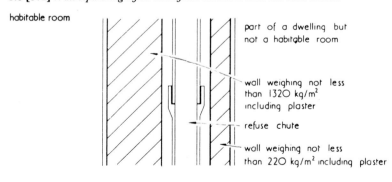

habitable room

part of a dwelling but not a habitable room

wall weighing not less than 1320 kg/m² including plaster

refuse chute

wall weighing not less than 220 kg/m² including plaster

Mass of masonry walls   **1.4/1.6**   A means of determining mass is given in Appendix A. The density of any particular material may be taken from a current Agrément certificate, a European Technical Approval or from the manufacturer in which case the Building Control Authority may ask for confirmation.

Diagrams

In the diagrams [5.5–5.8] measurements and weights are written simply in figures and so:

(*a*)   All references to dimensions are in millimetres.

(*b*)   All references to mass of walls and floors are in kg/m².

(*c*)   All references to density are in kg/m³.

Diagrams [5.9] and [5.10] show sectionally the general principle for the types of wall.

[5.5] *Walls: Type 1. Solid masonry.*

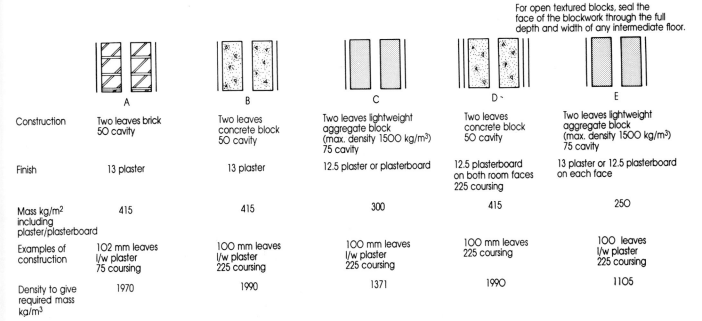

	A. brickwork	B. concrete block	C. brickwork	D. concrete block	E. concrete (in situ or panel) (min. density 1500)
Core	A. brickwork	B. concrete block	C. brickwork	D. concrete block	E. concrete (in situ or panel)
Finish	Plaster 13	Plaster 13	plasterboard 12.5 (any normal fixing method)	plasterboard 12.5 (any normal fixing method)	(min. density 1500) optional
Mass kg/m² including plaster/plasterboard	375	415	375	415	415
Examples of construction	215 brick l/w plaster 75 coursing	215 block l/w plaster 110 coursing	215 brick 75 coursing	215 block 150 coursing	190 unplastered
Density kg/m³ to give required mass	1610	1840	1610	1840	2200

Points to watch
1. Fill and seal all joints with mortar, to achieve the mass and avoid air paths.
2. Lay bricks frog up and in a bond including headers.
3. Blocks should extend to full thickness of wall.
4. Control sound paths around wall to reduce flanking transmission.

These constructions will give suitable resistance to direct transmission
NOTE   Plasterboard includes wall lining laminates of plasterboard and mineral wool.

[5.6] *Walls: Type 2. Cavity masonry.*

Additional constructions only where a step and/or stagger of at least 300 mm is used.

For open textured blocks, seal the face of the blockwork through the full depth and width of any intermediate floor.

	A	B	C	D	E
Construction	Two leaves brick 50 cavity	Two leaves concrete block 50 cavity	Two leaves lightweight aggregate block (max. density 1500 kg/m³) 75 cavity	Two leaves concrete block 50 cavity	Two leaves lightweight aggregate block (max. density 1500 kg/m³) 75 cavity
Finish	13 plaster	13 plaster	12.5 plaster or plasterboard	12.5 plasterboard on both room faces 225 coursing	13 plaster or 12.5 plasterboard on each face
Mass kg/m² including plaster/plasterboard	415	415	300	415	250
Examples of construction	102 mm leaves l/w plaster 75 coursing	100 mm leaves l/w plaster 225 coursing	100 mm leaves l/w plaster 225 coursing	100 mm leaves 225 coursing	100 leaves l/w plaster 225 coursing
Density to give required mass kg/m³	1970	1990	1371	1990	1105

Points to watch
1. Fill masonry joints with mortar with frog up.
2. Maintain cavity to underside of roof.
3. Connect leaves only where necessary for structural reasons.
4. Use only butterfly pattern ties, spaced as for structural requirements*
5. If external walls are to be filled with an insulating material, other than loose wool, the
   insulating material should be prevented from entering the cavity in the separating wall
   by a resilient (eg mineral wool) cavity closer.
*BS 5628:Part 3:1985 limits this type and spacing of tie to cavities 50–75 mm wide with
   minimum masonry leaf thickness of 90 mm

[5.7] *Walls: Type 3. Masonry between isolated panels.*

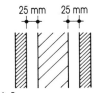

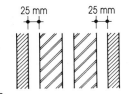

A, B
Masonry core (300 kg/m²)
Isolated panel each side
Min air space between
panels and core — 25 mm.
A. Brick. B. Concrete block

C
Lightweight concrete
(max. density 1500 kg/m3)
Mass 160 kg/m2

D
Cavity brickwork or blockwork
Two leaves brickwork or concrete
blockwork each leaf 100 mm thick
cavity 50 mm.
Only butterfly type wall ties should
be used

E
Two sheets plasterboard
joined by cellular core
Mass (inc. plaster finish
if used) 18 kg/m²
Fix to ceiling and floor only
Tape joints between panels

F
Two sheets plasterboard
with joints staggered
Each sheet 12.5 mm thick
if supporting framework
used.
Total thickness 30 mm if
no framework

Examples   A. 215 core
               75 mm coursing
               Density of
               brick
               1290 kg/m³

B. 140 core
    110 mm coursing
    Density of
    block
    2200 kg/m³

C. 200 core
    225 mm coursing
    Density of
    block
    730 kg/m³

Points to watch
1. Fill masonry joints with mortar, brick frogs up
2. Support panels only from floor to ceiling
3. Panels not to be fixed or tied to masonry core

[5.8] *Walls: Type 4. Timber frames with absorbent curtain.*

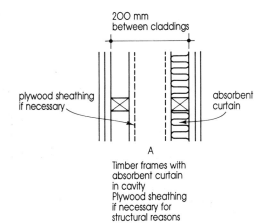
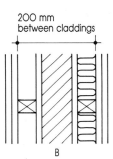

A
Timber frames with
absorbent curtain
in cavity
Plywood sheathing
if necessary for
structural reasons

B
Timber frames, masonry
core. Absorbent curtain
in cavity
Framing to be clear of core

NOTES
C. Masonry core: May be of any type but core connected to only one frame.
D. Cladding: On each side: two or more layers of plasterboard
                   Combined thickness 30 mm joints staggered
E. Absorbent curtain: Unfaced mineral fibre batts or quilt
                   (may be wire reinforced)
                   Density at least 12 kg/m³
       Thickness: 25 mm if suspended in cavity between frames
                   50 mm if fixed to one frame
                   25 mm per quilt if one fixed to each frame

Points to watch
1. Frames to be connected only if necessary for structural reasons
2. Use as few ties as possible. 14–16 gauge (40 mm x 30 mm) metal
   straps fixed at or just below ceiling level
3. Avoid penetration by services. Power points may be set in if
   cladding is repeated behind recess. They should not be back to back.

[5.9] *Section: general principle for all types. See diagram [5.10] for types 3 and 4 special details.*

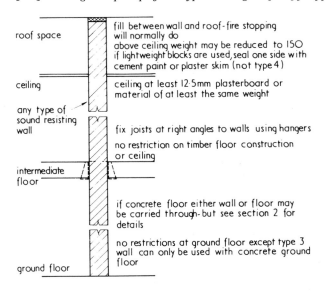

roof space — fill between wall and roof-fire stopping will normally do
above ceiling weight may be reduced to 150 if lightweight blocks are used, seal one side with cement paint or plaster skim (not type 4)

ceiling — ceiling at least 12·5mm plasterboard or material of at least the same weight

any type of sound resisting wall

fix joists at right angles to walls using hangers

no restriction on timber floor construction or ceiling

intermediate floor

if concrete floor either wall or floor may be carried through-but see section 2 for details

no restrictions at ground floor except type 3 wall can only be used with concrete ground floor

ground floor

1. Lightweight blocks are those with a density less than $1200 \, \text{kg/m}^3$.
2. It is not recommended that joists are built in, but where they are extreme care must be taken to avoid air paths through the construction.

NOTE   Although there was an attempt to harmonise the England and Wales regulations with those for Northern Ireland and Scotland which came into force before this Approved Document it is only in this document that building in of joists meets the provisions.

[5.10] *Section: details special to types 3 and 4.*

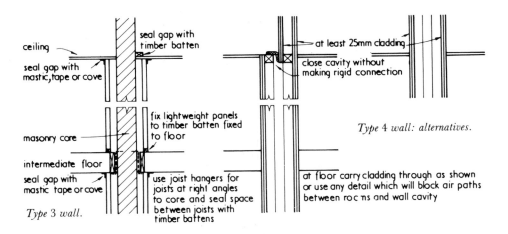

ceiling

seal gap with mastic, tape or cove

seal gap with timber batten

masonry core

fix lightweight panels to timber batten fixed to floor

intermediate floor

seal gap with mastic tape or cove

Type 3 wall.

use joist hangers for joists at right angles to core and seal space between joists with timber battens

at least 25mm cladding

close cavity without making rigid connection

Type 4 wall: alternatives.

at floor carry cladding through as shown or use any detail which will block air paths between rooms and wall cavity

Plans of junctions between separating walls of the four types with external walls are set out in diagrams [5.11] and [5.12] and the details are also tabulated in Tables 1 and 2.
Further details are given in diagrams [5.13] and [5.14].

NOTES   The guidance regarding the mass and nature of the external wall (solid or inner leaf) appear somewhat confused. Generally it would seem desirable that they should have a mass at least $120 \, \text{kg/m}^2$, but the following exceptions are mentioned.
○   In Type 1 walls, if the external wall (or inner leaf) has a mass less than 120, openings should be at least 1 m high and no more than 700 mm from the face of the SR wall.
○   In Type 2 walls (except for specification B) the weight of the inner leaf should be at least 120.

[5.11] *Junction: external wall/separating wall. Type 1.*

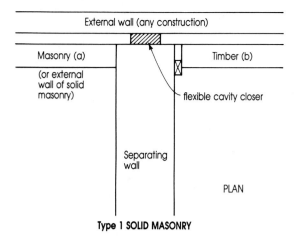

Type 1 SOLID MASONRY

Masonry
(a) 1. walls to be bonded together
      or
    2. masonry of external wall to abut separating wall and tied
    3. ties ≯ 300 centres and masonry to have mass of 120 kg/m²
    4. if mass < 120 kg/m² then length of external wall limited by openings
       i   not less than 1 m high
       ii on both sides of the separating wall at every storey and
       iii not more than 700 mm from the face of the separating wall on both
           sides with cavity closer between
Timber
(b) 5. should abut separating wall
    6. ties ≯ 300 centres vertically
    7. joints sealed with tape or caulking

NOTE A short length of wall will not vibrate strongly at low frequencies to cause
      flanking transmissions
      No restrictions on partitions

[5.12] *Type 2.*

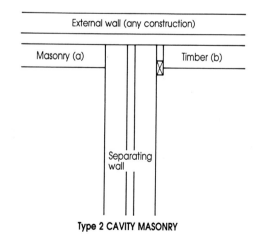

Type 2 CAVITY MASONRY

1. As for solid masonry

2. As for solid masonry
3. As for solid masonry
4. Mass of masonry should be 120 kg/m²
   No minimum mass if separating wall is Type B

5, 6 and 7. As for timber in solid masonry

NOTE The cavity in the separating wall should not be sealed in any material
      which connects the leaves together rigidly.
      Mineral wool is acceptable
      No restriction on partitions

[5.13] *Junction: external wall/separating wall. Type 3.*

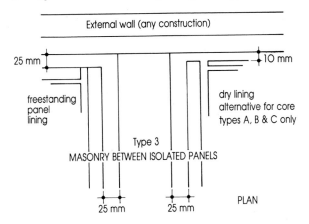

External wall (any construction)

25 mm — 10 mm

freestanding panel lining

dry lining alternative for core types A, B & C only

Type 3
MASONRY BETWEEN ISOLATED PANELS

25 mm   25 mm   PLAN

1. Inner leaf of a cavity wall should have internal finish of isolated panels as specified for separating wall except where core of separating wall has core A, B or C, when plaster or dry lining (with joints sealed with tape or caulking)
2. Insulation may be added but 25 mm & 10 mm gaps should be maintained
3. Inner leaf may be of any construction if dry lined with isolated panels
4. If inner leaf is plastered or dry lined, it must have mass of $\leqslant$ 120 kg/m² and butt jointed to the separating wall core with ties at 300 mm centres vertically

PARTITIONS:
Partitions abutting a type 3 separating wall must not be of masonry construction. Other loadbearing partitions should be fixed to the masonry core through continuous pad of mineral wool. Non loadbearing partitions should be tight butted to the isolated panels and all joints sealed with tape or caulking

[5.14] *Type 4.*

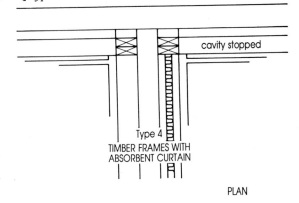

cavity stopped

Type 4
TIMBER FRAMES WITH
ABSORBENT CURTAIN

PLAN

1. If external wall of cavity construction, seal cavity between ends of separating wall and outer leaf
2. Internal finish should be 12.5 mm plasterboard or equally heavy material

PARTITIONS:
No restrictions on partitions

[5.15] *Stepped and staggered construction: plan and elevation.*
Limiting pathways between elements on opposite sides of SR wall.

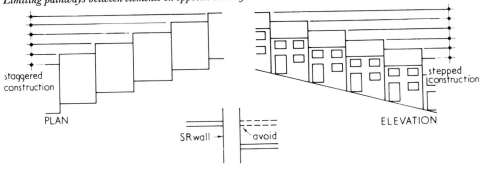

staggered construction

PLAN

SR wall   avoid

stepped construction

ELEVATION

Table 1   Junctions with roofs and floors

Junctions with	Wall Type 1	Wall Type 2	Wall Type 3	Wall Type 4
ROOF	Firestop joint – wall/roof	As for Type 1	Firestop joint – masonry core/roof	As for Type 1
ROOF SPACE AND CEILING	12.5 mm minimum ceiling Mass of wall above – can be reduced to 150 kg/m^2	As for Type 1 but cavity should be maintained As for Type 1	As for Type 1 (or Type 2) and free-standing panels omitted in roof space	(a) carry both frames through to underside of roof finish – cladding on each side may be reduced to at least 25 mm (b) close cavity at ceiling level without connecting frames together Use one frame with at least 25 mm cladding both sides Seal frame/roof finish by firestopping
	Open-textured lightweight aggregate block for wall – one side to be sealed – cement paint or plaster skim		As for Type 1 Junction-ceiling/panels seal with tape or caulking Maintain cavity	
INTERMEDIATE FLOORS	*Timber floor* Joists supported on hangers or built in	As for Type 1	Joist hangers for joists supported on wall Seal spaces between joints with full depth timber blocking	Carry cladding through floor or use solid timber edge to floor Where joints at right angle to wall, seal spaces with full-depth timber blocking
	Concrete floor If Type 1 or 2 (see Section 2) ie concrete base with either soft covering or floating layer, wall or floor may be carried through	Floor carried through only to cavity face of each leaf	Floor base carried through only if mass at least 365 kg/m^2 Seal junction – ceiling/ panel with tape or caulking Cavity not to be bridged	
GROUND FLOOR	*Suspended* As intermediate floors	*Suspended* As intermediate floors	*Suspended* Mass at least 365 kg/m^2	*Suspended* As wall Type 3
	Slab As above	*Slab* May be continuous	*Slab* Solid slab laid on ground	*Slab* As wall Type 3

In Type 1 the notes state 'Control sound paths around the wall (to reduce flanking transmission)'. What this means is not entirely clear, but it may suggest that where possible walls or partitions abutting the SR wall on each side should be staggered (see diagram [5.15]).
○   In Type 2 walls there is mention of 'step and stagger' situations. These are not explained but no doubt refer to the type of arrangement shown in diagram [5.15].

Table 2 Junctions with walls

Junctions with	Wall Type 1	Wall Type 2	Wall Type 3	Wall Type 4
EXTERNAL WALL SOLID MASONRY	As for inner leaf below	N/A	N/A	N/A
OUTER LEAF OF CAVITY WALL	Any construction	Any construction	Any construction	–
INNER LEAF OR MASONRY	Masonry bonded together OR Masonry of external wall should abut separating wall and be tied with ties at max. 300 mm centres vertically creating a homogeneous unit and masonry mass of 120 kg/m² unless length of the external wall is limited by openings (i) not less than 1 metre high (ii) on both sides of the separating wall at every storey and (iii) not more than 700 mm from the face of the separating wall on both sides with a cavity closer between	As for Type 1 and masonry mass of 120 kg/m² except where separating wall Type B is used where there is no minimum required mass Cavity in separating wall stopped with material such as mineral wool.	INNER LEAF OF ANY CONSTRUCTION (if lined with isolated panels) Panels as specified for the separating wall for core C. Core A, B and D, plaster or dry lining with sealed joints may be used. Insulation may be added to the internal finish but 25 mm and 10 mm gaps should be maintained. If inner leaf is dry lined or plastered, masonry must have mass of 120 kg/m² butt jointed to the core with ties at max. 300 mm centres vertically	
INNER LEAF OF TIMBER	Abut separating wall tied with ties at max. 300 mm centres Joints sealed with tape or caulking	As for Type 1	–	No restrictions on timber framed wall. If of cavity construction cavities to be sealed between ends of separating wall and outer leaf. Internal finish to be 12.5 mm plasterboard or equivalent
PARTITIONS	No restrictions	No restrictions	Must not be of masonry. Other loadbearing partitions should be fixed to masonry core through continuous pad of mineral wool. Non-loadbearing panels should be tight butted to the panels. All joints should be sealed	No restrictions

Section 2   Separating floors for new building

The requirements are that floors shall resist the transmission of airborne sound (E 2) and if the floor is above the dwelling, shall also resist impact sound (E 3).

2.1   There are the same limitations as for walls and diagram [5.16] illustrates exactly which floors must be sound-resistant.

E 2/E 3 **[5.16]** *Floors in dwellings which must be sound resisting.*

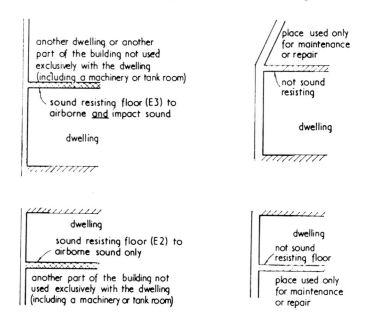

2.1/2.2   Three types of floor are illustrated:

Type 1   Concrete base with soft covering: resistance to airborne sound depends on the mass of the base and on eliminating air paths. The soft covering reduces sound at source. This type, and this type only, may be used without the soft covering if only resistance to airborne sound is required. The other two types cannot be changed.

Type 2   Concrete base with floating layer: resistance to airborne sound depends on the mass of both the base and the floating layer, which also reduces the transmission of impact sound to the base and to adjacent construction.

Type 3   Timber base and floating layer: resistance to airborne sound depends on the mass of the base (especially type C with pugging) and of the floating layer, which also reduces the transmission of impact sound. This type needs less weight because the materials are softer and radiate sound less efficiently.

The following diagrams show several specifications for each type, identifying features requiring special attention and illustrate suitable details for junctions with walls and pipe penetrations. As with walls the diagrams in the guide have been redrawn to illustrate the general principles, together with details of individual circumstances.

Mass of floors

2.3/2.5   This is expressed in kg/m^2. The density of the materials used on which these depend is in kg/m^3. These may be taken from a current Agrément certificate, a European Technical Approval or the manufacturers (in which case the Building Control Authority may require confirmation).

Floors: Type 1: Concrete base with soft covering

The resistance to airborne sound depends on the mass of the concrete base and the elimination of air paths. Impact sound at source is reduced by the soft covering. Where resistance to *airborne sound only* is required, the soft covering may be omitted.

No other part of the construction should be omitted. All joints between parts of the floor should be filled to avoid air paths and sound paths around the floor should be controlled to reduce flanking transmission.

At the perimeter and where the floor is penetrated by a pipe or duct, detailing and workmanship should be given special attention to avoid air paths and to reduce flanking transmission.
Diagrams
In diagrams [5.17] – [5.23] the same conventions apply as for walls.

[5.17] *Floors: Type 1. Concrete base; soft covering. In each case the mass of the base floor including any floor screed or ceiling finish bonded to the floor to be at least 365. All joints to be filled.*

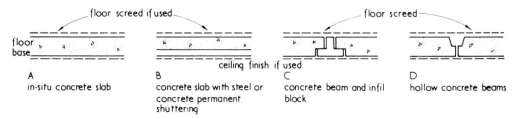

A
in-situ concrete slab

B
concrete slab with steel or concrete permanent shuttering

C
concrete beam and infil block

D
hollow concrete beams

Soft covering: use resilient material or material with a resilient base; thickness including any backing to be at least 4.5.

Suitable resilience will also be provided by a floor covering with a weighted impact sound improvement

(ΔL_W) *of not less than 17 dB. Use annex A to BS 5821: Part 2: 1984 for calculating the* ΔL_W.

The soft covering should be bonded to the floor base. (Resilient material is one which returns to its former thickness after compression.)

[5.18] *Type 2: concrete base; floating layer.*
Floor base: the same four types (A–D) illustrated in Type 1 may be used, but in each case the mass including any screed or the ceiling finish should be at least 300.

Floating layer: two types may be used: see below.

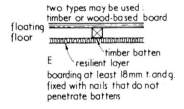

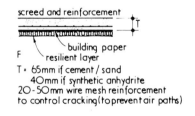

Resilient layer:
G flexible material. 25 mm minimum mineral fibre, density at least 36 kg/m³ laid tightly butted, and turned up at edges.

13 mm mineral fibre if battens have an integral closed cell resilient foam strip.

NOTE   Under a timber raft, fibre may be paper faced on the underside. Under a screed, fibre should be paper faced on upper side. Should not be combined with

batten and plasterboard suspended ceiling – may resonate and reduce sound insulation.

H Board material (to be used only with screed type F) – 13 mm pre-compressed expanded polystyrene (impact sound duty grade) laid tightly butted. Use on edge at edges of floating screed.

I 5 mm extruded (closed cell polyethylene foam, density 30–45 kg/m³. Lay over levelling screed to protect from puncture, lap joints and run up at edges of floating screed.

Combination: any of the four bases can be combined with either of the floating layers.

[5.19] *Type 3: timber base; floating layer.*

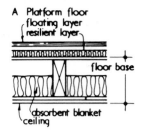

A Platform floor
floating layer
resilient layer
floor base
absorbent blanket
ceiling

All sizes and weights are minima.

Floating layer: 18 thick t and g timber or wood-based board with all joints glued, spot bonded to substrate of 19 thick plasterboard or material of the same weight or two thicknesses of cement bonded particle board with joints staggered, glued and screwed together, total thickness 24 mm.

Resilient layer: 25 thick mineral fibre of density 80–100 kg/m³. (Note. the low figure gives the best insulation but a 'softer' floor.)

Floor base: 12 thick timber or wood-based board nailed to joists, ceiling 30 plasterboard in two layers, joints staggered.

Absorbent material 100 thick 10 kg/m³ laid on ceiling. Unfaced rock fibre.

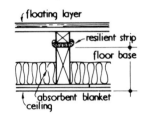

B Ribbed floor with absorbent blanket
floating layer
resilient strip
floor base
absorbent blanket
ceiling

Floating layer: 18 thick timber or wood-based board with tongued and grooved edges and all joints glued, spot bonded to substrate of 19 thick plasterboard or material of the same mass nailed to 45 × 45 timber battens, placed on the joists.

Resilient strip: 25 thick mineral fibre of density 80–140 kg/m³ (see note to Type C below).

Floor base: 45 (nom) wide joists, ceiling 30 plasterboard in two layers; joints staggered. Absorbent blanket as for Type A.

Take care nails do not penetrate through battens into resilient strip (also applies to C).

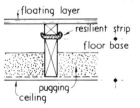

C Ribbed floor with heavy pugging
floating layer
resilient strip
floor base
pugging
ceiling

Floating layer: 18 thick t and g or wood-based board (joints glued) nailed to 45 × 45 battens.

Resilient strip: as for B but density stated as 80–140 kg/m³ (a fine distinction which seems a little pointless).

Floor base: 45 side joists; ceiling 19 thick dense plaster on expanded metal.

Pugging: of traditional ash (75 mm); whin aggregate (60 mm); dry sand (50 mm); thicknesses shown will achieve 80 kg/m². Do not use pugging where it may become wet and overload the ceiling.

Ceiling: Either 19 dense plaster on expanded metal lath or 6 plywood fixed under joists plus 2 layers plasterboard, staggered joints 25 thick.

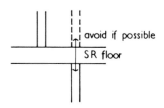

avoid if possible
SR floor

NOTE
In all three types limit the pathways between elements on opposite sides of the floor (to avoid flanking transmission).

[5.20] *Wall and floor junctions – floor Type 1*

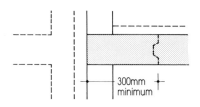

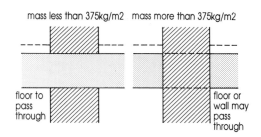

mass less than 375kg/m2   mass more than 375kg/m2

floor to pass through

floor or wall may pass through

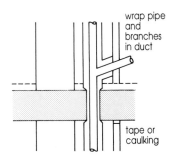

wrap pipe and branches in duct

tape or caulking

[5.21] *Wall and floor junctions – floor Type 2*

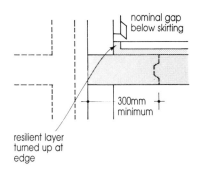

nominal gap below skirting

300mm minimum

resilient layer turned up at edge

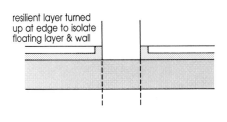

resilient layer turned up at edge to isolate floating layer & wall

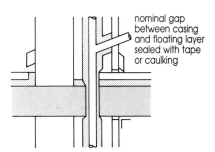

nominal gap between casing and floating layer sealed with tape or caulking

[5.22] *Wall and floor junctions – floor Type 3*

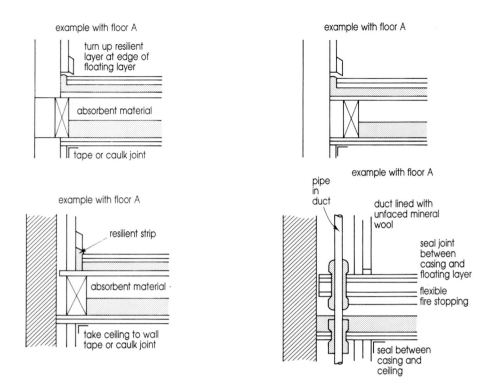

example with floor A

turn up resilient
layer at edge of
floating layer

absorbent material

tape or caulk joint

example with floor A

example with floor A

resilient strip

absorbent material

take ceiling to wall
tape or caulk joint

example with floor A

pipe
in
duct

duct lined with
unfaced mineral
wool

seal joint
between
casing and
floating layer

flexible
fire stopping

seal between
casing and
ceiling

[5.23] *Independent leaf and absorbent material.*

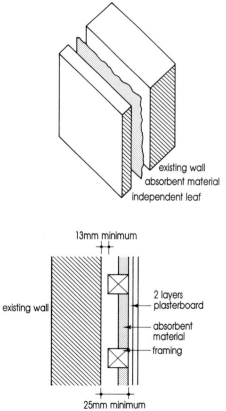

existing wall
absorbent material
independent leaf

13mm minimum

existing wall

2 layers
plasterboard

absorbent
material

framing

25mm minimum

Floors: Type 2: Concrete base with floating layer

Airborne sound resistance depends mainly on the mass of the concrete base and partly on the mass of the floating layer. Impact sound resistance is achieved by the resilient layer isolating the floating layer from the base and from the surrounding construction.

Where resistance to airborne sound only is required, the full construction should still be used. Similar remarks to those made for floor Type 1 apply to detailing and workmanship. Care should also be taken not to create a bridge between the floating layer and the base, surrounding walls, or adjacent screeds.

A screed should be laid on bases C and D to accommodate surface irregularities.

Floors: Type 3: Timber base with floating layer

Airborne sound resistance depends partly on the structural floor with absorbent blanket or pugging and partly on the floating layer. Impact sound resistance is achieved by the resilient layer isolating the floating layer from the base and surrounding construction.

Where resistance to *airborne sound only* is required, the full construction should be used.

Special attention should be given to detail and workmanship as mentioned for floor Types 1 and 2 and the floating layer and the base of surrounding walls should not be bridged.

Movement of materials should be allowed for, eg expansion of chipboard after laying.

Junctions

Details of junctions with floor types 1, 2 and 3 are shown in diagrams [5.20], [5.21] and [5.22] and Table 3 (p. 232).

The methods to be used when pipes penetrate separating floors are also illustrated.

NOTE The Gas (Safety) Regulations contain requirements for ventilation of ducts at each floor where they contain gas pipes.

Section 3 Similar construction method for new building

3.1   This method depends on repeating as closely as possible an existing construction which has been tested under paragraphs 3.5/3.7 and which achieved the sound transmission values given in Table 4.

It will be necessary to provide evidence of values achieved and similarly of construction.

3.2   Sound insulation between rooms on either side of a separating wall or floor depends on the wall or floor construction and size and shape of rooms. Doors and windows in masonry walls may affect flanking transmission dependent upon their position. 'Floor' includes stairs which perform the same separating function.

Conditions on the use of a similar construction

3.3   Similar features

(*a*)   Separating walls and floors (SW and SF). The following should be similar but not necessarily identical –

construction of SW and SF – mass not reduced;

construction of other walls and floors adjacent to SW and SF;

shape and size of rooms adjacent to SW and SF;

arrangement of windows and doors in external walls of masonry inner leaf adjacent to SW and SF.

(*b*)   Separating walls only.

Extent of step and stagger.

If there is none in tested construction one may be provided in proposed construction.

Allowable differences

3.4(*a*)   For SW and SF

Construction of outer or inner leaf of masonry cavity wall provided that the inner leaf is of the same general type and its mass is not reduced.

(*b*)   For SW only

The floating layer of a floor with a concrete or timber base. (Floor Type 2, Section 2).

Timber floor which is not a separating floor.

Table 3   Separating floors – junctions

	Floor Type 1	*Floor Type 2*
EXTERNAL WALL OR CAVITY SEPARATING WALL	External wall with openings at least 20% of its area in each room – no requirement. Otherwise mass including finish to be 120 kg/m^2	As for Type 1
Floor base	excluding any screed should pass through leaf whether spanning at right angles or parallel to wall	As for Type 1
Cavity	not to be bridged	As for Type 1
Floor base Type C or D	if beams parallel to wall. First joist to be 30 mm from cavity face of wall leaf	As for Type 1, but carry resilient layer up all edges to isolate floating layer. Leave gap between skirting and floating layer or turn under skirting. Use flexible seals
INTERNAL WALLS	If mass less than 375 mm including finishes – floor base except screed should pass through. If mass more than 375 mm – either the wall (excluding finishes) or floorbase should pass through.	As for Type 1
	Where wall passes through – floor base tied and grouted to wall	As for Type 1
PENETRATIONS	Ducts or pipes in enclosure. Mass of enclosure – 15 kg/m^2. Line enclosure or wrap duct or pipe within enclosure with 25 mm unfaced mineral wool	As for Type 1 but leave nominal gap between enclosure and floor and seal with acrylic caulking or neoprene
	Fire protect to AD B.	As for Type 1
	Fire stopping to be flexible – no rigid contact between pipe and floor	As for Type 1
TIMBER FRAME WALL	Seal gap between wall and floating layer with resilient strip glued to wall. Leave 3 mm gap between skirting and floating layer. Block airpaths between floor base and wall including space between joists. Seal junction of wall and ceiling lining with tape etc when joists are at right angles to the wall	
HEAVY MASONRY WALL	Mass of leaf (including finish) 375 kg/m^2 both above and below floor. Seal gap between wall and floating layer with resilient strip. Leave 3 mm gap between skirting and floating layer. Seal not necessary but if used should be flexible. Connect floor base to wall with any normal method. Seal junction of wall and ceiling lining with tape etc.	
LIGHT MASONRY LEAF	Use freestanding panel as in *Wall Type 3* if mass is less than 375 kg/m^2. Seal gap between panel and floating layer with resilient strip. Leave 3 mm gap between skirting and floating layer. Seal not necessary but if used should be flexible. Connect floor base to wall with any normal method but block air paths between floor and wall cavities. Take ceiling through to masonry. Seal junction with freestanding panel with tape etc.	
FLOOR PENETRATIONS	Ducts or pipes penetrating floors separating habitable rooms to be in an enclosure both above and below the floor. Material of enclosure to be at least 15 kg/m^2. Leave 3 mm gap between enclosure and floating layer. Seal with acrylic caulking or neoprene. If specification A is used, floor may go down to floor base. Ensure isolation of enclosure from floating layer. Penetrations to be fire protected – See Approved Document B. Flexible fire stopping and prevent rigid contact between pipe and floor.	

Testing existing construction

3.5 Test method

Carry out the tests in accordance with:

BS 2750: Part 4: 1980 *Field measurements of airborne sound insulation*

and Part 7: 1980 *Field measurement of impact sound insulation* to determine the:

Standardised Level Difference D_{nT} for airborne sound and

Standardised Impact Sound Pressure Levels L'_{nT} for impact sound.

Tests should be conducted in completed but unfurnished dwellings. Doors and windows should be closed.

Each separating wall or floor should be tested with eight sets of measurements. Where eight pairs of rooms are not available, four pairs of rooms can be used.

Each set of measurements should:

(*a*) Use pairs of large rooms if possible.

(*b*) Use pairs consisting of a room and some other space only where necessary to make up the sets of four.

(*c*) Take only one set of measurements between each pair.

Airborne sound transmission should be measured with the sound source

– in the larger room if the rooms are of unequal volume;

– in the other space if between a room and some other space.

A test report should be provided which describes the performance of the existing construction and includes details, set out in Table 3.

From each set of measurements calculate:

(a) for airborne sound insulation, the weighted standardised level difference (D_{nTw}) in accordance with BS 5821: *Method for rating the sound insulation in buildings and building elements.* Part 1 1984 *Method for rating the airborne sound insulations in buildings and interior building elements*, or

(b) for impact sound transmission, the weighted standardised impact sound pressure level (L'_{nTw}) in accordance with BS 5821: Part 2: 1984 *Method for rating the impact sound insulation*

Assessment of results

3.6 *Separating walls and floors*

For airborne sound insulation individual values of the weighted standardised level difference (D_{nTw}) should be not less than that given in the individual value column in Table 4.

Separating floors

For impact sound transmission individual values of the weighted standardised impact sound pressure level (L'_{nTw}) should be not more than that given in the individual value column of Table 4.

Mean values

3.7 The arithmetic mean of calculated values should be no worse than that given in the appropriate 'mean value' column in Table 5. Where only two or three sets of measurements have been possible the mean value for up to four sets should still be achieved, and where only one set is possible the value achieved should be no worse than the mean value.

Limits on the use of test evidence

3.8 The test procedure is intended to enable satisfactory evidence to be provided by a person intending to use the method of similar construction and the values in Table 4 are provided to enable an existing construction to be assessed before new construction is undertaken. A failure of a new construction to achieve the values in the table is not in itself evidence of a failure to comply with the requirements of the Regulations.

Table 4   Test report details: test of existing construction

1. Organisation conducting test
   (a) name
   (b) address
   (c) NAMAS accreditation number (if appropriate)

2. Name of person in charge of test

3. Date of test

4. Address of building tested

5. Brief details of test
   (a) equipment
   (b) test procedures

6. Description of building
   (a) sketch showing relationship and dimensions of rooms tested
   (b) description of external and separating walls, partitions and floors including details of materials used for their construction and finishes
   (c) estimate of surface mass kg/m² of external and separating walls, partitions and floors.
   (d) dimensions of any step and stagger between rooms tested.
   (e) dimensions of any windows or doors within 700 mm of the separating wall

7. Results of test, shown in tabular and graphical form
   (a) single number rating
   (b) underlying data, from measurements on which the single number rating is based

Section 4   Test chamber evaluation – new construction

4.1   This section describes a way of meeting the functional requirements for walls by means of tests in an approved type of test chamber. BRE will give details of test chamber construction.
4.2   It has to be shown that the sound insulation between at least two pairs of rooms is not less than the prescribed value.

Test procedure
4.3   Insulation against airborne sound should be measured between the lower pair of rooms and between the upper pair of rooms as BS 2750: Part 4: 1980. Measurement is to be in the 1/3 octave bands between 100 Hz and 3150 Hz and standardised to a reverberation time of 0.5 s.

Sound insulation value required
4.4   The modified weighted standardised level difference value from each measurement should not be less than 55 dB. The modified weighted standardised level difference value is affected by room dimensions. To calculate, add constant K to the weighted standardised level difference value. So modified D_{nTw} =

$D_{nTw} + K$

$K = 10 \log_{10} (3/L) + 1$

L = metres – length of room perpendicular to the separating wall.

Limits on use of test results
4.5   The information contained in the test report should include:–
Name and where appropriate NAMAS accreditation number of organisations which operate the test chamber and which conduct the measurements.

Description of test chamber, details of test equipment and procedure.

Full details of materials used and of test construction.

Dates both of construction and tests.

The D_{nT} and the D_{nTw} and R'_w for each measurement according to BS 5821: Part 1: 1984.

The two modified D_{nTw} obtained by adding correction K.

A test report may be accepted as evidence tending to show compliance with the Regulations but is only valid for the specific type of construction tested. The following features may, however, be changed:

Dimensions of separating wall and flank wall;

Door or window openings may be positioned in the flank wall;

Internal partitions may be attached to the separating wall.

Table 5   Sound insulation values

Airborne sound test in up to four pairs of rooms
Minimum values of weighted standardised level different (D_{nTw}) as defined in BS 5821: Part 1: 1984:

	Mean value (dB)	Individual value (dB)
Walls	53	49
Floors	52	48

Impact sound
Maximum values of weighted standardised impact sound pressure level (L^1_{nTw}) as defined in BS 5821: Part : 1984:

	Mean value (dB)	Individual value (dB)
Floors	61	65

Airborne sound test in at least eight pairs of rooms
Minimum values of weighted standardised level different (D_{nTw}) as defined in BS 5821 Part 1: 1984:

	Mean value (dB)	Individual value (dB)
Walls	52	49
Floors	51	48

Impact sound
Maximum values of weighted standardised impact sound pressure level (L^1_{nTw}) as defined in BS 5821 Part 2: 1984:

	Mean value (dB)	Individual value (dB)
Floors	62	65

Section 5   Remedial work in conversions

Introduction

Part E has been extended to cover a material change of use to a dwelling including conversion to flats.

5.1   Some existing walls and floors of properties to be converted into flats may well meet the requirements for sound insulation. This would generally be the case where the constructions were similar to those shown in Sections 1 and 2 (for example, within 15% of the mass of a construction listed there) or was a type which met the test requirements of Section 6.

5.2   If it cannot be shown that the existing construction meets the sound insulation requirements then this section gives guidance on one wall treatment as well as guidance on three floor treatments and one stair treatment to improve the level of sound insulation.

Wall treatment 1 shows an independent leaf and absorbent material. Diagram [5.24].

The resistance to airborne sound depends on the form of the existing construction, the mass of the independent leaf, its isolation from the existing wall and the absorbent material.

Where the existing wall is at least 100 mm thick and plastered on both faces the construction can be used on one side only.

With other existing walls the construction should be built on both sides.

The independent leaf and its supporting frame should not be in contact with the existing wall and although the absorbent material may bridge the cavity it should not be tightly compressed.

Construction
Independent leaf
Two layers 12.5 mm plasterboard fixed to any type of framing or plasterboard lining of 30 mm thickness if not framework is used.

Joints should be staggered with a gap of at least 25 mm between the inside face of the plasterboard and the face of the existing wall.

There should also be a gap of at least 13 mm between the framing and the face of the existing wall.

Perimeter of independent leaf should be sealed with tape or mastic.

Absorbent material – mineral wool at least 25 mm thick with a density of at least 10 kg/m³.

Diagram [5.25] shows floor treatments 1, 2 and 3 which show respectively:
an independent ceiling with absorbent material;
a platform floor;
a raft floor.

[5.24] *Conversions – wall treatment 1, typical junction details.*

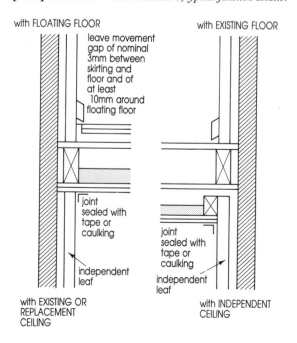

[5.25] *Conversions – floor treatments*

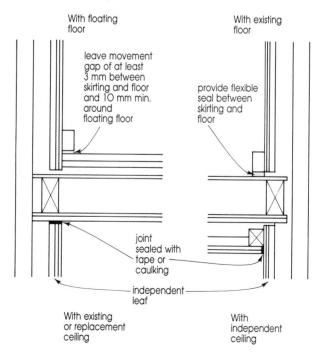

[5.26] *Stair treatment 1*

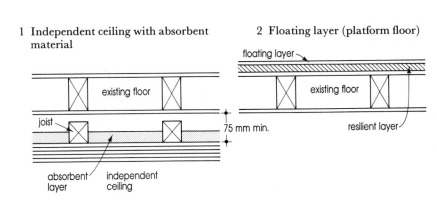

1 Independent ceiling with absorbent material

2 Floating layer (platform floor)

(a) NEW CEILING

Independent
2 layers plasterboard
Total thickness 30 mm
Joints staggered
≮ 75 mm below ex. ceiling
Fixed to independent joists

(b) TO BE SEALED

Perimeter of ind. ceiling

(c) EXISTING CEILING

If lath and plaster Retain if acceptable
for fire resistance
If replaced Use 2 layers plasterboard
≮ 30 mm thick overall with staggered
joints

If lath and plaster Retain if acceptable
for fire resistance
If replaced Use 2 layers plasterboard
as 1(c) with layer of 50 mm mineral
wool*

(d) ABSORBENT MATERIAL

Mineral wool
50 mm thick
Density 10 kg/m^3

(e) FLOATING LAYER

t and g boards or other boards 18 mm
thick with glued joints on substrate of
plasterboard ≮ 19 mm thick or single
layer of material having same mass

(f) RESILIENT LAYER

Mineral wool
25 mm thick
Density 80–100 kg/mm^3

(g) EXISTING FLOORING

If replaced Use boards ≮ 12 mm thick
with layer of 50 mm mineral wool
between joists*

(h) OTHER DETAILS OF
CONSTRUCTION

Leave 10 mm gap around floating
layer and fill with resilient material
Leave small gap between skirting
board and floating layer

3 Floating layer with absorbent material between joists (raft floor)

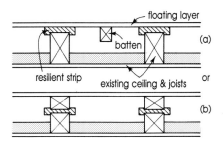

4 ALTERNATIVE independent ceiling with absorbent material

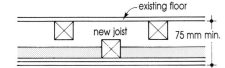

5 ALTERNATIVE floating layer (platform floor)

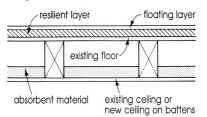

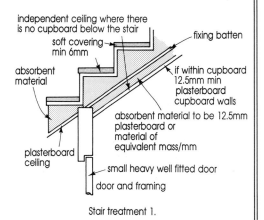

Stair treatment 1.

Independent
2 layers plasterboard
Total thickness 30 mm
Joints staggered
Ceiling may be supported on new ceiling joists or hangers $\not>$ thickness rather than 2 mm attached to original joists

Perimeter of ceiling

Perimeter of ceiling

Perimeter of ceiling

If lath and plaster Retain if possible.
If replaced use 2 layers plasterboard as 1(c)

If less than 25 mm thick Replace by at least 2 layers plasterboard as 1(c) supported from timber cross battens or suitable resilient hangers

Mineral wool
50 mm thick
Density 10 kg/m^3

Mineral wool
50 mm thick
Density 10 kg/m^3

Mineral wool
50 mm thick
(Need not be installed unless floorboards or ceilings are to be removed for other reasons)

t and g or other boards 18 mm thick nailed or screwed to battens $\not<$ 50 mm (nom) wide
Battens may run between or over the joists

t and g or other boards with glued joints

Resilient strips – mineral fibre
25 mm thick
Density 80–140 kg/m^3

Wool fibre insulation board
13 mm thick
(Ref. BS 1142:89

If replaced Use boarding at least 12 mm thick

If battens are run over joists the resilient strips should be between the battens and the joists
Leave gaps as 2(h)

Gaps in existing floor will necessitate covering floor with hardboard

Leave 10 mm gap around floating layer and fill with resilient material

[5.27] *Piped services – floor penetrations and casing*

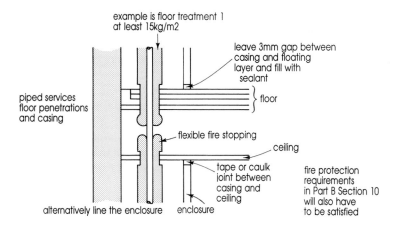

Where these are not practicable two further alternatives are given. These are similar to floor treatments 1 and 2 but in each case the change in ceiling to floor level will be smaller but the improvement in sound insulation will be less.

These disadvantages should be taken into account when considering construction methods.

Stair treatment 1 (see diagram [5.26]) can be used where a timber floor separates dwellings.

5.3　Upgrading measures will impose additional loads on the existing structure. The structure should be assessed to ensure that these loads can be safely carried out but appropriate strengthening may be necessary.

5.4　Old buildings sometimes contain architectural features such as cornices, decorative ceilings or floor coverings. When deciding what is reasonable the Approved Documents states that its guidance should be treated flexibly.

5.5　Piped services passing through separating floors in conversions to reduce sound insulation levels should be surrounded with sound absorbent material for their full height. See diagram [5.27].

Section 6　Field and laboratory tests

6.1　Tests may be carried out in the field or in a laboratory.

6.2　Better performance is required from laboratory tests because laboratory tests are made with minimal flanking transmission and when the building is used the insulation against airborne sounds may be lower.

6.3　For conversion work the following may be assumed:

Typical masonry wall　– half brick wall
　　　　　　　　　　　 – plastered both sides
　　　　　　　　　　　 – total mass not exceeding $200\,\mathrm{kg/m^2}$

Typical timber floor　– 22 mm plain edged boards and joists
　　　　　　　　　　　 – at 400 mm centres
　　　　　　　　　　　 – ceiling of lath and plaster or
　　　　　　　　　　　 – 30 mm plasterboard

6.4　The test results will only apply to remedial methods which are similar to those tested.

Field tests

Separating walls

6.5　Test in conjunction with at least two different half brick walls plastered both sides.

Test original walls alone and then with the remedial measure.

Provide both sets of results.

Tests to be conducted according to BS 2750: Part 4: 1980.

Calculate sound insulation values to BS 5821: Part 1: 1984.

Weighted standardised level difference achieved by both examples of combined wall and remedial measure should be not less than $D_{nTw} = 49\,\mathrm{dB}$.

Separating floors

6.6 Test two examples of the remedial measure.

If remedial measure uses parts of the original floor (other than the joints) test original floor alone and then with remedial measure.

Provide both sets of results.

If remedial measure replaces all the original floor elements (joists may be retained), test at least two typical installations.

6.7 Measure insulation against airborne sound and impact sound. If the improvement is only to airborne sound or only to impact sound, the test report should state this.

6.8 Tests for airborne sound – floors – BS 2750: Part 4: 1980

impact sound BS 2750: Part 7: 1984

Calculate according to BS 5821: Part 1: 1984 (airborne) and Part 2: 1984 (impact).

Value of floor with remedial measure against airborne sound should be not less than $D_{nTw} = 48\,dB$.

Value of floor against impact sound should be not more than $L_{nTw} = 65$.

Laboratory tests

Separating walls

6.9 Tests should be conducted according to BS 2750: Part 3: 1980.

Value of combined wall and remedial measure should be not less than $R_w = 53\,dB$.

Separating floors

3.10/3.12 Tests to be conducted according to BS 2750: Parts 3 and 6: 1980 respectively.

Values to be achieved – airborne – not less than $R_w = 52\,dB$

Impact – not more than $L_{nw} = 65$.

APPENDIX A

Method for calculating mass

A1 Where a mass is specified for walls or floor, it is expressed in kg/m^2.

The mass may be obtained from actual figures given by the manufacturers or it may be calculated by the method given in this appendix. To calculate the mass of a masonry leaf use the formulae from Table A1. These formulae are not exact but are accurate enough for this purpose. For coordinating heights other than those given in Table A1 use the formulae for the nearest height.

A2 Densities of bricks or blocks (at 3% moisture content) may be taken from a current BBA or ETA Certificate or from the manufacturer's literature, in which case the Building Control Authority may ask for confirmation, eg that the measurement was done by an accredited test house. Note that the quoted density of bricks or blocks is normally the apparent density, ie the weight divided by the volume including perforations, voids or frogs. This is the density appropriate to the formulae for the nearest height. Include any finish of plaster, render or dry lining in calculating the mass unless otherwise stated.

A3 A mortar joint of 10 mm and a dry set mortar density of $1800\,kg/m^3$ are assumed values. Values within 10% of these figures are acceptable.

A4 For in-situ concrete or screeds calculate the mass by multiplying the density (kg/m^3) by the thickness in metres. For slabs or composite floor bases divide the total mass of the element (kg) by the plan area of the element (m^2).

Table A1   Formulae for calculation of wall leaf mass

Coordinating height of masonry course (mm)	Formulae to be used
75	$M = T(0.79D + 380) + NP$
100	$M = T(0.86D + 255) + NP$
150	$M = T(0.92D + 145) + NP$
200	$M = T(0.93D + 125) + NP$

where
M = mass of 1 m^2 of leaf in kg/m^2
T = thickness of masonry in metres (ie unplastered thickness)
D = density of masonry units in kg/m^3 (at 3% moisture content)
N = number of finished faces
    (If no finish $N = 0$, if finish on one side only $N = 1$, if finish on both sides $N = 2$)
P = mass of 1 m^2 of wall finish in kg/m^2 (see below)

Finishes
Mass of plaster (assumed thickness 13 mm)

Cement render	29 kg/m^2
Gypsum	17 kg/m^2
Lightweight	10 kg/m^2
Plasterboard	10 kg/m^2

Notes on BS 2750 and BS 5821

Parts 4 and 7 of BS 2750 deal with field tests, as opposed to laboratory tests. The latter are useful for defining a sound reduction index for individual elements after blanking out all other routes for sound to pass. Field tests which take into account actual conditions, including flanking transmission, are necessary to define realistic standards.

In the tests for airborne sound the results are given as the difference in the level of sound between the room containing the sound source and the receiving room. Thus the figures to be achieved are minima. With impact sound tests only one measurement is taken in the receiving room and the standards to be achieved are therefore maxima (not to be exceeded). The measured results have to be adjusted to take account of the acoustic absorption of the receiving room which will also affect the final sound level in addition to the various transmission factors. The method used is to measure the actual absorption of the room and relate this to an assumed standard (taken in m^2 as 0.32 times the volume in m^3), thereby producing a factor by which the actual measured value can be adjusted. This adjusted figure is then known as the 'standardised' level difference or impact sound pressure level referred to in the Approved Document.

The BS gives details of how the sounds should be created and at what frequencies measurements should be taken. There are 16 of these from 100 to 3150 (not 3200, as one might expect) covering five octaves in 1/3 octave steps and recommended minimum (airborne) or maximum (impact) values for each frequency are given.

BS 5821 is intended to 'simplify' the formulation of acoustical requirements in building codes. It does this by defining a reference curve (graph) or values over the frequency band. This is placed next to the actual curve in accordance with specified rules. It is then possible to quote from the figure at the frequency of 500 Hz (which, being a logarithmic scale, is the mean frequency) as a single figure standard. These are known as the 'weighted' standardised level difference and sound pressure levels.

The nature of sound and its effects.

Sound is one of those earthly phenomena to which animals (including *homo sapiens*) are receptive. In physics it is usually grouped with heat and light. All three are transmitted by creating vibration at the source, which sets up a wave motion. Since the speed of the wave remains constant, the faster the vibration, the shorter the wave length. Sound and heat have comparatively slow speeds which can easily be comprehended by the human brain. Sound at around 700 mph is slow enough for the ear to detect echoes when the difference between the direct and reflected routes is only about 30 m. Light, on the other hand (together with electricity and radio waves), travels at 186,000 miles per second, a velocity which only means anything in terms of inter-stellar space (eg light could circle the earth eight times in one second). The speed of sound is also affected by the medium through which it is passing, thus the aircraft sound barrier is less at high altitudes. The expert manipulation of sound (music) has brought enormous pleasure to the human ear which is an instrument of extraordinary refinement and accuracy. It can, however, be equally repellent and at high intensities can produce actual physical pain and deafness. This is where it becomes a matter of concern to the Building Regulations.

There are two main divisions in the need for the control of sound in buildings. The first concerns the acoustics of internal spaces; mainly the period of reverberation, controlled by introducing sound absorptive material. The second concerns the transmission of sound between internal spaces and two kinds of sound are considered, *airborne* and *impact* sound.

The transmission of sound is related not only to its strength or intensity, measured in decibels (dB), but also to its frequency expressed in Hertz (Hz) ie cycles per second.

The disturbance or nuisance value of sound generated in another room increases as the frequency rises, hence the table in the 1976 Regulations required higher decibel reduction values for sound in the upper frequency ranges. This, however, is not so with impact sound. In this case the highest permitted levels are in the 200 to 500 Hz frequency band. This implies that such sound can best be tolerated at these frequencies and nuisance value is more at both the lower and upper frequency levels. The question of acoustic absorption in the rooms does not affect the resistance value of the separating wall or floor, but a high level of absorption will reduce the overall sound level in the room.

Although of no technical value it is interesting to consider the octave band structure. There are seven distinct notes in the musical scale (eight if one includes *doh* twice) which are clearly discernible to the human ear and which the human voice cannot only reproduce exactly but can also move from one note to another, jumping a whole octave or more if necessary. Although one might consider the musical scale as an arbitrary selection of progressively increasing frequencies, it clearly is not, as the frequency at the top is exactly double (from *doh* to *doh*) that at the bottom. To achieve this the frequency of each note (*ray, me, fah* etc) is 1.104× its predecessor. That the human ear and voice can tune in exactly to these very fine limits with the greatest of ease (at least for some) is really quite remarkable.

The subject of sound and its suppression is a highly complex and technical affair. Part E offers a particularly good example of how the statutory rules concerning the design of buildings now require a detailed knowledge of highly complex technology which must be beyond the scope of the average (or even above average) architect, calling for increasing resort to the specialist consultant.

References

The following British Standards are referred to in this Approved Document.

BS 1142: 1989 *Specification for fibre boards*.

BS 2750 *Measurement of sound insulation in buildings and of building elements*: Part 3: 1980 *Laboratory measurement of airborne sound insulation of building elements*: Part 6: 1980 *Laboratory measurement of impact sound insulation of floors*.

BS 5628 *Code of practice for use of masonry*: Part 3: 1985 *Materials and components, design and workmanship*.

BS 5821 *Methods for rating the sound insulation of building elements*: Part 1: 1984 *Method for rating the airborne sound insulation in buildings and interior building elements*: Part 2: 1984 *Method for rating the impact sound insulation*.

Chapter 6

Approved Document F
Ventilation

This document is in two parts:
F 1   Means of Ventilation
F 2   Condensation

Introduction

F 1

The previous requirement to provide zones of open space outside windows was omitted by the 1985 regulations. This was not regarded as a matter directly related to health and safety and can be left to designers. There is no requirement to provide windows.

The 1990 amendments include provision for mechanical extract ventilation in kitchens and bathrooms. Background ventilation is now essential in kitchens and habitable rooms.

F 2

The scope of requirement F 2 (previously only applicable to dwellings) has been extended to include all buildings

F 1   MEANS OF VENTILATION

The requirement is as follows:

Requirement	Limits on application
Means of ventilation F 1. There shall be adequate means of ventilation provided for people in the building.	This requirement applies only to – (*a*) dwellings; (*b*) the spaces within any building containing two or more dwellings which are used solely or principally with those dwellings; (*c*) rooms containing sanitary conveniences; and (*d*) bathrooms.

The requirement will be met if the ventilation, under normal conditions, is capable of restricting the accumulation of such moisture which could lead to mould growth and pollutants originating inside the building which would become a hazard to the health of occupants.

From the limits on application it can be seen that the general requirements apply only to dwellings and buildings containing dwellings. The requirement regarding sanitary conveniences and bathrooms applies to all buildings. Necessary security or comfort should not be affected to a significant extent so that the use of ventilation is encouraged.

0.2   A ventilation opening can include any opening whether permanent or closable which opens directly to external air, such as a door, window, louvre, airbrick, progressively openable ventilator or window trickle ventilator.

Other than in a screen, fascia, baffle etc, the smallest dimension of a ventilation opening should be at least 8 mm so as to minimise resistance to the flow of air.

0.3   *Common space* means a space associated with two or more dwellings.

0.4   *Habitable room* means a room used for dwelling purposes. A kitchen is not a habitable room.

0.5   *Bathroom* includes shower room.

0.6   *Sanitary accommodation* means a space containing one or more closets or urinals. If there is free circulation of air throughout the space, sanitary accommodation containing one or more cubicles can count as a single space.

0.7   *Objective*

The objective of the requirement is to provide a means of extracting moisture and to achieve rapid ventilation through natural means, background ventilation through trickle ventilators etc and extract ventilation by mechanical means.

Kitchens, bathrooms and shower rooms produce significant quantities of moisture and measures for extracting this moisture are given.

In habitable rooms and sanitary accommodation, moisture is likely to produce condensation and rapid ventilation is required to dilute the moisture and any pollutants.

Background ventilation which will not significantly reduce comfort and at the same time is adequately secure has been introduced so as to encourage persons living in dwellings to use the ventilation provided.

Background ventilation, eg trickle ventilators, should therefore be located to avoid undue draughts.

Means of ventilation

Habitable rooms

1.1   The requirement will be satisfied if both rapid and background ventilation are provided as shown in diagram [6.1].

F l **[6.1]** *Ventilation of habitable rooms.*

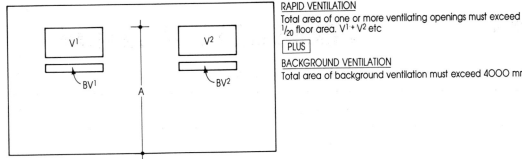

RAPID VENTILATION
Total area of one or more ventilating openings must exceed $\frac{1}{20}$ floor area. $V^1 + V^2$ etc

PLUS

BACKGROUND VENTILATION
Total area of background ventilation must exceed 4000 mm²

A to be not less than 1.75 m
V = ventilation opening
BV = background ventilation opening

Kitchens in dwellings

2.1   The requirement will be satisfied if both mechanical extract and background ventilation are provided as shown in diagram [6.2].

NOTE: As difficulties can occur with mechanical extract where there is a flue in the same room, ammendments to the AD may allow the omission of a fan where there is an open flue.

F l **[6.2]** *Ventilation of kitchens in dwellings.*

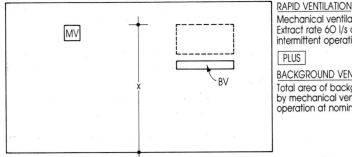

RAPID VENTILATION
Mechanical ventilation
Extract rate 60 l/s or if in cooker hood 30 l/s and capable of intermittent operation

PLUS

BACKGROUND VENTILATION
Total area of background ventilation not less than 4000 mm² OR by mechanical ventilation additionally capable of continuous operation at nominally one air change per hour

MV = Mechanical ventilation
BV = Background ventilation
 x = Minimum height of opening is not applicable as a kitchen
     is not regarded for Part F as a habitable room

Common spaces in buildings containing dwellings

3.1/3.2   These should have one or more ventilation openings with a total area of at least 1/50 of the floor area. If the space is used for access only and is wholly internal, mechanical extract ventilation at the rate of not less than one air change per hour may be provided.

Bathrooms in any building (including shower rooms)

4.1   The requirement will be satisfied if bathrooms are provided with mechanical extract ventilation. The extract rate should be not less than 15 l/s and be capable of being operated intermittently.

Sanitary accommodation in any building

5.1   Sanitary accommodation means a space containing a closet or urinal, whether or not it contains any other equipment. Cubicles which do not form a complete seal count as part of the general space (see diagram [6.3]).

F 1 **[6.3]** *Ventilation of sanitary accommodation.*

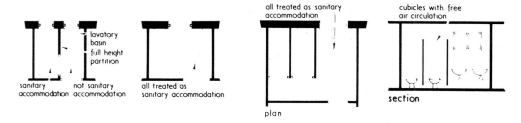

Like habitable rooms, one or more openings should be provided totalling at least 1/20 of the floor area with some part of the opening at least 1.75 m above floor level.

Alternatively, mechanical extract ventilation may be provided having a rate of extraction of not less than three air changes per hour. This may be operated intermittently with an overrun of 15 minutes.

If sanitary accommodation, eg a water closet, is installed within a bathroom mechanical extract ventilation must be installed as well as an opening window.

If the option is taken not to have an opening window but to have mechanical extract ventilation, the sizing of the extract will have to be calculated because there are two criteria – 15 l/s and three air changes per hour. 15 l/s = 54 m³/h, therefore if the bathroom is less than 18 m³ in floor area the extract rate of 15 l/s may be used. Larger bathrooms will require extract at a greater rate.

Ventilation through other spaces

6.1/6/2   Two rooms can be treated as one space if there is a permanent opening equal to 1/20 of their combined floor area.

If a habitable room adjoins a conservatory or similar space it may be ventilated through that space in the circumstances illustrated in sketch [6.4].

Ventilation openings into courts

6.3   If a ventilation opening serving a habitable room opens into a court (either fully enclosed or open one side) and is within 15 m of the opposite wall the provisions illustrated in sketch [6.5] apply.

Alternative approaches

7.1   The requirement will also be satisfied by using one of three alternative approaches:

(*a*)   provision throughout the dwelling of mechanical ventilation designed to be capable of continuous operation; or

by following the relevant recommendations of:

(*b*)   BS 5720: 1979 *Code of practice for mechanical ventilation and air conditioning in buildings*, the relevant clauses being 2.3.2.1, 2.5.2.10, 2.5.2.11, 3.1.1.1.

(*c*)   BS 5250: 1989 *Code of practice: the control of condensation in buildings*, clauses 9.9 and 9.10.

F l [6.4] *Ventilation through other spaces.*

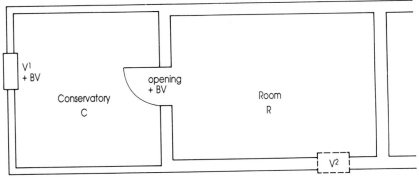

V = Ventilation opening — part at least 1.75 m above floor level
BV = Background ventilation

Opening — area at least 1/20 combined floor area
Room (R) may be ventilated through a conservatory or similar space if area of ventilator:

$$V^1 = \frac{(\text{area C} + \text{area R})}{20}$$

or if room already has a ventilator

$$V^1 + V^2 = \frac{(\text{area C} + \text{area R})}{20}$$

PLUS　Background ventilation to the conservatory and to the opening(s) between room and space EACH not less than 4000 mm²

F l [6.5] *Ventilation openings into courts.*

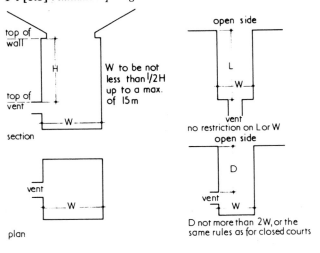

BS 5720: 1979

This code deals with the work involved in the design, installation, commissioning, operation and maintenance of mechanical ventilation and air conditioning systems, which automatically brings in heating and cooling. It has not been written simply for experts and includes brief descriptions of some systems and equipment to assist those without specialist training. The Approved Document refers only to four specific clauses regarding fundamental requirements (Section 2) and design considerations (Section 3).

Fresh air supply
2.3.2.1 This is required to dilute odours, tobacco smoke and carbon dioxide exhaled by people. A tables gives recommended quantities for various spaces. In deciding quantities account should be taken of natural infiltration. The amount of air introduced may be increased to provide a cooling effect, or reduced to limit the heating load (or the cooling load in warm conditions).

Fire and smoke detection
2.5.2.10 When recirculation of air is involved, consideration must be given to the installation of detection devices to either shut off the plant and close dampers or discharge the smoke laden air outside. This should not be near to any escape stairs etc. Smoke detectors can be used to operate alarms and/or dampers.
The Fire Research Station publish a number of notes on various building types.

Smoke control

2.5.2.11 Smoke can spread for a number of reasons (eg the stack effect in tall buildings). Centralised ducted ventilation systems have a potential for spreading smoke far beyond the source, so that many regulations and authorities require fan systems to be shut down automatically when smoke or a temperature rise is sensed. Even then smoke dangers may be needed to prevent migration of smoke through the ductwork. Systems should be designed with smoke in mind, including if possible arrangements to permit their operation in a positive way for controlling smoke.

One method of using ventilation for smoke control is the positive pressuration of escape routes, mainly stairways and lobbies. These may operate at slow speeds, switching to high speed if smoke is detected, or switch on only in emergency.

Mechanical extract/natural supply

3.1.1.1 This is the simplest form of ventilation system, comprising either one or more fans in the walls or roof, or ductwork connected to a central fan with suitable extract points and dampers. Provision for replacement air must be made.

It should be regarded as a palliative system to meet the need for ventilation in crowded rooms, offices or restricted areas with local conditions which might otherwise be objectionable such as lavatories, kitchens, plant rooms or parts of workshops and laboratories, or to meet a statutory requirement.

BS 5250: 1989

Clause 9.9

Occupation of buildings produces moisture. Ventilation to the outside air is necessary to avoid condensation and mould growth. Humidity level should be controlled to between 40 per cent and 70 per cent.

Occupants of buildings are concerned about draughts and the effect of ventilation on heating costs, so there is a tendency to reduce ventilation rates. The ideal system should provide controlled background ventilation with increased moisture extraction from areas such as kitchens and bathrooms.

Clause 9.10

The amount of water electric dehumidifiers extract is dependent on the temperature and vapour pressure of the air. They are much more effective in warmer dwellings where condensation problems are caused by high vapour pressures than in the more typical condensation-prone houses where low temperatures create the problem.

F 2   CONDENSATION

The requirement is as follows:

Requirement	Limits on application
Condensation in roofs F 2 Adequate provision shall be made to prevent excessive condensation (*a*) in a roof: or (*b*) in a roof void above an insulated ceiling.	

The requirement now applies to all buildings.

The standard of performance required is stated as being to limit condensation in spaces above insulated ceilings to such an extent that under normal conditions:

(*a*)   the thermal performance of the insulating materials, and

(*b*)   the structural performance of the roof construction will not be permanently reduced.

0.1 Provisions for ventilation of cold deck roofs are in two sections. Section 1 deals with roofs with a pitch of 15° or more and Section 2 is for roofs with a pitch of less than 15° and those where the ceiling follows the pitch of the roof.

0.2   Warm deck roofs or inverted roofs do not need ventilation as, unlike cold deck roofs, moisture from the building will not permeate the insulation.

0.3   Ventilation of small roofs over porches and bay windows may not always be necessary for health and safety purposes.

0.6   Although part of a roof with a pitch of over 70° is treated as a wall for other purposes, the guidance in this document applies to roofs of any pitch.

0.7   Ventilation openings may be continuous or distributed along the length providing the equivalent area is maintained. Care must be taken to see that insulation does not block the ventilation gap at eaves. (Purpose-made components are available.)

0.8   Further detailed guidance can be found in *Thermal insulation – Avoiding risks*. This is a guide to good practice building construction produced by the Building Research Establishment.

BR 143 Thermal insulation – Avoiding risks

This guidance was prepared specifically for Part L of the Building Regulations – Conservation of fuel and power – but technical issues that were not important for uninsulated constructions become more significant when buildings are better insulated.

The guide, which contains some 94 illustrations and nearly 300 recommendations, includes an explanation of the technical risks relative to ventilation and condensation which may be associated with meeting the building regulation requirements for thermal insulation.

The document does not have Approved Document status but explains potential technical risks and recommends avoiding action on roofs, walls, windows and floors.

Section 1

Roofs with a pitch of 15° or more (pitched roofs).

1.1   Where ceilings follow the roof pitch, Section 2 applies.

1.2/1.4   The provisions are illustrated in sketch [6.6].

Section 2

Roofs with a pitch of less than 15° and those where the ceiling follows the pitch of the roof.

2.1   This section also applies to roofs over 15° if the ceiling follows the roof pitch.

2.2/2.5   The provisions are also illustrated in sketch [6.6].

2.6   When the edges of a roof abut a wall or other obstruction in a way that prevents free cross-ventilation, or restricts the movement of air from ventilation openings, a different form of roof construction should be used.

2.7   Vapour checks can reduce the amount of vapour reaching the void but cannot be relied upon as an alternative to ventilation. A complete moisture barrier is needed for this. (See also Approved Document B3 regarding cavity barriers in roof spaces.)

British Standard approach

1.5 and **2.8**   Alternatively, the recommendations of BS 5250: 1989 *Code of practice: the control of condensation in buildings* may be used. The relevant clauses are 9.1, 9.2 and 9.4.

BS 6229: 1982 *Code of practice for flat roofs with continuously supported coverings*, clause 18, contains further information.

BS 5250: 1989 Code of practice: the control of condensation in buildings

Although the Approved Document refers only to clauses 9.1, 9.2 and 9.4 (see below) the whole of this BS is very useful. In Section Two there is a clear explanation of the terms used in heat loss and condensation calculations which are frequently confusing to the less technically minded. There are sections on the nature of condensation, the basis of design for the control of condensation and recommended design principles. The fundamental principle of designing to minimise condensation is to maintain a balance of three factors: thermal and vapour properties of the structure, heat input and ventilation rate.

There are two types of condensation: surface and interstitial. The first is the more obvious but the second may be more damaging to the structure. Both occur when the temperature of the surface of the point within the structure falls below the dewpoint temperature at that position.

F 2 **[6.6]** *Ventilation of roofs.*

(a) pitched roof.

ventilation at eaves equivalent
in area to a continuous gap along
total run of eaves of width 'w'

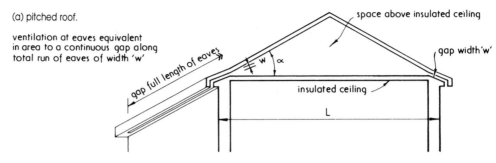

when angle ∝ > 15°   w ⩾ 10 mm (10,000 mm² per m length)
when angle ∝ ⩽ 15°   w ⩾ 25 mm (25,000 mm² per m length)

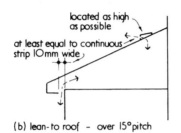

(b) lean-to roof – over 15° pitch

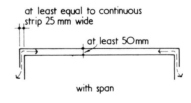

(d) ceiling follows roof pitch
(lean-to, mono or double pitch)

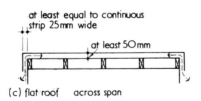

(c) flat roof   across span

with span

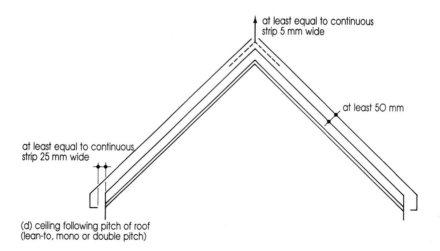

(d) ceiling following pitch of roof
(lean-to, mono or double pitch)

9.1   This is a general clause on the application of design principles. Particular attention should be paid to restrictions to air flows through ventilation openings, including the effect of mesh. External air outlets from appliances such as balanced flue heaters should be placed away from ventilation air inlets.

9.2   Performance of vapour control layers depends very much upon the material selected, workmanship and buildability.

The concept of a vapour barrier is misleading and the construction of an impervious layer is extremely difficult to achieve. Where such a layer is used it should be placed on the 'warm' side of the insulation and carefully sealed round all openings.

9.4   Covers most types of roof construction and gives recommendations in line with those in the Approved Document.

References

British Standards and other documents referred to in the AD.

BS 5720: 1979 *Code of practice for mechanical ventilation and air conditioning in buildings.*

BS 5250: 1989 *Code of practice: the control of condensation in buildings.*

BR 143: *Thermal insulation – Avoiding risks* (HMSO).

Chapter 7

Approved Document G   Hygiene

Part G contains three requirements:

G 1   Sanitary conveniences and washing facilities.

G 2   Bathrooms.

G 3   Hot water storage.

G 1, which was originally the requirement for adequate accommodation for the storage of food, was deleted by the Building Regulations (Amendment) Regulations 1989.

Refrigerators are now almost universally used and space for a refrigerator is thought likely to be made available in dwellings without regulation.

The requirement for sanitary conveniences and washing facilities, previously G 4, now becomes G 1.

The requirements for bathrooms and sanitary conveniences, originally in the Public Health Act 1936 and dealt with as 'linked powers', were incorporated into the Building Act 1984 as Sections 26 and 27. They were brought into the 1985 Building Regulations when they came into force on 11 November 1985 and these sections were repealed.

Hot water storage systems were previously considered to be a matter for control under the water by-laws but the powers of the water authority did not include those relating to public safety. It was considered that unvented hot water storage systems could present a risk of explosion and therefore be subject to building regulation control.

NOTE   In the Approved Documents to G 1 and G 2 there are references to a 'house in multiple occupation'. For the purposes of these regulations, the term means a house in which the occupants do not form part of a single household, and in such cases the same provision is required as for a dwelling anad must be accessible to all the occupants.

G 1   SANITARY CONVENIENCES AND WASHING FACILITIES

The requirement is:

Requirement	Limits on application

sanitary conveniences and washing facilities

G 1(1)   Adequate sanitary conveniences shall be provided in rooms provided for that purpose, or in bathrooms. Any such room or bathroom shall be separated from places where food is prepared.

(2)   Adequate washbasins shall be provided in –

(*a*)   rooms containing water closets, or

(*b*)   rooms or spaces adjacent to rooms containing water closets.

Any such room or space shall be separated from places where food is prepared.

(3)   There shall be a suitable installation for the provision of hot and cold water to washbasins provided in accordance with paragraph (2).

(4)   Sanitary conveniences and washbasins to which this paragraph applies shall be designed and installed so as to allow effective cleaning.

In the Stage 2 consideration of the building regulations, a report commissioned by the Department of the Environment concluded that the most important single feature in the prevention of the spread of infection from sanitary conveniences is the provision of adequate and convenient hand washing facilities.

The requirement has therefore been extended to include the provision of adequate washbasins. In this Approved Document:

Sanitary conveniences means closets and urinals.

Sanitary accommodation means a room containing closets or urinals, whether or not it also contains other sanitary fittings. Sanitary accommodation containing one or more cubicles counts as a single space if there is free circulation of air through the space.

Performance

The requirement will be met if provision is made for:

1　　　　sanitary conveniences in sufficient numbers for the sex and age of persons using the building;

2　　　　washbasins which should have a hot and cold water supply and be sited in or adjacent to rooms containing water closets, designed and installed so as not to be prejudicial to health.

Section 1　Sanitary conveniences and washing facilities

Number, type and siting

1.1　　　A dwelling, including a house in multiple occupation (see note before G 1), should have at least one closet, accessible to all occupants.

1.2　　　A space which contains a closet or urinal should be separated from a space used for the preparation of food. This includes a kitchen and any space where washing up is done.

1.3　　　Washbasins should be located –

(*i*)　in the room containing the closet;

(*ii*)　in a room or space giving direct access to the room containing the closet (provided it is not used for the preparation of food), or

(*iii*)　in a dwelling, in a room adjacent to the room containing the closet.

It is not intended that the spaces should be separated by a lobby. It is intended to mean that a WC compartment should not open directly onto a kitchen immediately adjacent to areas where food is stored or prepared. This is to avoid the risk of WC users washing their hands in sinks used for food preparation.

A room containing both a WC and a washbasin would be acceptable if it was separated from the kitchen by a door.

1.4　　　Regulations made under other legislation lay down rules as to the number, type and siting of sanitary appliances to be provided in certain types of buildings. Reference should be made to the requirements made under other legislation, eg

Offices, Shops and Railway Premises, Act 1963

Factories Act 1961

Food Hygiene (General) Regulations 1991

Part M of the Building Regulations also contains requirements for sanitary accommodation for disabled persons.

Design

1.5　　　A closet, urinal or washbasin should have a smooth, non-absorbent, easily cleaned surface.

1.6　　　Flushing apparatus should be capable of cleaning the receptable effectively and no part of the receptacle should connect with any pipe other than a branch discharge or flush pipe.

1.7　　　Hot water should be provided to washbasins which are situated in or adjacent to sanitary accommodation.

Installation

1.8　　　A closet should discharge through a trap and branch pipe into a discharge stack or drain.

1.9　　　A urinal should discharge through a grating, a trap and a branch pipe into a discharge stack or drain (see Approved Document H 1).

1.10   A closet with a macerator and pump may be connected to a small-bore drainage system discharging into a stack if:
(*a*)   there is also access to a closet on a normal gravity system;
(*b*)   the macerator, pump and small-bore system are the subject of and the conditions of use are in accordance with a current European Technical Approval issued by a member of EOTA (eg the British Board of Agrément).

1.11   A washbasin should discharge through a trap and branch discharge pipe to a discharge stack or where the washbasin is on the ground floor, discharge into a gully or direct to a drain.

Alternative approach

1.12   Where there is no suitable water supply or means of disposal of foul water, closets and urinals which use chemical or other treatment may be used.

1.13   Alternatively, the recommendations of Clauses 2, 3, 6, 7 and 8 of BS 6465 *Sanitary installations*, Part 1: 1984 *Code of practice for scale of provision, selection and installation of sanitary appliances*, may be followed.

NOTE   The Approved Document refers only to certain clauses of the British Standard. Clauses 2 and 3 deal with definitions and information and clauses 6–8 cover design, scale of provision and workmanship.

There are recommendations on siting in public buildings, layout of appliances, grouping for economy of service installations, noise, doors and locks, ventilation, ease of cleaning, partitions and cubicles, finishes, selection of appliances and their support.

Clause 7 contains a series of tables showing the recommended scale of provision for 12 types of building or accommodation which virtually covers the whole range of purpose groups in the Regulations.

Clause 8 deals with work on site and inspection.

Reference G 1

BS 6465 *Sanitary installations.*
Part 1: 1984 *Code of practice for scale of provision, selection and installation of sanitary appliances.*

G 2   BATHROOMS

The requirement is as follows:

Requirement	Limits on application
Bathrooms G 2. A bathroom shall be provided containing either a fixed bath or shower bath, and there shall be a suitable installation for the provision of hot and cold water to the bath or shower bath.	This requirement applies only to dwellings

The usual acceptable level of performance statement says the same thing as the Regulation plus a requirement that the bath must be connected to the foul drainage system.

This is Section 2 of the Approved Document G 1/2/3.

2.1   All dwellings must have at least one room with a fixed bath or shower (see Part F for ventilation).

Multi-occupation: see note 1.1.

2.2   There must be a piped supply of cold water and of hot water from a central source or unit heater.

2.3   The bath or shower should discharge via a trap and branch pipe into a gully or discharge stack or directly to a foul drain (see Approved Document H 1 for details).

2.4   Alternatively, they may be connected to a macerator and pump small-bore drainage system which is the subject of a current Agrément Certificate if the conditions of use are in accordance with the terms of the certificate.

G 3   HOT WATER STORAGE

The requirement is as follows:

Hot water storage

G 3. A hot water storage system that has a hot water storage vessel which does not incorporate a vent pipe to the atmosphere shall be installed by a person competent to do so and there shall be adequate precautions to:

(*a*)   prevent the temperature of the stored water at any time exceeding 100°C; and

(*b*)   ensure that the hot water discharged from safety devices is safety conveyed to where it is visible but will not cause danger to persons in or about the building.

Requirement G 3 does not apply to:

(*a*)   a hot water storage system that has a storage vessel with a capacity of 15 litres or less;

(*b*)   a system providing space heating only;

(*c*)   a system which heats or stores water for the purposes only of an industrial process.

NOTE G 3 is not restricted to dwellings. The use of this type of system has been common on the Continent for some time, but has only recently been accepted here. Previously, all systems had to have an open vent (or expansion pipe) which virtually ruled out the possibility of an explosion. Such systems do, however, have the disadvantage of requiring a storage tank of adequate capacity, in which the purity of the water cannot be guaranteed. Clearly, unvented systems must have very foolproof anti-explosion devices and it is with this aspect that the Regulation is concerned.

Reference should be made to the Requirements of Regulations 11(1), 12(4) and 13(3). By-laws of the appropriate water undertaking also apply.

Performance

A hot water system that has a storage vessel with no vent pipe to the atmosphere will meet the performance if it:

(*a*)   has been installed by a competent person;

(*b*)   has safety devices that prevent the temperature of the stored water at any time exceeding 100°C; and

(*c*)   has pipework that safely conveys the discharge of hot water from safety devices to where it is visible but will cause no danger to persons in or about the building.

Definitions – now called 'Meaning of terms'

Unvented hot water storage system

This is an unvented vessel for either

(*a*)   storing domestic hot water for subsequent use; or

(*b*)   heating domestic water that passes through an integral pipe or coil (for example, a water-jacketed tube heater/combi boiler), fitted with safety devices to prevent water temperatures exceeding 100°C and other applicable operating devices to control primary flow, prevent backflow, control working pressure and accommodate expansion.

Unit is an unvented hot water storage system, having the safety devices described in paragraph 3.3 or 3.4 and all operating devices factory fitted by the manufacturer.

Package is an unvented hot water storage system, having the safety devices described below together with a kit containing other applicable devices supplied by the package manufacturer, to be fitted by the installer.

Domestic hot water

Water that has been heated for ablution, culinary and cleansing purposes. The term is used irrespective of the type of building in which such a system is installed.

There are now two sections to the Approved Document.

Section 3 for hot water storage systems of not more than 500 l capacity having a heat input of not more than 45 kW.

Section 4 for systems larger than 500 l capacity or with a heat input of more than 45 kW.

Section 3	**3.1** Hot water storage systems can be heated either directly (immersion heater) or indirectly (calorifier). **3.2** Such systems may be either a unit or package which has been *'approved'*. *Approved* means approved as meeting the relevant requirement by – (1) a body operating a technical approvals scheme under the European Organisation for Testing and Assessment (EOTA) (for example the British Board of Agrément); (2) a certification body having NACCB accreditation and testing to the requirements of and appropriate standard that will ensure the requirement will be met; or (3) the subject of a satisfactory assessment that will provide an equivalent level of performance to (1) or (2) above.
Direct heating	**3.3** To meet the requirements a directly heated unit or package should have a minimum of two temperature-activated safety devices operating in sequence: (*a*) A non-self-resetting thermal cutout to BS 3955: 1986 or to BS 4201: 1991, (*b*) one or more temperature relief valves to BS 6283: Part 2: 1991 (temperature relief valves for pressures up to 10 bar) or Part 3: 1982 (combined temperature and pressure relief valves for pressures up to 10 bar). These devices are additional to any thermostatic control fitted to maintain the temperature of the stored water. **3.4** Other *'approved'* safety devices can be used. **3.5** *Temperature relief valves* In both units and packages, the temperature relief valve(s) – should be located directly on the storage vessel; – should be sized to give a discharge rating measured in accordance with BS 6283 Part 2 1991 Appendix F or Part 3 1991 Appendix G which is at least equal to the power input to the water; – should not be disconnected other than for replacement; – should not be relocated in any other device or fitting; – should discharge via a short length of metal pipe (D 1) of a size not less than the outlet of the temperature relief valve either by way of a manifold sized to accept the total discharge pipes connected to it through an air break over a tundish located vertically as near as possible to the valve.
Indirect heating	**3.6** Safety devices listed in 3.3 for direct heating are also required for indirectly heated units and packages, but the non-self-resetting thermal cut-out(s) should be wired up to a motorised valve or some other *approved* device which will shut off the flow to the primary heater. If the unit incorporates a boiler the thermal cut-out may be on the boiler. The temperature relief valve should be sized and located and the discharge pipe (D1) provided all in accordance with paragraph 3.5. **3.7** Where an indirect unit or package has an alternative direct method of water heating, a non-self-resetting thermal cut-out will also be needed on the direct source.
Installation	**3.8** Units or packages shouldbe installed by a competent person. The Approved Installer system operated through the British Board of Agrément has been terminated. A competent person is a person who holds a current Registered Operative Identity Card for the installation of domestic UVHWSSs issued by the Construction Industry Training Board (CITB), the Institute of Plumbing or the Association of Installers of UVHWSSs (Scotland and Northern Ireland) or registered operatives employed by companies on the BBA list of Approved Installers up to 31 December 1991 or an equivalent body.
Discharge pipes	**3.9** The discharge pipe(s) from any tundish should be included in the installation and should: – be vertical; – be in the same space as the UVHWSS; – be fitted as close as possible (within 500 mm) of the temperature relief valve. The discharge pipe from the tundish (D2) should: – terminate in a safe place: the discharge will be of scalding water and steam and there should be no risk of contact by persons in the vicinity; – be of metal;

– be at least one pipe size larger than the outlet pipe on the safety device unless its total equivalent hydraulic resistance exceeds that of a straight 9 m long pipe; bends should be taken into account in any calculations of flow resistance;

– have a vertical section of pipe at least 300 mm long, below the tundish before any elbows or bends in the pipework;

– be installed with a continuous fall;

– have discharges visible at both the tundish and the final point of discharge; if this is not practicable, at least one of the points should be visible.

Asphalt, roofing felt and non-metallic rainwater goods may be damaged by these discharges. The Approved Document gives examples of acceptable discharge arrangements. These are not given here and reference should be made to the Approved Document.

The size of the discharge pipe (D2) may be calculated from the Table to 3.9.

An alternative approach for sizing discharge is given in BS 6700, Appendix E, Section E2 and Table 21. See also diagram [7.1].

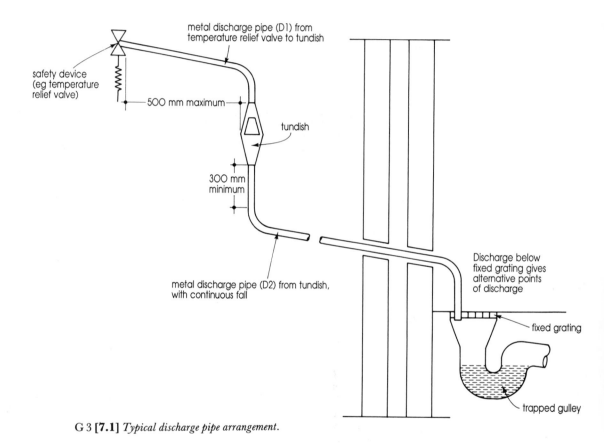

G 3 **[7.1]** *Typical discharge pipe arrangement.*

3.10   Electrical non-self-resetting thermal cut-outs should be connected to the direct heat source or indirect primary flow control device in accordance with the IEE Regulations.

Inspection of installations   **3.11**   Inspection of *approved* UVHWS systems comprising units or packages which are installed by a competent person is not thought to be unnecessary. Other systems may require inspection.

A worked example is given for ascertaining the permitted length of the D2 pipe. Another example is given here.

G1 type temperature relief valve with a discharge pipe (D2) having three No. 35 elbows and length of 4 m from the tundish to the point of discharge.

Max. resistance allowed for 35 mm D2 pipe from G1/2 trv   = 9.0 m
Deduct the resistance of three No. 35 mm elbows at 1.4 m each = 4.2 m
Max. permitted length   = 4.8 m
This length is satisfactory.

Table to 3.9 **Sizing of copper discharge pipe (D2) for common temperature relief valve outlet sizes**

Valve outlet size	Minimum size of discharge pipe (D1) (mm)	Minimum size of discharge pipe (D2) from tundish (mm)	Maximum resistance allowed, expressed as a length of straight pipe (ie) (m)	Resistance created by each elbow or bend (m)
G1/2	15	22	up to 9	0.8
		28	up to 18	1.0
		35	up to 27	1.4
G3/4	22	28	up to 9	1.0
		35	up to 18	1.4
		42	up to 27	1.7
G1	28	35	up to 9	1.4
		42	up to 18	1.7
		54	up to 27	2.3

Section 4 Unvented hot water storage systems over 500 litres or over 45 kW

4.1/4.2 These systems will generally be to individual design and inappropriate to be *approved*. Where this is the case, the storage system should be designed to the same safety requirements by an appropriately qualified engineer and installed by a competent person (see paragraph 3.8).

4.3 Safety devices on these installations should be in accordance with Clause 7, Section 2 of BS 6700: 1987 or other equivalent specification.

4.4 There should be an appropriate number of temperature relief valves either to BS 6283 Parts 2 and 3 (see paragraph 4.3) to give a combined discharge rating at least equivalent to the power input.

The valves should be factory fitted to the storage vessel and the sensing element located as described in paragraph 3.5.

4.5/4.6 Thermal cut-outs appropriate to the heat source should be incorporated into the system as described in paragraphs 3.6, 3.7 and 3.10 and discharge pipes should be installed in accordance with paragraph 3.9.

References

The following British Standards and other documents are referred to in the Approved Documents.

G1

BS 6465 *Sanitary appliances.* Part 1: 1984 *Code of practice for scale of provision, selection and installation of sanitary appliances.*

G3

BS 3955: 1986 *Specification for electrical controls for household and similar general purposes*, p. 6.
BS 4201: 1979(1984) *Specification for thermostats for gas burning appliances.*
Amendment slip No.1: AMD 4531, p. 6. No.2: AMD 6268.
BS 6283: *Safety devices for use in hot water systems.*
Part 2: 1991 *Specification for temperature relief valves for use at pressures from 1 bar to 10 bar.*
Part 3: 1991 *Specification for combined temperature and pressure relief valves for pressures from 1 bar to 10 bar.*
BS 6700: 1987 *Specification for design, installation, testing and maintenance of services supplying water for domestic use within buildings and their curtilages.*
BS 7206: 1990 *Specification for unvented hot water storage units and packages.*
Institution of Electrical Engineers *Regulations for electrical installations.* Current edition.

Chapter 8

Approved Document H
Drainage and Waste Disposal

H 1   SANITARY PIPEWORK AND DRAINAGE

The requirement is:

Requirement	Limits on application

Foul water drainage

H 1. (1) Any system which carries foul water from appliances within the building to a sewer, cesspool or a septic or settlement tank shall be adequate.

(2)   'Foul water' in sub-paragraph (1) means waste water which comprises or includes

(*a*)   Waste from a sanitary convenience or other soil appliance;

(*b*)   Water which has been used for cooking or washing.

Performance

The requirement will be met if a foul water drainage system –

(*a*)   conveys the flow of foul water to a foul water outfall (meaning a foul or combined sewer, cesspool, septic or settlement tank);

(*b*)   minimises the risk of blockage or leakage;

(*c*)   prevents foul air from the drainage system entering the building under working conditions;

(*d*)   is ventilated; and

(*e*)   is accessible for clearing blockages.

There are two sections:

Section 1   Sanitary pipework (within the building)

Section 2   Foul drainage (external)

There is also an Appendix dealing with larger buildings.

Introduction to the provisions

0.1/0.4   The capacity of the whole system, which depends on the size and gradient of the pipes, should be large enough to carry the expected flow at any point. The flow depends on the type, number and grouping of appliances and the table below shows the flow rate which can be assumed for most types.

As appliances are rarely used simultaneously, the minimum stack and drain sizes will be capable in normal use of carrying the flow from a large number of them.

Previously this table showed flow rates from appliances but these have been grouped to equate with usage from a typical household.

Flow rates for dwellings are now given for those which have been used for design purposes in BS 8301, ie a WC, a bath, a sink and one or two washbasins.

Table to 0.2   Flow rates from dwellings

Number of dwellings	Flow rate (l/s)
1	2.5
5	3.5
10	4.1
15	4.6
20	5.1
25	5.4
30	5.6

Pipe sizes

0.5   Pipe sizes in the Approved Document are nominal sizes in convenient round numbers approximately equal to manufactured sizes. Equivalent pipe sizes are in BS 5572 for sanitary pipework and in BS 8301 for building drainage.

Section 1   Sanitary pipework

Traps

1.1/1.4   All points discharging into the system should be trapped to prevent foul air entering the building. Under working and test conditions traps should always retain 25 mm minimum seal.

Ventilation of branch discharge pipes may be needed to prevent seals being broken by negative pressure in the system (but see later). For clearing blockages, appliances with integral traps should be removable and all other traps should be fitted after the appliance and should either be removable or have a cleaning eye.

The minimum sizes and seal depth are given in the table below.

Table to 1.2   Minimum trap sizes and seal depths

Appliance	Diameter of trap (mm)	Diameter of seal (mm)
washbasin bidet	32	75
sink* bath* shower* food waste disposal unit urinal bowl	40	75
WC pan	75 (minimum)	50

*Where these appliances are installed on a ground floor and discharge to a gulley the depth of seal may be reduced to not less than 40 mm.

Branch discharge pipes

1.5/1.6   Branch discharge pipes should always discharge either into another branch pipe or into a stub stack or discharge stack or directly into a drain. For waste water only they should discharge into a gulley.

1.7/1.11   These provisions are illustrated in diagrams [8.1, 8.2, 8.3, 8.8].

Sizes

1.12   Pipes serving one appliance only should have at least the diameter of the trap. Sizes and other details for *unvented* branches are shown in the table below.

Table to 1.12   Common branch discharge pipes (unvented)

Appliance	Max number to be connected	Max length of branch (m)	Min size of pipe (mm)	Gradient limits (fall per metre)		
				min (mm)		max (mm)
WCs	8	15	100	9	to	90
Urinals: bowls	5	*	50	18	to	90
stalls	6	*	65	18	to	90
washbasins	4	4 (no bends)	50	18	to	45

NOTE

*No limitation as regards venting but should be as short as possible.
 A fall of 18 mm equals 1°.

[8.1] *Single stack system: discharge pipe and stack details.*

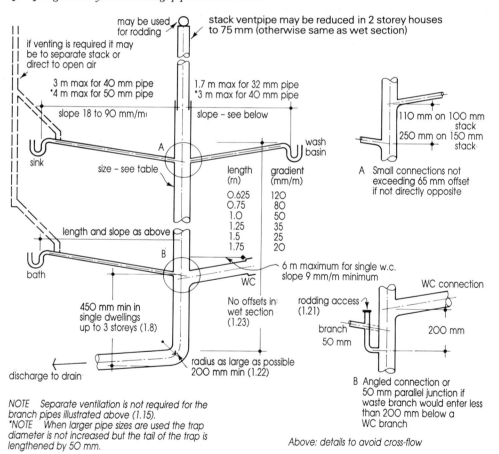

1.13/1.19   These provisions are also illustrated in diagrams [8.1 and 8.4–8.7].

1.20   Branch ventilating pipes serving one appliance should be 25 mm diameter unless the branch exceeds 15 m in length or has over five bends, when it should be increased to 32 mm.

1.21   Rodding points should be provided for access to any length of pipe which cannot be reached by removing traps.

Discharge stacks

1.22/1.23   Discharge and offsets are shown in diagram [8.1]. Offsets in the 'wet' portion of a discharge stack should be avoided if possible, but where they are unavoidable there should be no branch connection within 750 mm of the offset. In buildings over three storeys high, stacks

1.9 **[8.2]** *Ground floor closet direct to drain.*

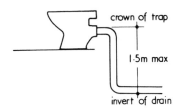

1.11 **[8.3]** *Branch pipe discharge to gulley.*

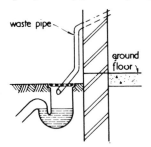

[8.4] *Branch of ventilation pipe.*

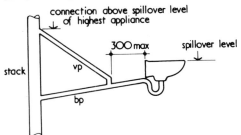

1.18 **[8.5]** *Bends in branch pipes.*

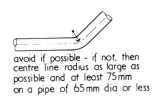

avoid if possible - if not, then centre line radius as large as possible and at least 75 mm on a pipe of 65 mm dia or less

1.14 **[8.6]** *Alternative junctions.*

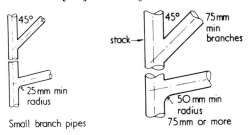

Small branch pipes

1.19/1.27 **[8.7]** *Termination of ventilating stacks or ventilation part of stack.*

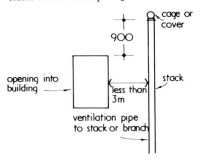

1.10/1.25 **[8.8]** *Stub stacks and ventilation pipe outlets.*

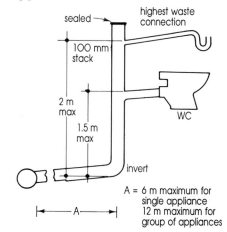

should be run inside and a ventilation stack may be needed with connections above and below the offset.

1.24   Stacks should not reduce in the direction of flow and should have the least diameter given in the table below.

Table to 1.24   Maximum capacities for discharge stacks

Stack size (mm)	Max capacity (l/s)
50 (min for urinals)	1.2*
65	2.1*
75	3.4†
90	5.3
100	7.2

* No wcs.
† No more than one siphonic wc with 75 mm outlet.

1.25/1.29 Details of stub stacks and ventilation pipe outlets are shown in diagram [8.8].

1.30 Rodding points should be provided for access to any lengths of pipe wshich cannot be reached from any other part of the system. Pipes should be accessible for repair.

Materials for pipes, fittings and joints

1.31 Any of the materials in the table below may be used. Different metals should be separated by non-metallic material to avoid electrolytic corrosion.

Pipes should be firmly supported without restricting thermal movement.

Table to 1.31   Materials for sanitary pipework

Material	British Standard
Pipes:	
cast iron	BS 416
copper	BS 864, BS 2871
galvanised steel	BS 3868
upvc	BS 4514
polypropylene	BS 5254
plastics	BS 5255
ABS	
Mupvc	
polyethylene	
polypropylene	
Traps:	
copper	BS 1184
plastics	BS 3943

NOTE   Some of these materials may not be suitable for conveying trade effluent.

Airtightness

1.32 The system should withstand an air or smoke test to a pressure of 38 mm watergauge for 3 minutes, during which time every trap should maintain a water seal of 25 mm min. Smoke testing is not recommended for upvc pipes.

Alternative approach

1.33 The recommendations of BS 5572: 1978 *Code of Practice for sanitary pipework*, Clauses 3, 4 and 7–12, can be followed. A note on this follows.

Note on BS 5572: 1978

This deals with sanitary pipework above ground and covers the requirements of domestic, commercial and public buildings. It does not cover the special requirements of hospitals, laboratory buildings, trade effluents and the like.

It outlines the general principles involved and gives performance data. There are detailed recommendations for the design of traps, discharge pipes and stacks, ventilating pipes and stacks and access.

Four types of discharge systems are described but the Approved Document generally details the single-stack system. In the additional guidance for large buildings Appendix A refers briefly to ventilating stacks.

The differences between the systems are illustrated below by diagram [8.9]. This shows the arrangement for one storey but can be applied to any number of storeys.

[8.9] *Types of discharge systems.*

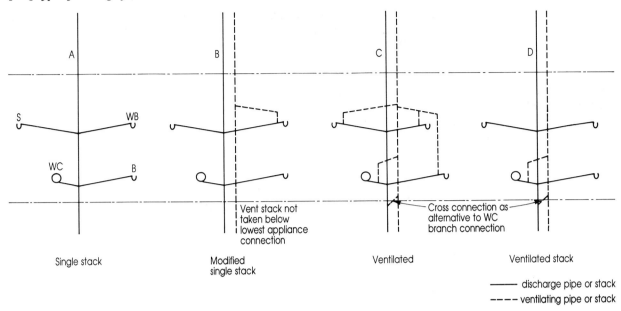

Single stack   Modified single stack   Ventilated   Ventilated stack

Vent stack not taken below lowest appliance connection

Cross connection as alternative to WC branch connection

———— discharge pipe or stack
– – – – ventilating pipe or stack

Type A. Single-stack system
This can be used only where the discharge stack is large enough to limit pressure fluctuations without requiring a separate ventilating stack.

Type B. Modified single-stack system
When the disposition of appliances (ie length and gradient) of branch discharge pipes could cause loss of trap seals, ventilation is provided only to those branches. The ventilating pipework can be extended to the atmosphere or connected to a ventilating stack.

Type C. Ventilated system
This is used where there are large numbers of sanitary appliances in ranges or where they are widely dispersed and it is not practical to provide discharge stacks in close proximity to the appliances. Both the stack and the individual branch pipes are fully ventilated.

Type D. Ventilated stack
Where the length and gradient of branch pipes is such that individual venting is unnecessary there is a possibility that the flow in the stack will cause loss of seal. To prevent this, the discharge stack itself is ventilated by cross connection to a separate vent stack.

Section 2   Foul drainage

2.1/2.2   Public sewers sometimes carry both foul and rainwater. If the drainage system is also designed to carry both (a combined system) pipe sizes may need to be increased above those required for foul water. Combined systems should not discharge to a cesspool or septic tank. Sewage lifting equipment will be needed where connection to a sewer by gravity is impracticable (see note on BS 8301).

Layout

2.3   Keep the system simple. Changes of direction and gradient should be as few and as gentle as possible. Provide access points only where blockages cannot be cleared without them. Connections to drains or sewers should be made obliquely or in the direction of flow.

2.4   The system should be ventilated at the head of each main drain, at any branch over 6 m long serving a single appliance or 12 m serving a group of appliances or on a drain fitted with an intercepting trap.

2.5   Lay pipes to even gradients; any changes to be at access points.

2.6   Lay in straight lines where practicable, but slight curves are permissible if blockages can be cleared. Bends should be in or close to inspection chambers and have as large a radius as possible.

2.7   Allow for settlement where drains run under or close to a building (see Appendices A9 to A14) on piles or beams, in common trenches or in unstable ground.

Where drains are liable to surcharge or where sewer rats are a problem, further precautions may be necessary.

Depth of pipe cover

2.8/2.9   The depth of drains will mainly depend on the required gradients and ground levels. However, protection from damage must also be considered, and if the primary factors result in too little cover for pipe protection (or too much, when the weight of the backfill becomes a problem) different combinations of cover, pipe strength and bedding may need to be considered, or special protection provided (see Appendices A15–A17).

Pipe gradients and sizes

2.10/2.12   The size and gradients of drains should be such as to accommodate the flow (see table to 0.2).

NOTE   These flow rates are what might be expected from dwellings under normal use.

The provisions acknowledge that appliances are seldom in use simultaneously and the flow rates have been calculated from BS 8301.

2.10 **[8.10]** *Discharge capacities of foul drains running 0.75 proportional depth.*

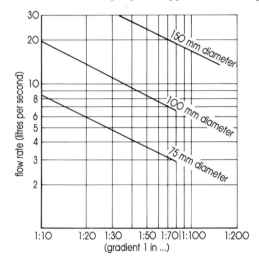

NOTES

1   No waste water drain to be less than 75 mm. No soil water drain or drain carrying trade effluent to be less than 100 mm.

2   Drains carrying a peak flow of less than 1 l/s should not be laid at less than 1:40. (These would be limited to drains not connected to a wc.)

3   For drains carrying more than 1 l/s gradient to be not less than 1:80 for 75 mm or 100 mm if at least one wc is connected; not less than 1:150 for 150 mm with at least five wcs connected.

2.13   Combined systems which carry both foul and rainwater should be designed to accommodate the total peak flow of both (see Requirement H 3).

Materials for pipes and jointing

2.14   Acceptable materials and the appropriate British Standards are shown in the table below and:

1   All joints should be appropriate to the material of the pipes and should remain watertight under working and test conditions.

2   Nothing should project into the pipe or cause obstruction.

3   Different metals should be separated by non-metallic materials to avoid electrolytic corrosion.

4   Pipes should have flexible joints.

Item 4 means that cement or lead-caulked joints do not meet the requirement (although the BS gives some situations in which they can be used).

NOTE   Some of these materials may not be suitable for conveying trade effluent.

Table to 2.14   Materials for below ground gravity drainage

Material	British Standard
Rigid pipes:	
asbestos	BS 3656
vitrified clay	BS 65
concrete	BS 5911
grey iron	BS 437
Flexible pipes:	
upvc	BS 4660
	BS 5481

NOTE   Some of these materials may not be suitable for conveying trade effluent.

Bedding and backfilling

2.15   The choice of bedding and backfilling will depend on the depth, size and strength of the pipes.

Rigid pipes

2.16   Four classes of bedding are shown in the diagram for rigid pipes of standard strength. Standard strength is the crushing strength of the pipe as given in the relevant British Standard or as stated by the pipe manufacturer and the classes given in the Approved Document are D, N, F and B, each having a bedding factor.

The bedding factor is the ratio of the strength of the pipe in a crushing machine to its strength when bedded in the ground and varies with the support angle of granular material under the pipe. Research has shown that bedding factors can be increased to 1.9 and 2.5 respectively and

2.16 **[8.11]** *Bedding for rigid pipes.*

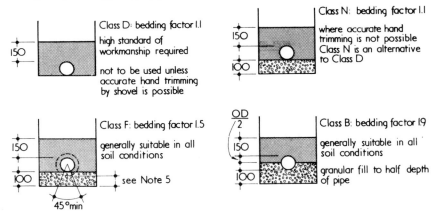

Table to 2.16   Limits of cover for standard strength rigid pipes in any width of trench

Pipe bore	Bedding class	Fields and gardens		Light traffic roads		Heavy traffic loads	
		Min	Max	Min	Max	Min	Max
100	D or N	0.4	4.2	0.7	4.1	0.7	3.7
	F	0.3	5.8	0.5	5.8	0.5	5.5
	B	0.3	7.4	0.4	7.4	0.4	7.2
150	D or N	0.6	2.7	1.1	2.5	–	–
	F	0.6	3.9	0.7	3.8	0.7	3.3
	B	0.6	5.0	0.6	5.0	0.6	4.6

that clay pipes with sleeve joints can be laid with only 50 mm of granular material under the barrels. Socketed clay pipes should have 100 mm of granular material under the barrels and not less than 50 mm under the sockets.

Granular material should have a compaction fraction value not greater than 0.3 (see note on BS 8301).

The table to 2.16, which is taken from BS 8301, gives figures relative to pipes with the lowest crushing strength (20 kN/m).

Flexible pipes
2.17   These will deform under load and require support to limit this to 5 per cent of the diameter. The diagram shows the recommended systems which will presumably achieve this. Minimum depth should be 0.9 m under any road and 0.6 m under fields and gardens; maximum 10 m in all cases (see also A12/A14).

2.17 **[8.12]** *Bedding for flexible pipes.*

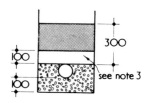 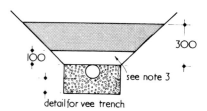

KEY (to **[8.11]** *and* **[8.12]***)*

1 *Selected fill: free from stones larger than 40 mm, lumps of clay over 100 mm, timber, frozen material, vegetable matter.*

2 *Granular material: should conform to BS 882: 1983 Table 4 or BS 8301: 1985 Appendix D.*

3 *Selected fill or granular fill free from stones larger than 40 mm.*

4 *Provision may be required to prevent ground water flow in trenches with Class N, F or B type bedding.*

5 *Where there are sockets these should be not less than 50 mm above the floor of the trench.*

Comment
Note 4 below the diagram presumably means that the granular bed may act as an undesirable subsoil water drain and some means of dealing with this may be needed.

Clearance of blockages   **2.18/2.22**   Sufficient and suitable access for clearing blockages should be provided. The provisions described are for normal rodding and not where mechanical means are available. Access points are of four types:

(*a*)   Rodding eyes – capped extensions of the pipe.
(*b*)   Access fittings – small chambers on the pipes (or on an extension of the pipes).
(*c*)   Inspection chambers – chambers with working space at ground level.
(*d*)   Manholes – large chambers with working space at drain level.
Access should be provided:
(*a*)   At or near the head of a drain.
(*b*)   At a bend or change of gradient.
(*d*)   At a junction unless each run can be cleared from another access point (some junctions can only be rodded through from one direction).
(*e*)   At maximum intervals on long runs.
The tables show greatest depths and least dimensions for access points and maximum distances between them according to type.

Construction   **2.23**   Access points should contain the foul water under working and test conditions and resist the entry of ground and rainwater. The materials which may be used include the traditional bricks, blocks and in-situ concrete and also vitrified clay, precast concrete and plastics, in which a range of factory-made units are available.

2.24/2.25   Detailed provisions for manholes and inspection chambers are shown in diagrams [8.13] and [8.14].

2.22 **[8.13]** *Maximum spacing of access points (m).*

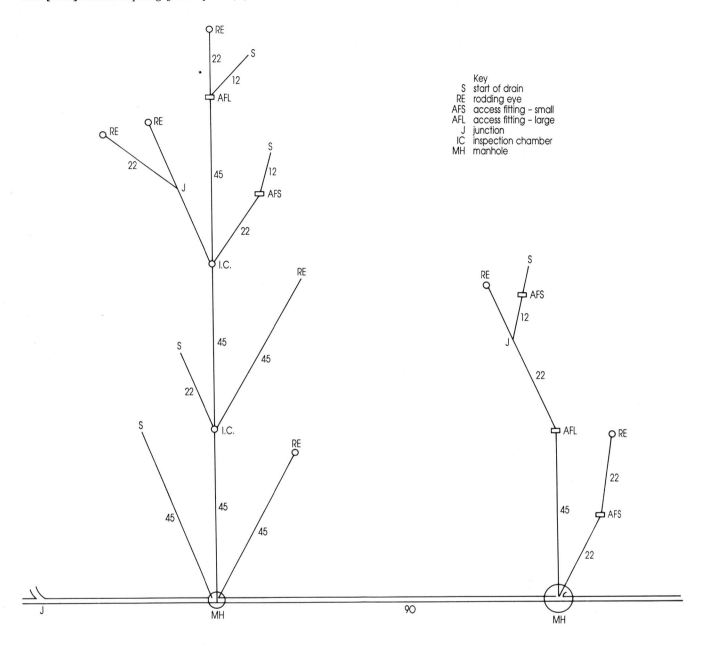

Key
S   start of drain
RE   rodding eye
AFS   access fitting – small
AFL   access fitting – large
J   junction
IC   inspection chamber
MH   manhole

Watertightness

2.26/2.28 After laying, including any necessary haunching or surrounding and after backfilling, drains up to 300 mm should be capable of withstanding:

(*a*) either an air test to give a maximum loss of head on a manometer of 25 mm in 5 minutes for 100 mm gauge or 12 mm for a 50 mm gauge, or

(*b*) a water test to 1.5 m head measured above the invert at the head of the drain. The section being tested should be filled, left to stand for 2 hours and topped up. The leakage over the next 30 minutes should not exceed 0.05 litres for each metre run of 100 mm drain (a drop of 6.4 mm/m) or 0.08 litres for a 150 mm drain (a drop of 4.5 mm/m). The head of water should never exceed 4 m, so it may be necessary to test in sections.

Table to 2.20   Minimum dimensions for access fittings and chambers

Type	Depth to invert (m)	Internal sizes	
		Length × width (mm × mm)	Circular (mm)
Rodding eye	–	As drain but min 100	
Access fitting			
small	0.6 or less	150 × 100	150
large		225 × 100	–
Inspection chamber	0.6 or less	–	190*
	1.0 or less	450 × 450	450
Manhole	1.5 or less	1200 × 750	1050
	over 1.5	1200 × 750	1200
	over 2.7	1200 × 840	1200
Shaft	over 2.7	900 × 840	900

NOTES
* Drains up to 150 mm
Covers should be the same size as fittings or chambers. Manhole covers may be 600 mm square or diameter.
Inspection chambers with depth 0.6–1 m may have covers of 430 mm diameter.

Table to 2.23   Materials for access points

Material	British Standard
1. Inspection chambers and manholes	
Clay:	
bricks and blocks	BS 3921
vitrified	BS 65
Concrete:	
precast	BS 5911
in situ	BS 8110
plastics	BBA Certificates
2. Rodding eyes and access fittings (excluding frames and covers)	as pipes See table to 2.14 BBA Certificates

2.24/2.25 **[8.14]** *Inspection chambers and manholes.*

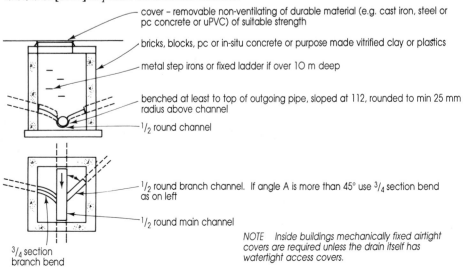

cover – removable non-ventilating of durable material (e.g. cast iron, steel or pc concrete or uPVC) of suitable strength

bricks, blocks, pc or in-situ concrete or purpose made vitrified clay or plastics

metal step irons or fixed ladder if over 10 m deep

benched at least to top of outgoing pipe, sloped at 112, rounded to min 25 mm radius above channel

¹/₂ round channel

¹/₂ round branch channel. If angle A is more than 45° use ³/₄ section bend as on left

¹/₂ round main channel

³/₄ section branch bend

NOTE   Inside buildings mechanically fixed airtight covers are required unless the drain itself has watertight access covers.

| **Alternative approach** | **2.29** Alternatively, the relevant recommendations of BS 8301: 1985 *Code of practice for building drainage* may be followed. The relevant sections are One, Two, Three (except Clause 10), Four (except Clause 23), Five (Clause 25 only) and Appendices. A note on this follows. |

| **Note on BS 8301: 1985 Building drainage** | This British Standard contains detailed recommendations for the design, layout, construction, testing and maintenance of foul, surface and ground water drainage systems constructed in the ground under and around buildings and their connection to sewers, treatment works, cesspools, soakaways and water courses. |

It covers drains not exceeding DN 300 (DN = nominal diameter in mm). For larger sizes of pipework CP 2005 is appropriate.

The excluded Clauses mentioned in 2.29 relate to groundwater and maintenance and periodic inspection. Section 15 – Sewerage and surface water lifing installations – is now included.

Section 3 contains the general design considerations and gives details on hydraulic design. It contains details on how to calculate the flow in a system using probability of discharge factors and discharge unit ratings.

The simple design information on flow rates in the introduction to the provisions has been calculated from the Code.

The ability of a pipe to carry a load may be increased by the provision of suitable bedding. There is more information on the bedding considered necessary for both rigid and flexible pipes, the backfill material and depth of cover.

'Cover' is not defined but must refer to the depth from the crown of the pipe to the surface.

The illustration in diagram 8 in the Approved Document of Class F is not the same as in the Code, and the correct version appears below. The code makes it clear that the illustration is shown after settlement and Clause 11.2.6 states that a pipe will normally settle under all bedding arrangements, the extent of settlement depending on various factors.

[8.15] *Bedding Class F. Pipe laid on flat layer of granular material with compaction fraction not greater than 0.2. Illustrated after settlement.*

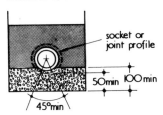

pipe laid on flat layer of granular material with CF not greater than 0·2 - illustrated after settlement

socket or joint profile

50 min   100 min

45° min

In no case should the settlement exceed that shown for Class F, ie the 45° angle from the centre of the pipe shows the minimum amount of the barrel of a socketed pipe which should rest on the granular material with the socket resting on at least 50 mm of granular material.

The new edition of the approved document contains amendments which have been made to harmonise more closely with the Code.

Appendix   Additional guidance for large buildings

It is not clear why this relatively small amount of additional information has been relegated to an Appendix and some of the guidance is also relevant to small buildings.

| **Capacity of pipes** | **A1** Two additional flow rates are given 0.06 l/s for a spray tap basin and 0.70 l/s for a washing machine. |
| | **A2** Some additional minimum trap sizes are given as shown in the table below. |

Table to A 2   Minimum trap sizes and seal depth additional to Table 2

Appliance	Diam of trap (mm)	Depth of seal (mm)
sanitary towel macerator	40	75
food waste disposal unit (industrial type)	50	75
urinal (stall, 1 to 6 person positions)	65	50

Discharge and ventilating pipes and stacks

A3/A4   These are some additional criteria generally applicable to multi-storey buildings both residential and commercial.

In buildings up to five storeys, the lowest branch connections should be at least 750 mm above the invert of the bend at the base of the stack (apart from single dwellings up to three storeys: see Section 1). In buildings from six to 20 storeys there should be ground floor branch connections and in buildings over 20 storeys both ground and first floor branch connections should be excluded.

These should be taken either into a separate stack, or if ground floor, into a drain or gulley.

A5   Where ventilation of branch pipes is necessary the ventilation pipes may be taken to the outside air or to a separate dry stack (ventilated system) (for all other buildings see paragraph 2.29).

A6   The lower end of a stack may be connected directly to a bend (see paragraph 1.22). This refers to a bend of at least 200 mm radius at the bottom of all stacks.

A8   The upper end may be carried to the outside air (as for the upper end of open discharge stacks) or cross connected to the discharge stack above the spill over level of the highest connected appliance.

Special protection – settlement

A9   Under a building a pipe should be surrounded by at least 1100 mm of granular material or other flexible fill. Where excessive subsidence may occur, additional flexible joints or suspended drainage may be a solution.

A10   A drain passing through a wall or foundation should be treated as shown in diagram [8.16].

A11   The trench for a drain near a building should be filled with concrete if the circumstances are as illustrated in diagram [8.17].

NOTE   There is no similar requirement for a building constructed near a drain trench.

A12   The local authority may be able to give information concerning sites where pipes may have to be laid on piles or beams, in a common trench or where the ground is unstable, particularly where there is a high water table.

A 10 **[8.16]** *Pipe penetrating wall.*

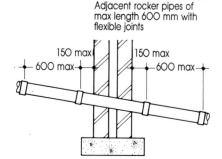

A 11 **[8.17]** *Drain trench near building.*

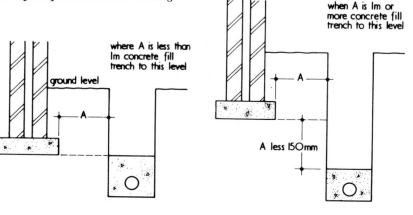

**Special protection –
surcharging of drains**

A13   On sites where surcharging could be a problem, measures should be taken to protect the building. The local authority may be able to provide information and guidance on these sites. Drainage unaffected by surcharge should by-pass any protection measures and should discharge by gravity.

**Special protection –
rodent control**

A14   Sealed drainage, ie drainage having access covers to the pipework in the inspection chamber, may be necessary in areas where infestation by rodents is a problem. The Approved Document suggests that some local authorities will be able to provide information on known locations and the most effective measures of control. Intercepting traps can give some protection but they must be regularly maintained to avoid blockages.

**Special protection –
ground loads**

A15/A17   Where ground cover is limited, special precautions are needed, as illustrated in diagrams [8.18] and [8.19].

A 15/A 17 **[8.18]** *Special protection: ground loads.*

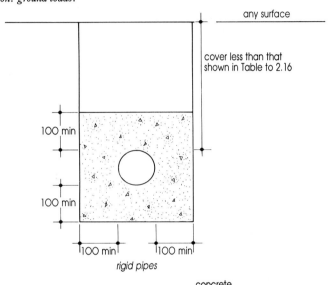

rigid pipes

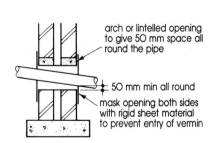

arch or lintelled opening to give 50 mm space all round the pipe

50 mm min all round

mask opening both sides with rigid sheet material to prevent entry of vermin

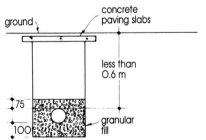

flexible pipes not below road (or as for rigid pipes)

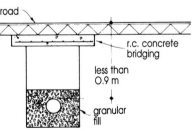

flexible pipes below road

[8.19] *Movement joint in concrete surround.*

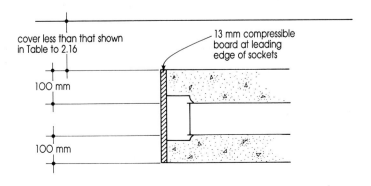

Note on BS 65: 1981

This covers vitrified clay pipes and fittings, with or without sockets, and includes normal, surface water, perforated and extra-chemically-resistant pipes. It applies to both glazed and unglazed products. Specifications cover dimensions and tolerances, as well as physical and performance characteristics and testing procedures. A range of preferred and other diameters is given but the BS does not include any details of recommended lengths, socket dimensions, radius and curvature of bends, etc. It merely specifies allowable tolerances on the manufacturers' stated values, plus a test for straightness. The diameters range from 75 mm to 1000 mm.

Performance standards specified include crushing strengths, bending moment resistance, impermeability, internal pressure test, chemical and acid resistance and water absorption.

H 2   CESSPOOLS AND TANKS

There are still locations where connection to a public sewer is not possible and the need for other solutions will still recur. Requirement H 2 of Schedule 1 is as follows:

Requirement	Limits on application
H 2. Any cesspool, septic tank or settlement tank shall be (a) of adequate capacity and so constructed that it is impermeable to liquids; (b) adequately ventilated; and (c) so sited and constructed that – (i) it is not prejudicial to the health of any person, (ii) it will not contaminate any underground water or water supply, and (iii) there are adequate means of access for emptying.	

Performance

The requirement will be met if the performance level is:

(a)   Cesspools have enough capacity to store the foul water until they are emptied.

(b)   Septic tanks and settlement tanks have enough capacity to break down and/or settle out the solid matter in the flow.

(c)   Cesspools, septic tanks and settlement tanks are constructed so as to prevent leakage and also entry of subsoil water, and have adequate ventilation.

(d)   Cesspools, septic tanks and settlement tanks are sited so as not to be prejudicial to health, not to contaminate water supplies and are accessible for emptying.

Introduction

It may be helpful to explain the basic differences between the three types of unit.

1   Cesspools are simply storage tanks which hold the whole of the piped foul waste (solids and liquids) with no (planned) biological action. They have to be emptied frequently.

2   Settlement tanks are chambers in which the solids are separated out as sludge and removed at frequent intervals. This may be done hydraulically. Liquid waste is filtered.

3   Septic tanks are a form of settlement tank in which the sludge is retained for sufficient time for organic matter to undergo anaerobic decomposition. Filtration of liquid waste may be necessary. They are the best solution to the small installation providing ground conditions permit, as desludging is normally required only once every 12 months.

The provisions of the Approved Document itself are as follows.

Capacity

1.1   Cesspools: at least 18 m^3 below the inlet level (18 000 litres).

1.2   Septic tanks and settlement tanks: at least 2.7 m^3 below the inlet level (2700 litres).

Siting

1.3   Cesspools, septic tanks and settlement tanks, if they are to be desludged using a tanker, should be within 30 m of a vehicle access and arranged so that they can be emptied and cleaned without hazard to the building's occupants or the contents being taken through a dwelling or place of work. Access may be through a covered open space.

Design and construction

1.4, 1.6/1.10   The main points are illustrated in diagram [8.20].

Materials may include brickwork, concrete or glass reinforced concrete. Brickwork should be at least 220 mm engineering brick in 1:3 cement mortar and in-situ concrete at least 150 mm thick of C/25/P mix.

The entry velocity into a septic tank should be limited to minimise turbulence by laying the last 12 m of incoming drain at a gradient not steeper than 1:50 (for drains up to DN 150). Where the width of the tank does not exceed 1200 mm the inlet should be via a dip pipe. Septic tanks should incorporate at least two chambers or compartments operating in series.

1.4, 1.6/1.10 **[8.20]** *Design of cesspools and septic tanks*

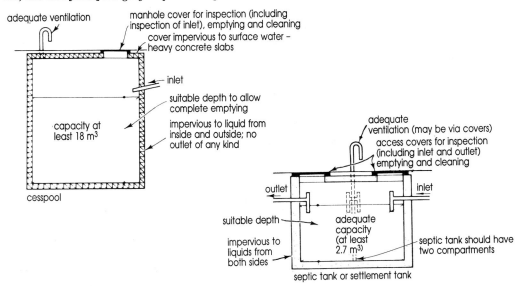

NOTES 1. Cesspools should be covered and ventilated.
          Septic and settlement tanks may be left uncovered
          but if so, they should be fenced.
        2. Access should be at least 600 mm x 600 mm.
          Access covers should be of durable quality because
          of the corrosive nature of the contents of the tank.
          Covers should be lockable.

1.5   Factory-made cesspools and septic tanks should comply with a BBA Certificate and be installed in accordance with the manufacturer's instructions. Particular care is necessary in ensuring stability of these tanks.

Alternative approach

Alternatively the relevant recommendations of BS 6297: 1983 *Code of practice for the design and installation of small sewage treatment works* may be followed. The relevant clauses are in Sections One, Two, Three (Clauses 6 to 11), Four and Appendices. A note on this follows.

Note on BS 6297: 1983

Its scope includes small sewage treatment plants for domestic type discharge ranging from single households to about 1000 population equivalent, and also sewage storage in cesspools. It does not deal with trade effluents.

It is strongly recommended that the information should be supplemented by skilled engineering advice.

There is a note on materials which as well as the traditional brick and concrete include GRC, GRP and steel which should be corrosion protected both inside and out.

Sewage treatment works operate by the settlement and retention of solids and usually include biological treatment by the use of biological filters or by biological treatment of the raw sewage followed by the separation of solids.

Cesspools receive and retain raw sewage and form no part of sewage treatment.

Surface water should always be excluded or, if not possible, specialist advice sought. Collective treatment is better than a number of individual units. Small treatment works (two or more premises) should be sited at least 25 m from any dwelling and this distance is increased for larger works. Good access is needed to enable the tanker to operate its suction lift facility. All tanks must be impervious to both contents and ground water. Cesspools should always be covered to exclude rain. Other tanks may be covered or protected by fencing but all must have access for cleaning and inspection, including inspection of inlets and outlets. Access openings should have at least 600 mm clear opening. They should also be vented and have rodding access.

Cesspools

An average household of three persons may produce 7 m³ (the capacity of an average tanker) every three weeks. Cesspools should be sited at least 15 m from any dwelling and away from any source of drinking water. There should be vehicle access to within 30 m.

The capacity should be based on 1 m³ per head per week, which allows for some infiltation of ground water via the drains. The best shape is as shown in diagram [8.21].

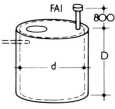

[8.21] *Septic tanks venting via the house drainage system. FAI with non-return valve 800 mm above ground.*

d = D
D (depth from cover to floor)
to be not more than 4m

May be rectangular

Septic tanks

The capacity where desludging is once per year should be:

C (litres) = 180 P + 2000

where P is the design population with a minimum of 4. Thus the minimum size becomes 2720 l (approximately, as stated in the Approved Document). This formula is adjusted for other types of building by deciding the degree of partial occupancy as compared to dwellings. Multi-compartment tanks may be needed in which case the settlement (first) zone takes up ⅔ of the total capacity.

For rectangular tanks two in series or two compartments is a good arrangement. A typical two-compartment arrangement is shown in the diagram [8.22] (redrawn from the BS).

[8.22] *Typical septic tank, two in series, for up to 30 persons. For larger installations base of first tank to be sloped at 1:4 and baffles used instead of dip pipes.*

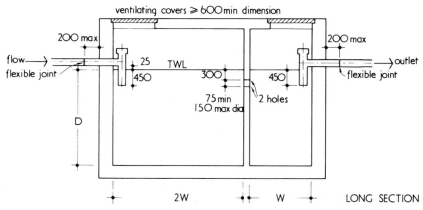

W = width ≤ 1200mm - (if more than 1200 two inlets required at the same level)
Single inlets to be placed on longitudinal centre of tank
D = 1200mm for up to 10 persons 1500 for over 10
TWL = top water level (ie invert of outfall)

Sometimes a small integral inspection chamber is included on the inlet side which makes rodding so much easier.

For populations over 60, duplicate tanks should be provided in parallel, allowing one to be in use whilst the other is desludged.

If further treatment of the effluent is required a biological filter is usually provided. This is simply a bed of inert material such as clinker or slag to promote natural aerobic degradation of the sewage (ie by contact with air, as opposed to the anaerobic action in the tank itself).

Settlement tanks

These usually form part of larger installations and the BS whilst giving recommendations stresses that specialist advice is essential.

Other stages

The BS also gives recommendations for biological filters, activated sludge units, tertiary treatment (where a better standard of effluent is required), final effluent disposal, pumping and automatic alarm systems.

H 3 RAINWATER DRAINAGE

The requirement is:

Requirement	Limits on application
H 3. Any system which carries rainwater from the roof of the building to a rainwater outfall shall be adequate.	

This is a prime example of a basic functional requirement. In itself it says very little but the Approved Document states that the requirement will be met if a rainwater drainage system:

(*a*)   Carries the rainwater from the roof to an outfall (a surface water or combined sewer, a soakaway or watercourse).

(*b*)   Minimises the risk of blockage or leakage.

(*c*)   Is accessible for clearing blockages.

As in H 1, there are two sections:

Section 1 Gutters and rainwater pipes:

Section 2 Rainwater drainage.

Introduction

0.1   Areas of 6 m² (including small roofs and balconies) can be ignored unless they receive a flow from other sources.

0.2/0.4   The capacity must be enough to accommodate a flow based on a rainfall rate of 75 mm per hour from the area to be drained and will depend on the size and gradient of the gutters and pipes. Figures are given later.

Note

BS 6367: 1983 *Code of practice for drainage of roofs and paved areas* explains that the time a particular intensity of rainfall has to be sustained to create a maximum run-off is assumed to be 2 minutes, being typical for most roofs.

It gives a number of alternatives to the 75 mm figure, based on differing return periods (T). See later note on BS 6367.

0.5   Rainwater or surface water should not be discharged to a cesspool or septic tank.

Section 1 Gutters and rainwater pipes

1.1   The flow from a roof depends on the area and pitch. For flat roofs the actual area is taken and the table shows the allowance to be made for various pitches. Roofs over 70° are treated as walls.

NOTE   The BS gives a method of calculating these factors for any pitch of roof (plan area + half area on elevation) which gives the same results for the pitches shown in the table. It is clear therefore that interpolation is in order.

Table to 1.1   Calculation of area drained

Type of surface	Effective design area (m^2)
1 flat roof	plan area of relevant portion
2 pitched roof at 30° pitched roof at 45° pitched roof at 60°	plan area of portion × 1.15 plan area of portion × 1.40 plan area of portion × 2.00
3 pitched roof over 70° or any wall	elevational area × 0.5

1.2   The maximum areas which can be drained by half-round gutters laid level with a sharp edged outlet at one end, where the distance from the stop end to the outlet is not more than 50 times the water depth, are shown in the table, which also gives minimum outlet sizes. It also includes flow capacities, but the provision of figures for areas of roof relieves the designer of having to do this calculation.

Table to 1.2   Gutter sizes and outlet sizes

Max roof area (m^2)	Gutter size (mm dia)	Outlet size (mm dia)	Flow capacity (l/s)
6.0	–	–	–
18.0	75	50	0.38
37.0	100	63	0.78
53.0	115	63	1.11
65.0	125	75	1.37
103.0	150	89	2.16

NOTE   Refers to nominal half round eaves gutters laid level with outlet at one end sharp edged. Round edged outlets allow smaller downpipe sizes.

1.3   Where the outlet is not at the end, the gutter should be sized to suit the largest area draining into it. Where there are two end outlets they may be 100 times the depth of flow apart.

Note

1.2/1.3   Although the BS contains these design methods, it would have been more helpful if the Approved Document gave an indication of maximum distances. The 1985 AD quoted 8 m and 16 m respectively.

1.4   If there is any fall it should be towards the nearest outlet. (The BS recommends a minimum fall of 1:350, really just to guard against backfall occurring). Other types of gutter section and outlets with rounded edges can increase the capacity (see BS 6367).

Any overflow in gutters caused by above normal rainfall should discharge clear of the building.

Rainwater pipes

1.5   These should discharge into a drain or gulley and any entry into a combined system must be trapped. They may however discharge onto another surface if it is drained.

NOTE   The BS describes the practice of connecting roof outlets into a discharge stack at roof level, but this would be ruled out by the above.

1.6   RWPs should be at least the size of the gutter outlet and, if serving more than one gutter, should have an area at least equal to the combined area of the outlets.

NOTE   This is not quite the same thing as saying 'large enough to serve the combined areas of roof', and would often result in a larger size than this.

Materials   **1.7**   The materials which may be used should be of adequate strength and durability. In addition:

(*a*)   All gutter joints should remain watertight under working conditions. Pipes within buildings must be able to withstand the airtightness test for sanitary pipework (see H 1. 1.32).

(*b*)   Gutters and RWPs should be firmly supported but allow for thermal movement.

(*c*)   Different metals should be separated by non-metallic material to avoid electrolytic corrosion.

The 1985 AD set out a list of suitable materials and this is reproduced below.

Materials for gutters and rainwater pipes

Material	*British Standard*
aluminium	BS 2997
cast iron	BS 416, BS 460
copper	BS 1431
galvanised steel	BS 5493
lead	BS 1178
low carbon steel	BS 5493
pressed steel	BS 1091
unplasticised pvc	BS 4514, BS 4576
zinc	BS 1431

Alternative approach   **1.8**   Alternatively, the relevant recommendations of BS 6367: 1983 can be followed. The relevant clauses are in Sections One, Two, Three (except Clause 9), Four, Five (except Clause 18) and Appendices. In fact the Approved Document itself contains so little information that in all but the simplest of buildings the designer will find a need to look to the BS for advice. A note on this follows.

Note on BS 6367: 1983 CP for drainage of roofs and paved areas   This code of practice is a very complete guide to surface water drainage. It also includes paved areas which are not covered by Requirement H 3. It has a section on materials, but the main body of the work is devoted to the hydraulic design of roof drainage. A rainfall of 75 mm/hour is taken as generally satisfactory (but see later). A simple calculation turns this into a figure of 0.02083 l/s m^2 (litres per second per square metre).

A method of allowing for roof slopes is given, namely to take the plan area of the roof plus half the area on elevation. This works for any angle, the outer limits being the net area for flat roofs and half the vertical area for walls.

Methods of design for eaves, valley and boundary or parapet wall gutters are given. Assuming adequate outlet sizes, gutter sizing depends largely on the area to be drained and the spacing of the outlets. The design method assumes that the distance between a stop end and an outlet is never more than $50 y_u$ or between two outlets more than $100 y_u$ when $y_u =$ the upstream water depth (which for eaves gutters can be taken as the depth of the gutter).

To take an example of a 100 mm half-round gutter (depth 50 mm) this would amount to a length limitation of 2.5 m and for longer lengths the BS states that a reduction factor should be applied. The 8 m length stated in the Approved Document would give a depth/length ratio of 1:160 which would require a reduction factor of 0.85, so that the figures in the Approved Document really overstate the true capacity.

Tables and graphs are given for sizing half-round and trapezoidal gutters.

The subject of outlets is dealt with in detail and the design of these has a great effect on the capacity of the whole system. Round, as opposed to sharp edged junctions, improve the performance, as also do tapered outlets and box receivers. Tables and charts are provided to determine the capacity of outlets and hence of the RWPs into which they discharge. Outlets from flat roofs are also dealt with.

Appendix A gives details for designing for higher rainfalls or higher categories of risk. A series of meteorological maps gives the return periods (T) in years where the chosen rate of rainfall sustained for two minutes may occur once. These are given for four intensities of 75, 100, 150 and 225 mm/hour. Strangely enough, the records show that although more rain falls on the upland areas of the north it is the lowland areas of the south and east that have the most short high-intensity bursts. From these maps the designer can decide, by using the appropriate return period, what intensity to use. The return period may be a fraction or multiple of the life of the building, depending on the degree of security required. The maximum security category 5 assumes a return period of 35 000 years, but this is a purely statistical figure.

Section 2   Rainwater drainage

Combined systems

2.1   Rainwater drains should only be discharged into a combined sewer if it has sufficient capacity to take the extra flow. If there is not enough capacity the rainwater should be run in a separate system with its own outfall.

Design

The following provisions apply if the system is to carry rainwater only. Surface water lifting equipment will be needed where sewers may surcharge or levels of the building or the site make impractical a gravity connection (see note on BS 8301).

Layout and depth

2.4/2.5   Paragraphs 2.3 to 2.9 of H 1 apply.

Gradient and size

2.6/2.7   Drains must have enough capacity to carry the flow. Although drainage from paved areas and other hard surfaces is not covered by building regulations, drains should have enough capacity to carry this run-off as well as drainage from the building.

2.6/2.7 **[8.23]** *Discharge capacities of rainwater drains running full. NOTE   The capacity can be increased by increasing the gradient or by using larger pipes (see solid lines).*

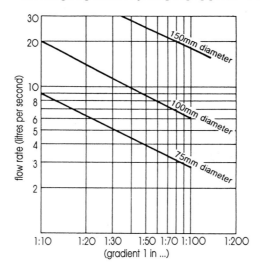

Comment
This is simply taken from the chart in BS 8301 for drains running full whereas the similar chart in H 1 is for drains running ¾ full. The capacity is only slightly increased (about 5 per cent). It should be noted that there are problems with drains running full, such as the creation of negative pressure, and this basis should therefore never be used for combined systems.

Materials, bedding, backfilling, blockages, watertightness	**2.8/2.11** The provisions are the same as those in H 1, see 2.15–2.28 (this only shows how unnecessary subdivision of subject matter leads to repetition).
British Standard method	Alternatively, the recommendations of BS 8301: 1985 *Code of practice for building drainage* may be adopted. The relevant clauses are in Sections One, Two, Three (except 7 and 10), Four (except 23), Five (25 only) and appendices. This is the same reference as for H 1.
Note on BS 8301: 1985 (regarding rainwater)	Clauses 8 and 9 of this BS deal with rainwater drainage. They make the same recommendations as the Approved Document but expand on these as follows.

Outlets
Soakaways may be suitably filled pits, lined roofed pits or seepage trenches, not closer than 5 m to a building. They work best in pervious soils. In soils of limited permeability they should have a storage capacity equal to at least 12 mm of rain below the inlet.
Entry into a watercourse should be at least 150 mm above normal water level and if backflooding is likely, a non-return valve should be fitted.
Balancing ponds or tanks may sometimes be needed upstream of the soakaway to cope with peak flows.

Flow calculations
The whole of the rainfall on impervious areas (roofs and paved areas) should be assumed to reach the drain. A formula for calculating the run-off from very large areas is given but this is not applicable to normal building drainage.

Trapping
RWPs should only enter a foul or combined drain via a trapped gulley, but may sometimes be used as vents if constructed to the standard of foul discharge pipes and vented to the open at points where they would not be a nuisance (away from any openings). Note that this would not be permitted by the Approved Document (1.5) but it seems likely that Local Authorities would accept a method approved in a British Standard. A series of RWPs may be connected together without trapping if an interceptor is provided at the point of entry into the foul drain.
Clause 15 deals extensively with sewerage and surface water lifting installations.
The installation should be sited as near as practicable to the appliances or areas to be served having regard to matters such as access and potential noise nuisance. Various types of apparatus are mentioned together with criteria to be considered in the selection of equipment, particularly durability and economy in whole-life cost.
A delivery main from a sewage lifting installation should rise continuously to its point of discharge.

H 4   SOLID WASTE STORAGE

The requirement is:

Requirement	Limits on application
Solid waste storage	H 4. (1) Adequate means of storing solid waste shall be provided. (2) Adequate means of access shall be provided – (*a*) for people in the building to the place of storage, and (*b*) from the place of storage to a street.

Performance	The requirement will be met by the following performance. Solid waste storage should be: (*a*) designed and sited so as not to be prejudicial to health, (*b*) of sufficient capacity having regard to the quantity and frequency of removal, (*c*) accessible for filling by people in the building and of ready access for emptying and removal.

Introduction	**0.1** The efficacy of a refuse storage system is dependent on its capacity and the ease of removal in relation to the collection service provided by the collecting authority. The Approved Document is now under two headings – domestic and non-domestic developments.

Domestic developments	*Capacity* **1.1/1.2** In low-rise developments, any dwelling should have access to a movable container of at least $0.12\,m^3$ per dwelling or a communal waste container with a capacity between $0.75\,m^3$ and $1\,m^3$. (This assumes a weekly collection and an output of $0.09\,m^3$ per dwelling, where the service is less frequent, more individual or larger capacity containers will be needed.) Dwellings up to the fourth storey may each have their own or share a container. Above four storeys refuse chutes should be provided, but if this is not practicable there should be a satisfactory management arrangement for taking refuse to the storage area. *Design* **1.3/1.5** Containers should have close-fitting lids unless fed by chute. Chutes should have a smooth non-absorbent surface, close-fitting access doors and be ventilated top and bottom. Containers need not be enclosed, but if they are, the enclosure should allow room for filling and emptying and provide a clear space of 150 mm between and around containers. For communal containers this space should be at least 2 m high with ventilation openings at top and bottom. *Siting* **1.6/1.7** Householders should not have to carry refuse further than 30 m and containers should be within 25 m of the vehicle access. In new buildings they should be capable of collection without passing through a building (except for garage, carport or open covered space).

Non-domestic developments	**1.8** The collecting authority should be consulted where other types of development such as high density are planned. Guidance should be sought on: (*a*) The volume and nature of the waste, and storage capacity required. This will have to be based on the size and type of the container and the frequency of collection. (*b*) The method of storage, including any on-site treatment proposed. (*c*) The location of storage and treatment areas and access to them for removal. (*d*) Hygiene arrangements. (*e*) Fire hazards and protection measures.

British Standard 5906	**1.9** It is significant that here the BS is referred to in the general guidance and is not quoted as an alternative approach. The relevant clauses in BS 5906: 1980 *Code of practice for storage and on-site treatment of solid waste from buildings* are Clauses 3 to 10, 12 to 15 and Appendix A. Under 'General principles' the BS stresses the importance of adequate storage space, maximum convenience for user and collector, hygiene, amenity, fire risk and sound insulation (also provision for salvageable material). Storage provision depends on the volume and nature of the waste and frequency of collection. An approximate figure per dwelling per week is 12 kg at a density of $133\,kg/m^3$ (both figures plus or minus 10 per cent). Individual containers (bins or sacks suitably protected) are recommended for houses. Shelters if provided should be open to the air and large enough to contain two bins, about $0.8\,m^3$, which is twice the capacity shown in the Approved Document. Blocks up to four storeys should have either chutes or communal containers sited to be within 30 m horizontally from each dwelling. Over four storeys chutes should always be provided. It is also recommended that chutes should be not further than 30 m from any dwelling they serve and that hoppers should not serve more than six dwellings.

[8.24] *Requirements for refuse hoppers. In addition, hoppers must not be situated in a dwelling, and must be made entirely of non-combustible material.*

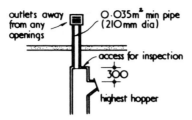

outlets away from any openings

0.035m² min pipe (210mm dia)

access for inspection

300

highest hopper

Alternative ventilation

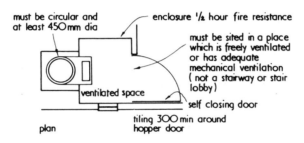

arranged to prevent the emission of dust, foul air and noise whether open or closed

does not project into refuse chute

hinged so that it cannot stay in any intermediate position and must be open or closed

section

Hopper detail

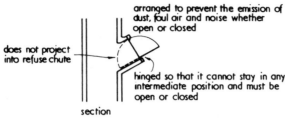

must be circular and at least 450mm dia

enclosure ½ hour fire resistance

must be sited in a place which is freely ventilated or has adequate mechanical ventilation (not a stairway or stair lobby)

ventilated space

self closing door

tiling 300 min around hopper door

plan

Hopper compartment

[8.25] *Chutes and storage chambers.*

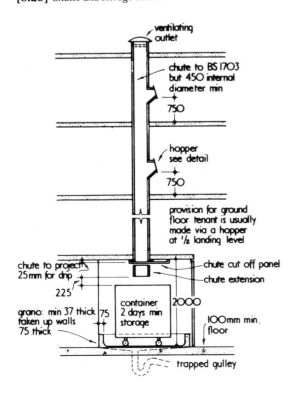

ventilating outlet

chute to BS 1703 but 450 internal diameter min

750

hopper see detail

750

provision for ground floor tenant is usually made via a hopper at ½ landing level

chute to project 25mm for drip

225

grano: min 37 thick taken up walls 75 thick

container 2 days min storage

75

2000

chute cut off panel

chute extension

100mm min. floor

trapped gulley

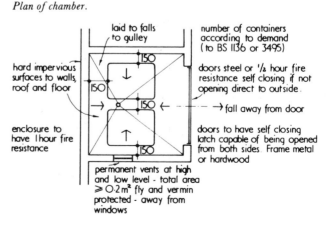

Section.

Plan of chamber.

laid to falls to gulley

hard impervious surfaces to walls, roof and floor

enclosure to have 1 hour fire resistance

number of containers according to demand (to BS 1136 or 3495)

doors steel or ½ hour fire resistance self closing if not opening direct to outside.

fall away from door

doors to have self closing latch capable of being opened from both sides. Frame metal or hardwood

150

150

150

150

permanent vents at high and low level - total area ≥ 0.2 m² fly and vermin protected - away from windows

References

The following British Standards and other documents are referred to in the Approved Document.

H1

BS 65: 1981 *Specification for vitrified clay pipes fittings and joints* Amendment 1: AMD 4328. Amendment 2: AMD 4394.

BS 416: 1973 *Cast iron spigot and socket soil, waste and ventilating pipes (sand cast and spun) and fittings* Amendment 1: AMD 3113.

BS 437: 1978 *Specification for cast iron spigot and socket drain pipes and fittings.*

BS 864 *Capillary and compression tube fittings of copper and copper alloy.* Part 2: 1983 *Specification for capillary and compression fittings for copper tubes.* Amendment 1: AMD 5097. Amendment 2: AMD 5651.

BS 882: 1983 *Specification for aggregates from natural sources for concrete.* Amendment 1: AMD 5150.

BS 2871 *Copper and copper alloys. Tubes.* Part 1: 1971 *Copper tubes for water, gas and sanitation* Amendment 1: AMD 1422. Amendment 2: AMD 2203.

BS 3656: 1981 *Specification for asbestos-cement pipes, joints and fittings for sewerage and drainage.*

BS 3868: 1973 *Prefabricated drainage stack units: galvanised steel.*

BS 3921: 1976 *Clay bricks.*

BS 3843: 1979 *Specification for plastics waste traps* Amendment 1: AMD 3206. Amendment 2: AMD 4191. Amendment 3: AMD 4692.

BS 4514: 1983 *Specification for unplasticised PVC soil and ventilating pipes, fittings and accessories* Amendment 1: AMD 4517.

BS 4660: 1973 *Unplasticised PVC underground drain pipe and fittings* Amendment 1: AMD 2514. Amendment 2: AMD 3708. Amendment 3: AMD 4006. Amendment 4: AMD 4081. Amendment 5: 4441.

BS 5254: 1976 *Polypropylene waste pipe and fittings (external diameter 34.6 mm, 41.0 mm and 54.1 mm)* Amendment 1: AMD 3588. Amendment 2: AMD 4438.

BS 5255: 1976: *Plastics waste pipes and fittings* Amendment 1: AMD 3565, 2: AMD 3854, 3: AMD 4472.

BS 5481: 1977 *Specification for unplasticised PVC pipe and fittings for gravity sewers* Amendment 1: AMD 3631. Amendment 2: AMD 4436.

BS 5572: 1978 *Code of practice for sanitary pipework* Amendment 1: AMD 3613. Amendment 2: 4202.

BS 5911 *Precast concrete pipes and fittings for drainage and sewerage.* Part 1: 1981 *Specification for concrete cylindrical pipes, bends, junctions and manholes, unreinforced or reinforced with steel cages or hoops.* Amendment 1: AMD 4035. Part 2: 1982 *Specification for inspection chambers and gullies.* Amendment 1. AMD 5904.

BS 8301: 1985 *Code of practice for building drainage* Amendment 1: AMD 5904.

BS 8110: *Structural use of concrete.* Part 1: 1985 *Code of practice for design and construction.*

H2

BS 5328: 1981. *Methods for specifying concrete including ready mixed concrete.* Amendment 1: AMD 4862. Amendment 2: 4970.

BS 6297: 1983 *Code of practice for design and installation of small sewage treatment works and cesspools.*

H3

BS 6367: 1983 *Code of practice for drainage of roofs and paved areas.* Amendment 1: AMD 4444.

BS 8301: 1985 *Code of practice for building drainage* Amendment 1: AMD 5904.

H4

BS 5906: 1980 (1987) *Code of practice for the storage and on-site treatment of solid waste from buildings.*

Chapter 9

Approved Document J Heat Producing Appliances

Although the requirement remains the same as in the 1985 Regulations, the Approved Document has been completely rearranged into four sections. The first deals with provisions which apply to all appliances followed by three sections covering appliances burning different fuels.

The sections are:

1.   General provisions.

2.   Additional provisions for solid fuel burning appliances with a rated output up to 45 kW.

3.   Additional provisions for individually flued (non-fan-assisted) gas burning appliances with a rated input up to 60 kW (and air supply for cooking appliances).

4.   Additional provisions for oil burning appliances with a rated output up to 45 kW.

There are quite a few changes and these deal with air extract fans, performance of chimneys and solid fuel effect fires.

The requirement is:

Requirement	Limits on application
Air supply J 1. Heat producing appliances shall be so installed that there is an adequate supply of air to them for combustion and for the efficient working of any flue-pipe or chimney. *Discharge of products of combustion* J 2. Heat producing appliances shall have adequate provision for the discharge of the products of combustion to the outside air. *Protection of building* J 3. Heat producing appliances and flue-pipes shall be so installed, and fireplaces and chimneys shall be so constructed, as to reduce to a reasonable level the risk of the building catching fire in consequence of their use.	The requirements in this Part apply only to fixed heat producing appliances which – (*a*) are designed to burn solid fuel, oil or gas; or (*b*) are incinerators.

The Approved Document sets out the performance which will meet the requirement in this case and says the same thing as the requirement in a slightly different way.

An installation will meet the requirement if it

(*a*)   receives sufficient air for the proper combustion of the fuel and the operation of the flue, and is capable of normal operation without –

(*b*)   the products of combustion becoming a hazard to health, and

(*c*)   causing damage by heat or fire to the fabric of the building.

Section 1 Provisions which apply generally

1.1　'Non-combustible' means able to be classified as such under BS 476. *Fire tests on building materials and structures,* Part 4: 1970 (1984): *Non-combustibility tests for materials.* Materials of limited combustibility as defined in Appendix A or Part B will not do.

Air supply to appliances

1.2　The appliance should either be room sealed or if it is not, the room containing the appliance should have a ventilation opening. This opening should not be in a wall which is required to be fire resisting. If the ventilation opening is to another room, then that room should have an opening of at least the same size direct to the open air.

Air extract fans

1.3　A heat producing appliance and its flue should be able to operate effectively whether or not the fan of any air extract plant in the building is running.
This, of course, does not apply to a room-sealed appliance.
Previously the Approved Document stated that extract fans should only be fitted where the appliance was room sealed but the 1990 amendments to Part F (Ventilation) impinge on this. The code of practice appropriate to the fuel used in the appliance should be consulted with regard to the level of effective operation.

Flue pipes and chimneys

1.4　Appliances should connect either with a balanced flue or a flue pipe or chimney which discharges to external air. Exception is made for appliances such as gas cookers which are designed to operate without a flue.

Openings into flues

1.5/1.6　The only openings into flues should be for:
(*a*)　inspection and cleaning – the opening should be fitted with a rigid, non-combustible gastight cover, or
(*b*)　fitting an explosion door, draught stabiliser or draught diverter.
A flue may serve more more than one appliance in the same room but should not open into more than one room except for cleaning or inspection purposes.

Chimneys built under former control

1.7　The regulations do not apply to chimneys which were constructed before the Building Regulations came into being, ie 1 February 1966. Where such a chimney is to be used and there is no obvious indication that the chimney is unsatisfactory it may be considered as satisfying the requirement. The fact is that all chimneys under former control are exempt, but it is certainly advisable to provide linings where appliances such as wood burning stoves are to be installed.

Section 2 Additional provisions for solid fuel burning appliances with a rated output of up to 45 kW

Air supply to appliances

2.1　Rooms containing solid fuel appliances should contain an air entry opening or openings as follows:
If the appliance is an open appliance – a total free area of at least 50 per cent of the appliance throat area.
　　　　　　　　　　　　　　　　　　– Defined in BS 8303: 1986.
Any other solid fuel appliance:　　a total free area of at least 550 mm per kW of rated output above 5 kW, and where a draught flue stabiliser is used, the total free area should be increased by 300 mm for each kW of rated output.

NOTE　The provision of the correct amount of air for both ventilation and combustion is very important.

Appliances need to draw air for combustion, and if insufficient air is provided, the appliance will take the oxygen from the air in a room. If an appliance cannot draw adequate air from the room, combustion may not be complete and the products of combustion may return to the room. Air vents for all appliances should preferably be direct to external air. If extract fans are fitted in rooms (now a requirement in kitchens and bathrooms – see Part F1) which also contain appliances, extra ventilation may be needed.

Size of flues

2.2   Minimum sizes – Flue pipes
At least equal to the size of the outlet on the appliance
– Chimneys
Never less than the size of the outlet on the appliance or that recommended by the manufacturer and at least the size shown in the Table.

Table to 2.2   Size of flues

Installation	Minimum flue size
Fireplace recess with an opening up to 500 mm × 550 mm	200 mm dia.
Inglenook recess appliances	A free area of 15% of the area of the recess opening
Open fire	200 mm dia.
Closed appliance up to 20 kW rated output	125 dia.
Closed appliance up to 20 kW burning bituminous coal or closed appliance above 20 kW and up to 30 kW	150 dia.
Closed appliance above 30 kW and up to 45 kW rated output	175 mm dia.

NOTE   Should an offset be necessary the flue size should be increased by 25 mm in diameter or where a square flue of equivalent area is used 25 mm on each side.

Outlets from flues

2.3   The provisions regarding outlets from flues have been considerably simplied, as diagram [9.1] shows.
There is now no reference to chimneys but areas above a roof are shown within which flues should not terminate.
NOTE   Section 73 of the Building Act 1984 gives local authorities special powers when a building is erected or raised to overreach existing chimneys. If these are in a party wall or within 6 feet of the new building, the owner may be required to raise them to the same height as his building or its chimneys.

2.3 **[9.1]** *Flue outlets.*

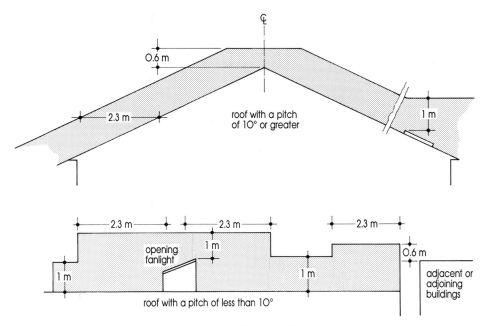

flue outlet should terminate outside the shaded area

Direction of flues

2.4/2.5 Flues should be vertical wherever possible and there should be no horizontal flue runs. Where an appliance has a back outlet, the length of the horizontal section should not exceed 150 mm. See diagram [9.2].

Where bends are necessary they should not make an angle of more than 30° with the vertical.

2.4/2.5 **[9.2]** *Direction of flues.*

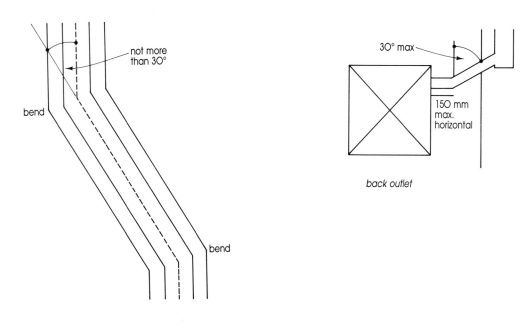

Flue pipes

2.6, 2.8/2.9 A flue pipe should only be used to connect an appliance to a chimney; flue pipes with spigot and socket joints should have the sockets uppermost. Flue pipes should not pass through a roof space and should be separated from combustible material by the distances shown in the diagram [9.3]. The previous Approved Document stated that flue pipes should not pass through any internal wall or partition or a floor but this is now omitted.

2.9 **[9.3]** *Separating flue pipe from surface of adjacent combustible material.*

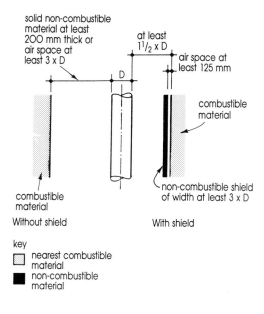

Materials for flue pipes

2.7 Any of the following may be used:

(*a*) cast iron as described in BS 41; 1973 (1981) *Specification for cast iron spigot and socket flue or smoke pipes and fittings*, or

(*b*) mild steel with a wall thickness of at least 3 mm

(*c*) stainless steel with a wall thickness of at least 1 mm and as described in BS 1449 *Steel plate, sheet and strip*, Part 2: 1983 *Specification for stainless and heat resisting steel plate, sheet and a strip for Grade 316 S11, 316 S13, 316 S16, 316 S31, 316 S33* or the equivalent Euronorm 88-71 designation, or

(*d*) vitreous enamelled steel complying with BS 6999: 1989 *Specification for vitreous enamelled low carbon steel flue pipes*, other components and accessories for solid fuel burning appliances with a maximum rated output of 45 kW.

Chimneys

General

2.10 Should withstand a temperature of 1100°C without impairing structural stability or performance of the chimney.

2.11 A debris collecting space which is accessible for emptying should be provided where the chimney is not directly over an appliance.

Brick (linings)

2.12 Brick chimneys should be lined with –

(*a*) clay flue liners with rebated and socketed joints to BS 1181: 1971 (1977) or

(*b*) imperforate clay pipes with socketed joints to BS 65: 1981 or

(*c*) high alumina cement and kiln burnt or pumice aggregate pipes with joints rebated and socketed or having steel collars around the joints (see diagram [9.4]).

2.12 **[9.4]** *Chimney linings to BS 1181: 1971. The BS also includes terminals, and gives maximum external diameters for circular pipes. These, with tolerances allowed for internal diameters, are based generally on a pipe wall thickness of about 20 mm. Linings of type (b) (mentioned above) are normal BS 65 Drain pipes, available in a wider range of diameters and bends.*

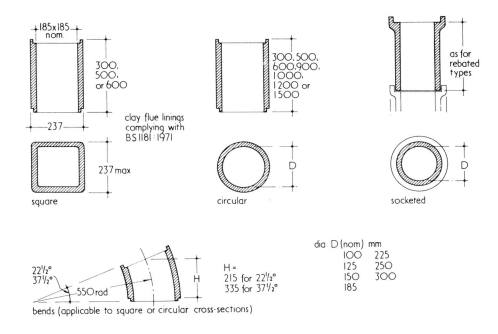

Blockwork

2.13 Chimneys should be made of refractory material or a combination of high alumina cement and kiln burnt or pumice aggregates or lined as in 2.12.

Wall thickness

2.14 Walls of masonry construction should have the thickness excluding the liner as shown in diagram [9.5].

2.14 **[9.5]** *Masonry chimneys: construction.*

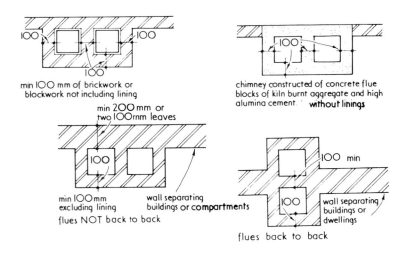

min 100 mm of brickwork or
blockwork not including lining

chimney constructed of concrete flue
blocks of kiln burnt aggregate and high
alumina cement. **without linings**

min 200 mm or
two 100mm leaves

min 100mm
excluding lining

wall separating
buildings or **compartments**

flues **NOT** back to back

100   min

wall separating
buildings or
dwellings

flues back to back

Combustible material
2.15   Should not be placed in the shaded area shown in diagram [9.6].

2.15 **[9.6]** *Combustible material adjacent to flues.*

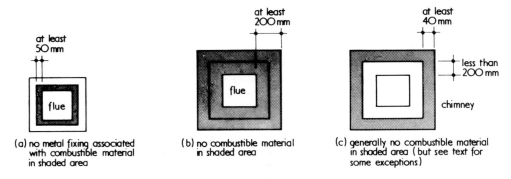

at least
50 mm

flue

(a) no metal fixing associated
with combustible material
in shaded area

at least
200 mm

flue

(b) no combustible material
in shaded area

at least
40 mm

less than
200 mm

chimney

(c) generally no combustible material
in shaded area (but see text for
some exceptions)

Exceptions referred to in (*c*) are a floorboard, skirting, dado or picture rail, mantelshelf or
architrave.

Factory made insulated
chimneys

2.16/2.17   Factory made insulated chimneys should be constructed and tested in accordance
with BS 4543 as follows:
Method of test   Part 1: 1976
Solid fuel appliances Part 2: 1976

These deal with prefabricated chimneys suitable for industrialised housing for use with
appliances up to 45 kW output. They consist of an internal corrosion and heat resistant pipe
surrounded by insulation and a weather resistant casing (although some are designed for
internal situations).
Chimneys complying with Part 2 are also suitable for oil and for gas appliances.
Linings are either stainless steel of a specific composition or vitrified clay to BS 1181. Outer
casings are aluminium, stainless steel or galvanised or aluminium coated sheet steel.
They must be designed for assembly and erection on site without any cutting, drilling or
alteration (ie purpose made for each situation). They must be properly supported and provided
with firestops.
For details of these recommendations and sizes see diagram [9.7].
A sequence of 8 tests must be carried through (one occurs three times) for support, joint leakage,
flue draught, thermal shock, thermal insulation and strength. A minimum standard for each is
specified. The test procedures are laid down in Part 1.
A factory made insulated chimney should not:
(*a*)   Pass through a separate compartment unless cased in non-combustible material with at
least half the fire resistance of the compartment wall or floor. Diagram [9.8] shows a possible

2.16/2.17 **[9.7]** *Factory made chimney detail.*

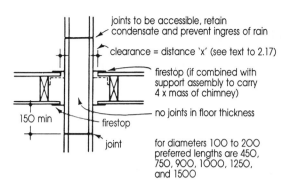

joints to be accessible, retain condensate and prevent ingress of rain

clearance = distance 'x' (see text to 2.17)

firestop (if combined with support assembly to carry 4 x mass of chimney)

no joints in floor thickness

150 min

firestop

joint

for diameters 100 to 200 preferred lengths are 450, 750, 900, 1000, 1250, and 1500

2.16/2.17 **[9.8]** *Factory made chimney passing through compartment wall.*

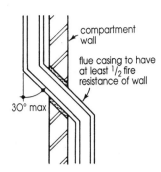

compartment wall

flue casing to have at least ½ fire resistance of wall

30° max

situation in relation to a compartment wall. (See Approved Document B 3 *Internal fire spread (structure)* for more information.)

(*b*)   Be positioned, with its outer wall nearer to combustible material than 'x'.

(*c*)   Pass through a cupboard, storage space or roof space unless surrounded by a non-combustible guard at least 'x' from the outer wall of the chimney.

The value of 'x' is explained in BS 4543: Part 1 and is either 40 mm or the distance stated by the manufacturer whose product is under test.

Constructional hearths, fireplace recesses and location of appliances

2.18/2.22   Constructional hearths must always be provided. The details of these, fireplace recesses, walls adjacent to hearths and location of appliances are shown in diagrams [9.9] to [9.12].

2.18/2.19 **[9.9]** *Constructional hearths.*

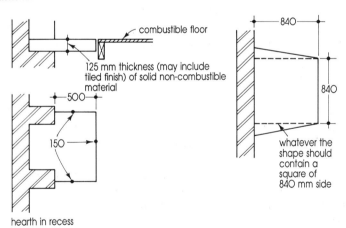

combustible floor

125 mm thickness (may include tiled finish) of solid non-combustible material

500

150

hearth in recess

840

840

whatever the shape should contain a square of 840 mm side

NOTES   *All dimensions are minima. Hearth to be of non-combustible material. If a solid fuel burning appliance is installed over a constructional hearth built before 1/2/66, that hearth need not comply with the minimum dimensions for projection (500 mm) and square size (840 mm) shown here.*

2.20 **[9.10]** *Permitted constructions of fireplace recesses.*

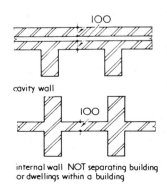

100

cavity wall

100

internal wall NOT separating building or dwellings within a building

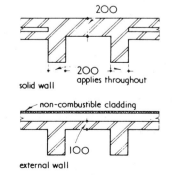

200

solid wall

200 applies throughout

non-combustible cladding

100

external wall

All dimensions are minima.
Construction to be solid non-combustible material.
Thickness of wall at back must extend to full height of recess.

2.21 [9.11] *Walls and partitions adjoining hearths for solid-fuel burning appliances.*

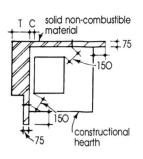
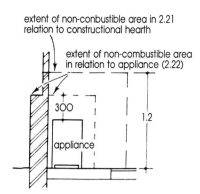

if clearance C is less than 50 mm
thickness T is at least 200 mm

C more than 50 mm
thickness T at least 75 mm

2.22 [9.12] *Appliance on constructional hearth.*

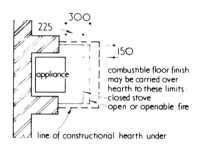
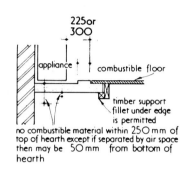

Alternative approach

The requirement may also be met by following the relevant recommendations of BS 8303: 1986. The Approved Document does not state which parts are relevant so it is presumed that all the recommendations should be used.

Note on BS 8303: 1986

This BS deals with four types of appliance –
(*a*)   open fires without convection
(*b*)   room heaters
(*c*)   independent boilers and free standing cookers
(*d*)   warm air heating appliances – natural convection.
Although this code of practice gives useful information the detail contained in BS 6461, Part 1: 1984 (the alternative approach in the previous Approved Document) is more pertinent to the designer. In fact BS 8303 reverts back to BS 6461 and the alternative approach should perhaps have referred to both standards.
It is regarded as essential to avoid the creation of negative pressure in the room or space in which the appliance is installed. Such negative pressure may lead to escape of products of combustion from openings in the appliance which may be drawn into the room. Extract fans should not be installed in the room or space in which the appliance is situated. Provision should be made for combustion and ventilation sufficient for the type of appliance in accordance with the manufacturer's instructions.

Note on BS 6461: Part 1: 1984

This deals with the installation of chimneys and flues for domestic appliances burning solid fuel (including wood and peat). Part 1 gives recommendations for flues whether in chimneys or flue pipes.
It includes recommendations for chimneys of brick, stone, concrete or flue blocks and also on materials for flue pipes and their installation, serving appliances up to 45 kW. The flue gas temperatures are assumed generally not to exceed 500°C but it is accepted that this may be exceeded for short periods. More information is available in BS 8303 with regard to chimney height and fireplace recess construction.
Flues built to this standard are also suitable for oil or gas appliances.
The BS does not conflict in any way with Approved Document J, which is clearly based upon it, but it provides more detail, particularly by way of explaining the basis of the recommendations.

It gives general principles for chimney design which include:

(*a*)   Totally non-combustible, durable, temperature and corrosion resistant construction.

(*b*)   Chimneys to be lined unless of special flueblocks.

(*c*)   Area and height chosen in relation to appliance.

(*d*)   Prevention of air leakage and excessive heat loss.

(*e*)   Avoidance of rough interiors, flat gradients and sudden changes of direction.

(*f*)   Limit the number of bends and keep angles as small as possible.

(*g*)   Locate terminals to avoid pressure zones and away from openings.

(*h*)   Build stacks in materials to suit exposed conditions (eg the bricks may need to be different from those used in general building).

(*i*)   Site chimneys on internal walls if possible (to conserve heat).

Size

The recommendations follow the Approved Document for open appliances with openings up to 500 × 550 mm. For larger sizes the flue area should be 14 to 16 per cent of the free area of the fire opening. For closed appliances a flue of 150 nominal diameter is suitable.

A total height of 4.5 m is usually adequate for draught.

Fireplace recesses: there are diagrams showing recommended dimensions and construction.

Other details: flues are best vertical, but if bends are necessary they should be limited to two and angles of 45° (preferably 30°) to the vertical. A flue should serve only one appliance and there should be no openings except for cleaning and inspection or a draught stabiliser.

External: the recommendations for projection above roofs are as in the Approved Document, but there are also notes on the design of flue terminals and chimney terminals (the top of the stack).

Structural: there is a rule about the height of chimneys above roofs in relation to width (4.5 × the least dimension) which is as laid down in Approved Document A Section 1D. There is also a lot more advice on foundations, general structural design and stays.

Fire precautions: the outside surface should not exceed 70°C under working conditions (usually achieved by 100 mm of masonry). Other recommendations are as those in the AD.

There are sections on flue linings, brickwork, stonework, blockwork and concrete construction, and also on the use of purpose made flue blocks which do not need lining and which should have rebated joints and rounded internal angles.

Flue pipes: There are the same recommendations as in the AD and in addition they should be as short as possible, contain not more than two bends and be accessible for inspection throughout. For pipes close to surfaces the effects of radiation may be reduced by insulation as well as by shielding. Access for cleaning should be provided where this cannot be done through the appliance or chimney soot door.

There are sections on site inspection and testing and appendices on remedial action, cleaning and maintenance, as well as a number of diagrams.

Section 3   Additional provisions for individually flued (non-fan assisted) gas burning appliances with a rated input up to 60 kW (and air supply for cooking appliances)

Solid fuel effect appliances

3.1   These gas appliances simulate the burning of coal and wood with a live flame. They should be installed in accordance with the manufacturer's instructions where they have been tested by the approved authority. There is no mention of what is considered to be an approved authority. Those not so tested should be installed in accordance with BS 6714: 1986 or with the provisions of Section 2 (ie as for solid fuel appliances).

Appliances in bathrooms and garages

3.2   Attention is drawn to the Gas Safety (Installation and Use) Regulations 1984 which require that any appliance in a bath or shower room or a private garage must be a room-sealed type.

Air supply to appliances (other than balanced flued or solid fuel effect appliances)

3.3   *Room or space containing cooker.*
Should have an opening window or other means of providing ventilation.
If in a small room, ie less than 10 m², a permanent ventilation opening of at least 5000 mm should be provided.

3.4   *Room or space containing open flued appliance.*
A permanent ventilation opening of at least 450 mm for each kW of appliance input rating over 7 kW, ie for a 12 kW appliance a ventilation opening of 5 × 450 mm = 2250 mm would be necessary.

Size of flues

3.5   The provisions are as shown in diagram [9.13].

3.5 **[9.13]** *Size of flues.*

(a) Gas fire

12,000 mm² cross sectional area

16,500 mm² cross sectional area with D≥ 90 mm

(b) any other appliance
Cross sectional area at least equal to that of appliance outlet.

Direction of flues (other than balanced flues)

3.6   There should be no horizontal runs and any necessary bends in a flue should not make an angle of more than 45° with the vertical.

Outlets from flues

3.7   Outlets from balanced flues as illustrated in diagram [9.14].
3.8   Outlets from any other appliance as in diagram [9.15].

3.7 **[9.14]** *Balanced flue terminals.*

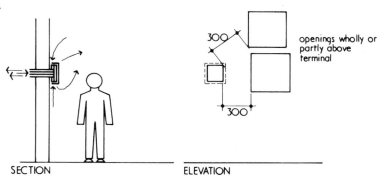

SECTION   ELEVATION

300

openings wholly or partly above terminal

300

• situated to allow free intake of air and dispersal of products
• protected by guard if it may be in contact with people or be damaged
• designed to prevent entry of matter which may restrict flue

3.8 **[9.15]** *(a) Detail of outlet terminal. (b) Siting of outlet terminals in respect of openings.*
NOTE   Terminal not required if flue outlet exceeds 175 mm across the axis.

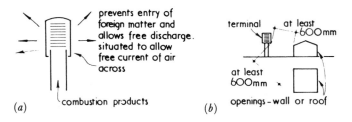

prevents entry of foreign matter and allows free discharge. situated to allow free current of air across

(a)   combustion products

terminal   at least 600mm

at least 600mm

openings – wall or roof

(b)

Flue pipes

Materials
3.9   Any material listed in Section 2 (for solid fuel appliances) may be used or any of the following:
(a)   sheet metal as described in BS 715: 1986 *Specification for metal flue pipes, fittings, terminals and accessories* for gas-fired appliances with a rated output not exceeding 60 kW, or

(*b*)   asbestos cement as described in BS 567: 1973 (1984) *Specification for asbestos-cement flue pipes and fittings, light quality*, or BS 835: 1973 (1984) *Specification for asbestos-cement flue pipes and fittings, heavy quality*, or

(*c*)   cast iron as described in BS 41: 1973 (1981), or

(*d*)   any material described in Section 2 for a solid fuel appliance, or

(*e*)   any other material fit for its intended purpose.

NOTE   3.9(e) is an interesting provision as it simply amplifies the whole concept of the Approved Documents (see Introduction).

Shielding

3.10   Flue pipes should be shielded from combustible material to reduce the risk of setting fire to the building. The provisions are illustrated in diagram [9.16].

3.10 **[9.16]** *Shielding of flue pipes.*

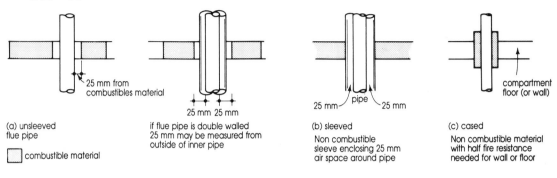

Chimneys

3.11/3.12   Brick chimneys should be lined with materials similar to those described for solid fuel appliances (see 2.12).

Blockwork chimneys should be constructed of flue blocks as described in BS 1289.

3.13   Flexible flue liners complying with BS 715: 1970 may be used if the chimney was built before 1 February 1966 or is already lined.

NOTE   These are no longer permissible for solid fuel burning appliances.

3.14   Chimneys which are not lined or constructed in accordance with 3.11 to 3.13 above should have a debris collecting space at the base of at least $0.012\,m^2$ and a depth of 250 mm below the point of connection of the appliance. Ready access for debris clearance should be available by removal of the appliance or otherwise.

Wall thickness

3.15   The thickness of a brick or blockwork chimney should be at least 25 mm. There are also special provisions for compartment walls and floors as shown in diagram [9.17].

Factory made insulated chimneys

3.16   Factory made insulated chimneys described in Sections 2 or 4 may be used for gas.

Hearths (other than for solid fuel effect appliances)

3.17/3.19   These should always be provided unless:

(*a*)   Any flame or incandescent material is not less than 225 mm above the floor (see diagram [9.18]) or

(*b*)   The appliance complies with the recommendations of the appropriate parts of BS 5258: *Safety of domestic gas appliances* or BS 5386: *Specification for gas burning appliances* which refer to installation without a hearth.

BS 5258 has a number of parts each dealing with a different type of appliance. They are mostly concerned with the safety standards of the appliances themselves, but include in each case a test rig to simulate the complete installation, designed to establish that floor and wall temperatures in the immediate vicinity do not rise by more than 50°C during operation. In such circumstances special provisions for protecting adjacent combustible material are not necessary. If these conditions are not met a hearth at least 12 mm thick of solid non-combustible material must be provided, as shown in diagram [9.19].

Back boilers require special attention. The Approved Document refers loosely to a 'back boiler whether installed alone or with another appliance' and the accompanying diagram (illustrated in diagram [9.20] to demonstrate the degree of ambiguity) is quite unsatisfactory, as is the terminology. A 'back boiler', by definition, is behind something else and cannot therefore be installed on its own. The usual arrangement is a combination of gas fire and small central heating boiler behind. Such boilers may however also be fitted in a fireplace recess behind a decorative closure screen (when they are usually known as circulators). In such cases the front projection of the hearth may be measured from the front of the boiler. If however there is a fire in front of the boiler, the 225 mm front projection must clearly be taken from the flame position of the fire, as for other appliances. Diagram [9.20] illustrates the situation.

In both cases the construction of the hearth for these appliances must be solid non-combustible material either:

125 mm thick (ie as for Section 2 hearths) or

25 mm thick on non-combustible supports at least 25 mm high.

3.15 **[9.17]** *Chimney walls.*

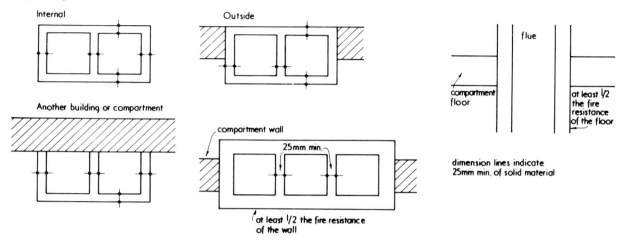

3.17/3.19 **[9.18]** *Appliance fixed above floor.*

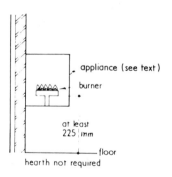

3.17/3.19 **[9.19]** *Hearth (general).*

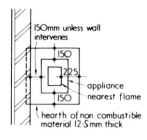

3.17/3.19 **[9.20]** *Hearth for backboiler.*

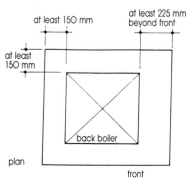

Backboiler (as in AD. J)

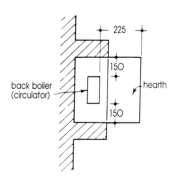

Circulator only

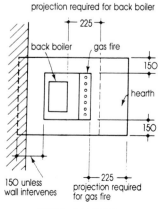

Combined appliance

Shielding of appliances

3.25 This really should be headed 'proximity to combustible material' because unless the appliance is within 75 mm no shield is needed. Diagram [9.21] shows the requirement. This does not apply to appliances which comply with the relevant recommendations of BS 5258: *Safety of domestic appliances* or BS 5386: *Specifications for gas burning appliances.*

3.20 **[9.21]** *Appliances: separation from combustible material.*

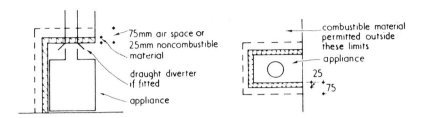

Section 4   Additional provisions for oil burning appliances with a rated output up to 45 kW

Air supply to appliances

4.1 Any room or space containing an appliance (other than a balanced flued appliance) should have a permanent ventilation opening of free area at least 550 mm² for each kW of rated output over 5 kW.

Flues (other than balanced or low level flues)

4.2/4.3 Size. A flue pipe should be at least the same size as the flue outlet. A chimney should have a diameter (or if square, an equivalent cross-sectional area) relative to the rated output of the appliance:

Rated output	Diameter (mm)
up to 20 kW	100
20 to 32 kW	125
32 to 45 kW	150

Horizontal runs should be avoided: bends should not be more than 45°.

Outlets from flues

4.4 Balanced flue terminals should be as shown in diagram [9.14] but note that the outlet should be 600 mm minimum from *any* opening either above or below it.

Flue pipes and brick and blockwork chimneys

4.7 The temperature of the flue gases under the worst operating conditions should be ascertained.
Flue pipes and chimneys should be constructed as for solid fuel appliances (paragraphs 2.6/2.8 and 2.10/2.14) if the temperature is likely to exceed 260°C and if not they may be constructed as for gas appliances, paragraphs 3.9/3.15.

Factory made insulated chimneys

4.8/4.9 These should be constructed and tested to BS 4543 Part 1: 1976 and Part 3: 1976 *Specification for chimneys for oil fired appliances* and installed in a manner similar to the provisions in the Approved Document for solid fuel appliances (2.16(*b*) and 2.17).

Hearths

4.10 If the surface temperature of the floor below the appliance is
(*a*)   likely to exceed 100°C a construction hearth should be provided (paragraphs 2.18 and 2.19 – solid fuel appliances), or
(*b*)   not likely to exceed 100°C, the appliance may stand on a rigid imperforate sheet of non-combustible material without a constructional hearth.

Shielding of appliances   **4.11**   If the surface temperature of the sides and back of the appliance is likely to exceed 100°C, the appliance should be shielded as described in paragraphs 3.20(*a*) or (*b*) – gas fired appliances.

Alternative approach   The requirements may also be met by following the relevant recommendations of BS 5410: *Code of practice for oil firing*: Part 1: 1977. *Installations up to 44 kW output for space heating and hot water supply purposes.*

Once again there are no relevant sections indicated.

References

BS 41: 1973 (1981) *Cast iron spigot and socket flue or smoke pipes and fittings.*

BS 65: 1981 *Specification for vitrified clay pipes, fittings and joints,* AMD 4328 and AMD 4394.

BS 476: *Fire tests on building materials and structures,* Part 4: 1970 (1984). *Non-combustibility tests for materials,* AMD 2483 and AMD 4390.

BS 567: 1973 (1984) *Specification for asbestos-cement flue pipes and fittings, light quality.*

BS 715: 1986 *Specification for metal flue pipes, fittings, terminals and accessories for gas-fired appliances with a rated input not exceeding 60 kW.*

BS 835: 1973 (1984) *Specification for asbestos-cement flue pipes and fittings, heavy quality.*

BS 1181: 1971 (1977) *Specification for clay flue linings and flue terminals.*

BS 1289: *Flue blocks and masonry terminals for gas appliances.* Part 1: 1986 *Specification of precast concrete flue blocks and terminals.* Part 2: 1989 *Specification for clay flue blocks and terminals.*

BS 1449: *Steel plate, sheet and strip.* Part 2: 1983 *Specification for stainless and heat resisting steel plate, sheet and strip,* AMD 4807.

BS 5546: 1979 *Code of practice for installation of gas hot water supplies for domestic purposes (2nd family gases).*

BS 5864: 1980 *Code of practice for installation of gas-fired ducted air heaters of rated output not exceeding 60 kW (2nd family gases),* AMD 3972.

BS 5871: 1980 (1983) *Code of practice for installation of gas fires, convectors and fire/back boilers (2nd family gases),* AMD 3973 and AMD 4638.

BS 6172: 1982 *Code of practice for installation of domestic gas cooking appliances (2nd family gases).*

BS 6173: 1982 *Code of practice for installation of gas catering appliances (2nd family gases).*

BS 6461 *Installation of chimneys and flues for domestic appliances burning solid fuel (including wood and peat).* Part 2: 1984 *Code of practice for factory made insulated chimneys for internal applications.*

BS 6714: 1986 *Specification for installation of decorative log and other fuel effect appliances (1st, 2nd and 3rd family gases).*

BS 6798: 1987 *Specification for installation of gas-fired hot water boilers of rated input not exceeding 60 kW.*

BS 4543 *Factory-made insulated chimneys.* Part 1: 1976 *Methods of test for factory-made insulated chimneys.* Part 2: 1976 *Specification for chimneys for solid fuel fired appliances.* AMD 2794, AMD 3475 and AMD 3878. Part 3: 1976. *Specification for chimneys for oil fired appliances.* AMD 2981 and AMD 3476.

BS 5258 *Safety of domestic gas appliances.* Part 1: 1986 *Specification for central heating boilers and circulators.* Part 4: 1987 *Specification for fanned-circulation ducted-air heaters.* Part 5: 1975 *Gas fires,* AMD 4076 and AMD 4745. Part 7: 1977 *Storage water heaters;* Part 8: 1980 *Combined appliances: gas fire/back boiler.* Part 12: 1980 *Decorative gas log and other fuel effect appliances (2nd and 3rd family gases),* AMD 5434. Part 13: 1986 *Specification for convector heaters.*

BS 5386 *Specification for gas burning appliances.* Part 1: 1976 *Gas burning appliances for instantaneous production of hot water for domestic use,* AMD 2990. Part 2: 1981 (1986) *Mini water heaters (2nd and 3rd family gases);* Part 3: 1980 *Domestic cooking appliances burning gas,* AMD 4162, AMD 4405, AMD 4878 and AMD 5220. Part 4: 1983 *Built-in domestic cooking appliances.*

BS 5410 *Code of practice for oil firing.* Part 1: 1977 *Installations up to 44 kW output capacity for space heating and hot water supply purposes,* AMD 3637.

BS 6999: 1989 *Specification for vitreous enamelled low carbon steel flue pipes, other components and accessories for solid fuel burning appliances with a maximum rated output of 45 kW.*

BS 8303: 1986 *Code of practice for installation of domestic heating and cooking appliances burning solid mineral fuels.* AMD 5732.

Chapter 10

Approved Document K
Stairs, Ramps and Guards

This Approved Document has two Parts and three Sections:

K 1   Stairs and ramps – Sections 1 and 2

K 2/3   Pedestrian and vehicle barriers – Section 3

The main changes include some simplification and some minor extensions to the provisions in the Approved Document.

Perhaps the major change is that there is no longer a provision for width of stairs in Part K. It will, however, be necessary to consdier the guidance given in Part B – regarding stairs for means of escape and also stairs provided under the provisions of Part M – Access for Disabled Persons.

A new term 'containment' is used when referring to the new provision regarding the guarding of windows at low level on upper floors.

Protection for children from falling through stairs and balconies has been extended to include all buildings. Previously only dwellings were covered. Stairs with a pitch greater than 42° and ladders are now included within the guidance.

Additional guidance is given on steps and short stairs, spiral stairs and alternating tread stairs and handrail heights and rise and going provisions have been simplified.

Although the question of guarding is dealt with generally under K 2/3, the guarding of stairways and ramps is dealt with under K 1. The need for this segregation is far from apparent but is no doubt the result, as we have already seen, of the effort to define the regulations in terms of functional requirements which tends to lead to an artificial separation of related elements and inevitably results in repetition.

K 1   STAIRS AND RAMPS

Requirement K 1 is:

Requirement	Limits on application
K 1. Stairs, ladders and ramps shall offer safety to users moving between levels of the building.	1. The requirements of this Part apply to stairs, ladders and ramps which form part of the building. 2. Requirement K 1 does not apply to stairs, ladders and ramps which provide access to levels used only for the purpose of maintenance.

Performance

The new performance criteria are that the requirement K 1 will be met by the use of stairs, ladders and ramps to afford reasonable safety between levels in

(*a*)   dwellings where the difference is more than 600 mm;

(*b*)   other buildings where the change of level is two or more risers (or 380 mm if not part of a stair).

Different standards of provision can give an acceptable standard of safety. For example, in public buildings higher standards may be needed because of unfamiliarity and the number of users.

Introduction

0.1   There are two sections:

Section 1 gives guidance on aspects of stairway geometry, special stairways and guarding of stairs.

Section 2 gives guidance on ramps and guarding of ramps.

0.2   The requirements do not apply to stairs, ladders or ramps outside a building unless these are part of the building structure.

Entrance steps attached to a building are controlled but steps on land leading to a building are not.

0.3   Where access routes are part of means of escape or form the only means of access for disabled people reference should be made to Part B and Part M.

0.4   Access within public buildings should conform to Part K. This includes arenas, cinemas, sports stadia and theatres, but where steps are part of gangways or where special consideration needs to be given to guarding, reference should be made to

Guide to Safety at Sports Grounds – access for spectators at sports grounds and arenas (1990) or

Guide to Fire Precautions in existing places of entertainment and like premises (1990).

(these are Home Office publications and available from HMSO) and for assembly buildings BS 5588 Part 6: 1991 *Code of Practice for places of assembly.*

Definitions

0.5   The following are defined for the purposes of Approved Document K:

Alternating tread stairs	– Paddle-shaped treads with the wide portion alternating side to side
Containment	– A barrier that prevents people from falling from one floor to a storey below
Flight	– Part of a stair or ramp having consecutive steps or a continuous slope
Going and rise	– See diagram [10.1]

0.5 **[10.1]** *Going and rise.*

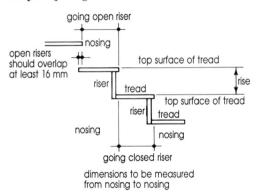

Ladder	– Has a series of narrow steps or rungs on which ascent and descent is made by facing the ladder
Ramp	– Means a slope steeper than 1 in 20 designed for a pedestrian or wheelchair user to get from one level to another
Stair	– A succession of steps and landings that makes it possible to pass on foot to another level
Helical stair	– A stair describing a helix round a central void
Spiral stair	– A stair describing a helix round a central column
Tapered tread	– A step in which the nosing is not parallel to the nosing of the step or landing above it.

Section 1   Stairs

Steepness of stairs

Rise and going

1.1/1.4   The steps in a flight should all have the same rise and going of suitable dimensions (see Table to 1.4 below). Tapered steps provisions are in 1.18–1.20.

Table to 1.4

		Rise (max)	Going (min)
1	private stair	220 mm [(a)]	220 mm[(a)]
2	institutional and assembly stairs	180 mm*	280 mm[(b)]
3	other stairs	190 mm*	250 mm

[(a)]The maximum pitch for a private stair is 42°.
[(b)]If the area of the building is less than 100 m^2 the going may be reduced to 250 mm.
*See also Approved Document for Part M for maximum rise of stairs for disabled people.

More definitions are given here of the different types of stair:
'Private' intended to be used by one dwelling.
'Institutional and Assembly' serve one place where a substantial number of people will gather.
'Other' stairs in buildings other than dwellings, institutional and assembly buildings.
The term 'common stair' is no longer used.
NOTE Although no longer mentioned in the Approved Document, it is usual where the landing is formed by ground which slopes across the stair to take the depth of the riser from the centre (diagrams [10.2] and [10.3]).

[10.2] *Sloping ground.*

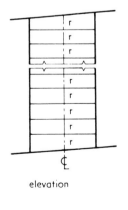

elevation

[10.3] *Comparison of gradients of stairs using maximum rise and minimum joins*

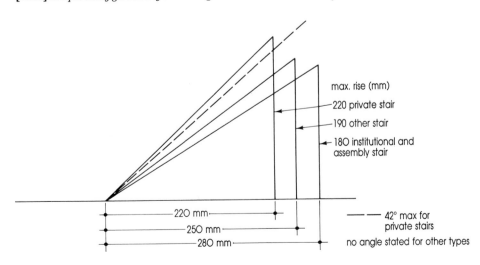

max. rise (mm)
220 private stair
190 other stair
180 institutional and assembly stair

220 mm
250 mm
280 mm

42° max for private stairs
no angle stated for other types

Curved nosings may be used provided the going stays the same across the width of the stair (diagram [10.4]).
The possible combinations which may be used within these limits are within the heavy lines on diagrams [10.5] to [10.7].

1.5   Twice the rise plus the going (2R+G) should be between 550 mm and 700 mm.

[10.4] *Possible use of curved nosings.*

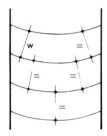

[10.5] *Private stairs within one dwelling.*

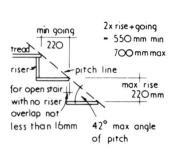

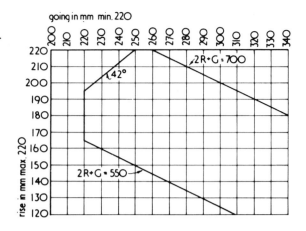

[10.6] *Institutional and assembly buildings.*

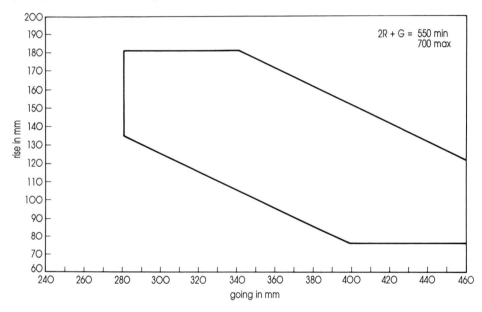

going in mm

[10.7] *Other stairs.*

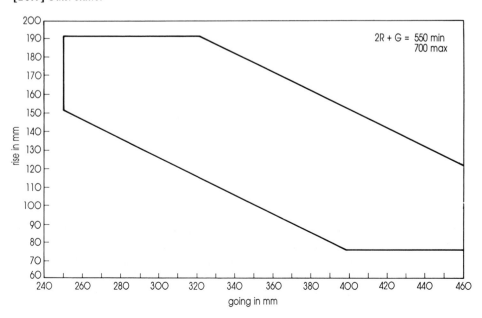

going in mm

[10.8] *Pitch.*

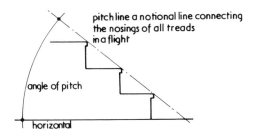

1.6   Gangways in assembly buildings, especially sports stadia, and arenas may need to be at different pitches to maintain sightlines for spectators. This may affect main stairways, etc. Aisles and gangways should not have a pitch of more than 35° (diagram [10.8]).

1.7   As an alternative approach, the relevant recommendations of BS 5395: Part 1: 1977 may be followed to meet the provision regarding steepness (see note on BS 5395).

Construction of steps   **1.8/1.9**   All steps must be level. If they have open risers they should overlap by at least 16 mm. If they have open risers in a flight all stairs likely to be used by children under 5 years old should be constructed so as to prevent the passage of a 100 mm diameter sphere through the open risers (diagram [10.9]).

[10.9] *Open risers.*

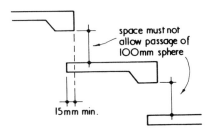

Headroom   **1.10**   The Approved Document states that a headroom of 2 m is adequate on the access between levels (diagram [10.10]).

For loft conversions, which often create difficulties in achieving headroom, it is suggested that where there is insufficient space, 1.9 m at the centre of the stair reducing to 1.8 m at the side of the stair would be acceptable (see diagram [10.11]).

1.10 **[10.11]** *Reduced headroom for loft conversions.*

[10.10] *Headroom.*

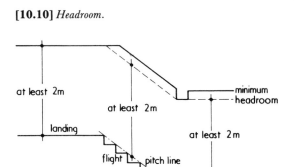

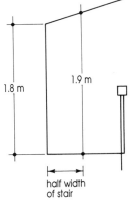

Width of flights   **1.11**   One of the major changes in the Approved Document is the removal of guidance on minimum stair widths. There was apparently no justification for retaining them, but, of course, there are other requirements for stair widths in the Regulations.

The Approved Document to Part B has guidance in relation to means of escape and Part M relates to access for disabled people. There is also guidance on stair widths in BS 5395: 1977.

1.12 **[10.12]** *Rule regarding the subdivision of stairs over 1 m wide.*

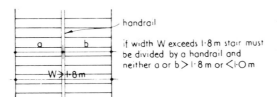

NOTE   The effect of this, whether intentional or not, is to rule out the use of stairways between 1.8 m and 2 m wide, since anything over 1.8 m must be divided, but the minimum width of any subdivision is 1.0 m.

1.12   A stair in a public building which is wider than 1800 mm should be divided into flights not wider than 1800 mm. In buildings where the minimum width is 1000 mm this exercises a certain limitation, as illustrated in diagram [10.12].

Length of flights

1.13   There should be no more than 16 risers to a flight in areas used for *shop or assembly purposes*.

This rule used to be universal and designers will clearly decide for themselves on the advisability of using long uninterrupted flights.

For gangways which have a shallow pitch and used in assembly buildings, ie sports grounds, theatres, etc, reference should be made to BS 5588: Part 6 *Guide to safety in sports grounds* and/or the *Guide to Fire Precautions in existing places of entertainment*, etc.

1.14   Stairways of over 36 risers should have a change of direction of at least 30° (diagram [10.13]).

1.14 **[10.13]** *Stairways over 36 risers.*

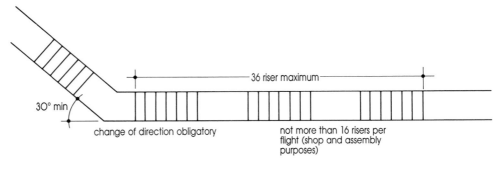

Landings

1.15   There should be a landing at the top and bottom of every flight and its width and depth should be at least equal to the width of the stair.

1.16   Part of the floor may count as a landing, but all landings should be clear of obstruction. A door may, however, swing across part of a landing at the *bottom of* a flight only if certain clearances are maintained (see diagram [10.14]). Door to cupboards and ducts may open in a similar manner, over the landing at the top of a flight (diagram [10.15]).

1.17   Landings may slope up to 1 in 20 if they are formed by the ground and the ground is paved or otherwise firm (diagram [10.16]).

1.15 **[10.14]** *Landings: obstruction.*

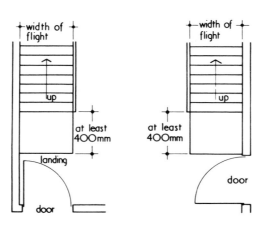

1.16 **[10.15]** *Cupboard on to landing*

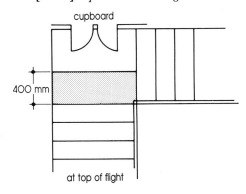

cupboard

400 mm

at top of flight

[10.16] *External stair or ramp.*

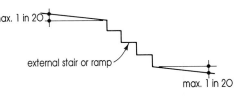

max. 1 in 20

external stair or ramp

max. 1 in 20

Tapered treads

1.18   The going of tapered treads should be measured:
(*a*)   If the flight is less than 1 m wide, in the middle.
(*b*)   If the flight is 1 m or wider, 270 mm from each side.
The rise and going should be within the same limits as shown in the table for parallel steps (Section 1.4) and going should measure at least 50 mm at the narrow end.
1.19   Consecutive steps should have uniform going (see diagrams [10.17 and 10.18]).
1.20   Where a stair consists of both straight and tapered treads, the going of the tapered treads should not be less than the goings of the straight flight.

Comment
The 2R + G formula and gradient rules also apply to tapered steps. Diagram [10.19] shows how these rules are applied to a spiral or helical stair and also to winders forming part of an otherwise parallel stair.

[10.17] *Tapered treads: width 'w' changes at constant rate.*

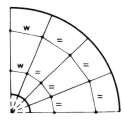

[10.18] *Tapered steps can have curved nosings provided the width reduces at a constant rate.*

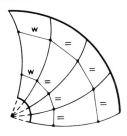

[10.19] *Spiral stairs and winders.*

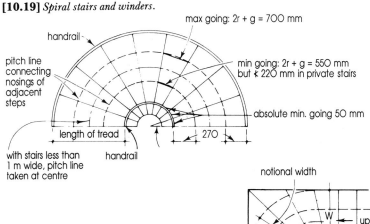

handrail

pitch line connecting nosings of adjacent steps

max going: 2r + g = 700 mm

min going: 2r + g = 550 mm but ≮ 220 mm in private stairs

absolute min. going 50 mm

length of tread

270

with stairs less than 1 m wide, pitch line taken at centre

handrail

notional width

W   up

270

W

pitch line 270 mm from the extremities of the width or notional width as appropriate with stairs less than 1 m wide pitch line taken at centre all steps have uniform goings for each consecutive step

length of nosing of lowest tapered step (W) equal to length of nosing of first parallel step above

To assist the reader in understanding how these controls affect the design of stairs in practice, diagrams [10.20–10.22] show three examples of tapered steps in different types of building with varying widths or riser dimensions. In Cases 1 and 3 it can be seen that the height of the riser controls the maximum going and hence the degree of taper and thus the minimum radius. In Case 2 this does not apply and the taper is controlled only by the minimum going at the centre and narrow end.

[10.20] *The diagram shows the effect of rise and width on taper and radius. The formula 2 × rise + going = 700 mm max or 550 mm min, together with the absolute minimum for going, controls the angle of taper and hence the minimum radius of the stair for any given width. The calculation is affected by the selected rise, which controls the maximum going on the outer pitch line.*

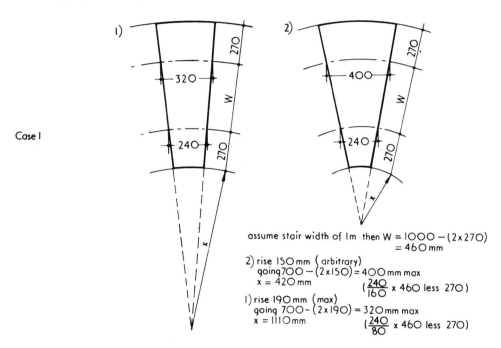

Case 1

assume stair width of 1m then W = 1000 − (2 x 270)
= 460 mm

2) rise 150 mm (arbitrary)
going 700 − (2 x 150) = 400 mm max
x = 420 mm   ($\frac{240}{160}$ x 460 less 270)

1) rise 190 mm (max)
going 700 − (2 x 190) = 320 mm max
x = 1110 mm   ($\frac{240}{80}$ x 460 less 270)

[10.21] *Tapered treads: method specified for stairways less than 1 m wide (example based on private stair). The rises in both cases will be the same – between 165 mm and 195 mm.*

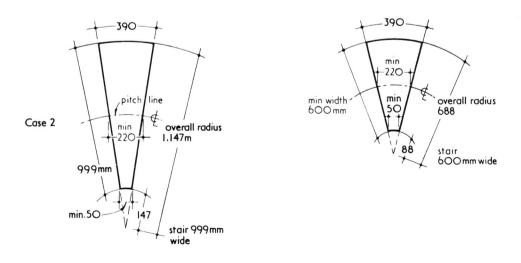

Case 2

[10.22] *This example is based on an institutional and assembly stair (see Table to 1.4). Other stairs (except private stairs) are similar but the minimum going is 250 mm and maximum rise 190 mm.*

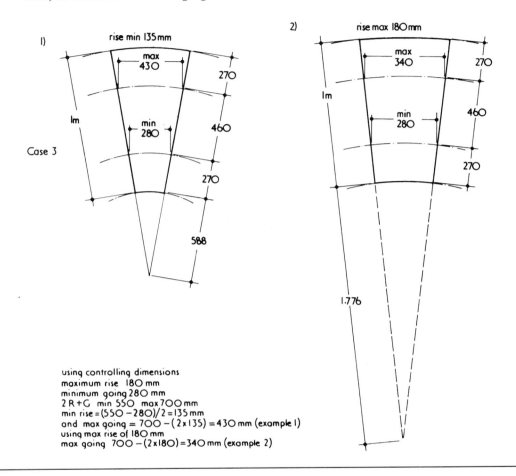

using controlling dimensions
maximum rise 180 mm
minimum going 280 mm
2 R+G min 550 max 700 mm
min rise = (550 − 280)/2 = 135 mm
and max going = 700 − (2 x 135) = 430 mm (example 1)
using max rise of 180 mm
max going 700 − (2 x 180) = 340 mm (example 2)

Alternating tread stairs

1.22/1.24   These stairs have caused a considerable amount of controversy as to whether they provide a safe passage for users. They are now specifically mentioned in the AD (see diagram [10.23]). The usual type of 'space saver' stairs has alternate handed steps with part of the tread cut away. It is said that familiarity and regular use provides a degree of safety which is reasonable.

The limitations on the use of this stair are:
1. Use in lift conversions when there is insufficient space to accommodate a stair satisfying the guidance on stairs in the first part of Approved Document K.
2. One or more straight flights.
3. Used for access to one habitable room together with a bathroom or WC (the WC should not be the only one in the dwelling).
4. Steps to be uniform with parallel nosing.
5. Handrails to be provided on both sides.
6. Treads should have slope-resistant surfaces.
7. Tread sizes over the wider part of the step should be as Table 1.

1.24 **[10.23]** *Alternating tread stairs.*

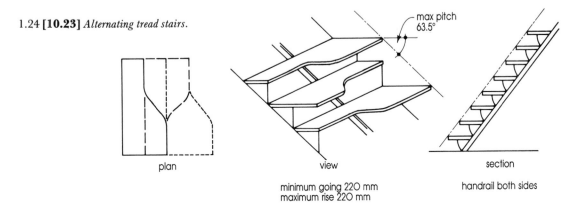

plan

view

minimum going 220 mm
maximum rise 220 mm

section

handrail both sides

Fixed ladders

1.25   Fixed ladders should only be used in a loft conversion when there is insufficient space to construct a proper stairway as para. 1.17.

There should be –

Fixed handrails on both sides and only be used for access to one habitable room.

Retractable loft ladders are not acceptable for means of escape. (See Approved Document B.)

1.26   Stair ladders – walkways should be to BS 5395: Part 3 or BS 4211: 1987.

1.27   All flights must have a handrail at one side and if over 1 m at both sides, but they need not extend beside the two bottom steps except for public buildings and for disabled people (see Approved Document M). If the heights match up, the handrails may form the top of the guarding (the usual balustrade and handrail). Diagram [10.24] illustrates the requirements.

1.27 **[10.24]** *Handrails.*

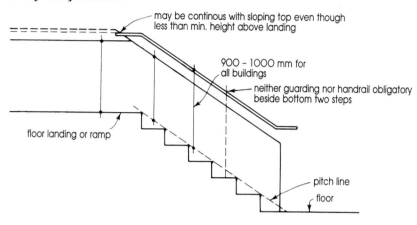

Guarding

1.28   Flights and landings should be guarded at the sides:

in dwellings – wherever there is a drop exceeding 600 mm;

in other buildings – wherever there are two or more risers.

1.29   The guarding to a flight should prevent children being held fast by the guarding. Children should not readily be able to climb it and there should be no openings which a 100 mm sphere can pass through. This does not apply to stairs not likely to be used by children under 5 years of age – perhaps accommodation for elderly people is one example of a building where this provision could be omitted.

1.28 **[10.25]** *Guarding.*

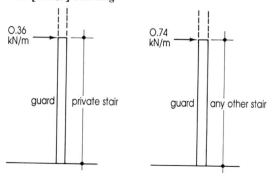

1.30   The horizontal force which guarding should be capable of resisting at the height given in diagram [10.25] is for each metre of length

in the case of a private stair   0.36 KN

any other stair   0.74 KN

Part N should be referred to where glazing is used in guarding.

Alternative approach

BS 5395: *Stairs, ladders and walkways* Part 1: 1977 *Code of practice for stairs*, Part 2: *Code of practice for helical and spiral stairs* and Part 3: 1985 *Code of practice for the design of industrial stairs, permanent ladders and walkways* give additional information which may be useful for setting out stairways. The Approved Document refers to Part 1 of this Code as an alternative design approach for steepness of stairs (1.7), Part 2 for spiral stairs (1.21) and Part 3 for fixed ladders (1.26).

BS 5395 Part 1 CP for straight stairs

Originally BS 5395 covered all types of stairs but subsequently all reference to circular stairs was transferred to Part 2. Part 1, however, still covers the use of winders in straight stairs. The geometry of stairs is covered rather more comprehensively than in the Approved Document. In addition, the BS deals with structural systems, materials, components, finishes, safety aspects, fire protection and lighting.

Part 2 CP for helical and spiral stairs

The defined difference between helical and spiral stairs is that a spiral stair describes a helix around a central column and a helical stair describes a helix around a central void.
The relationship between rise and going is given as

$$2R + G \geq 480 \, mm \leq 800 \, mm$$

This is a wider range than the normal guidance for parallel steps.

Part 3 CP for industrial stairs, etc

As fixed ladders are now included in the Approved Document, reference is made to this code which covers the design and construction of industrial stairs, permanent ladders and walkways.

BS 585: 1989 Wood stairs Part 1

This British Standard is referred to in para. 1.20 in connection with tapered treads.
Its title is *Specification for stairs with closed risers for domestic use, including straight and winder flights and quarter or half landings*.
The standard which is limited to widths not greater than 1220 mm and stairs with a total going not exceeding 3800 mm is primarily concerned with materials and construction requirements.

Section 2 Ramps

2.1 Ramps should not have a slope steeper than 1:12.
2.2 Headroom: clear headroom of at least 2 m.
2.3 Width: no recommendation. See Parts B and M of the Approved Document.
2.4 There should be no permanent obstructions.
2.5 Handrails: If ramps are less than 1 m – handrail on at least one side.
If wider – handrail on both sides.
No need for handrail if rise is 60 m or less.
Height between 900 mm and 1000 mm.
Should give firm support and allow good grip.
2.6 Landings ⎫
2.7 Guarding ⎬ As for stairs
⎭

K 2/3 PEDESTRIAN AND VEHICLE BARRIERS

This covers the provision of barriers and the containment of vehicles to reduce the risk to the safety of persons in or about buildings.
The requirements of Parts K 2/3 of Schedule 1 are:

Requirement	Limits on application
Protection from falling K 2. Stairs, ramps, floors and balconies, and any roof to which people normally have access, shall be guarded with barriers where they are necessary to protect users from the risk of falling.	1. The requirements of this Part apply only to stairs, ladders and ramps which form part of the building.
Vehicle barriers K 3. Vehicle ramps, and any floor and roof to which vehicles have access, shall be guarded with barriers where they are necessary to provide protection for people in or about the building.	2. Requirement K1 does not apply to stairs, ladders and ramps which provide access to levels used only for the purpose of maintenance.

This is backed up by an acceptable performance level which will be met if provision is made for

(*a*)   Pedestrian guarding to prevent people being injured by falling from a height of more than 600 mm. (Presumably this is accepted as being the minimum height from which people are likely to sustain significant injury.)

(*b*)   Pedestrian guarding beside stairways forming either a means of access for the public or along a means of escape (except within a dwelling), capable of preventing people from falling the height of two risers. Where there is no stairway to judge this, the height is 380 mm.

(*c*)   Vehicle barriers capable of resisting or deflecting the impact of vehicles.

Section 3   Guards and barriers

Pedestrian guarding

3.1/3.5   This should be provided wherever reasonably necessary to meet criterion (*a*) above. This includes the edges of any part of a raised floor (including an opening window) or gallery, balcony, roof (including roof lights etc), lightwell, basement area of sunken area next to a building, unless in a space used only for maintenance and repair. Diagram [10.26] illustrates some examples.

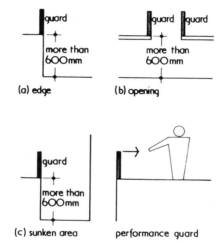

3.2 **[10.26]** *Location (guarding).*

Vehicle barriers

NOTE   The provision regarding containment is new and may serve to reduce accidents caused through persons falling from windows on upper floors.

Paragraph 1.29 in Section 1 regarding safety provisions for children under 5 years who may be using the building is repeated.

Where vehicles have access to any part of a building, barriers should be provided to all edges which are above the floor, ground or any other vehicle route.

Any walk, parapet, balustrade or similar obstruction may serve as a barrier. Barriers should be at least the height shown in diagram [10.27], and should be capable of resisting forces set out in BS 6180: 1982 *Code of practice for protective barriers in and about buildings* Part 1: 1984 *Code of practice for dead and imposed loads.*

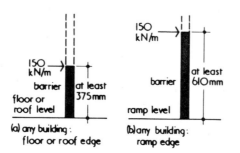

3.5 **[10.27]** *Barrier heights and strengths.*
NOTE   These loads do not agree with those quoted in BS 6399: Part 1: 1984, CP for dead and imposed loads (previously CP3: Ch V: Part 1) which were quoted in Approved Document A (see AD A Section 2 and note on BS 6180 below).

BS 6180: 1982: Protective barriers in and about buildings

This deals with all guard barriers in buildings and places of assembly including vehicle barriers. In the latter type it is mainly concerned with vehicles within the 2500 kg/16 km/h range but Appendix B does give a method of calculation for vehicles outside these limits.

The use of either method depends on establishing an estimated acceptable total displacement figure for the vehicle and barrier combined, as a starting point.

Reference is also made to a method for use within the limitations of mass and speed stated above in BS 6399: Part 1, which should suffice for most cases. On pedestrian barriers the BS recommends heights and minimum horizontal design loads, applied at design level as in the Approved Document, but also gives two other figures of a UDL per m^2 for infill panels and a point load on any part of the infill building usage. There is an additional table for audience, spectator and crowd protection. For external situations wind loading must also be taken into account. There is advice on the various available materials, including concrete, masonry, various metals and plastics for railings, handrails etc. Safety aspects apart from strength are dealt with, as well as fabrication, corrosion protection and fixing methods.

Note on BS 6339: Part 1: 1984

This is referred to in Approved Document A as the guide for dead and imposed loads. There would appear to be some conflict between Appendix B of BS 6180: 1982 and BS 6399, Clause 10. The latter gives a load of 150 KN on any 1.5 m length of barrier (not per metre), but this is not made clear in Appendix B.

References

The following British Standards and other documents are referred to in the Approved Document.

BS 585: *Wood stairs*: Part 1: 1989 *Specification for stairs with closed risers for domestic use, including straight and winder flights and quarter and half landings.*

BS 4211: 1987 *Specification for ladders for permanent access to chimneys, other high structures, silos and bins.*

BS 5395 *Stairs ladders and walkways.* Part 1: 1977 *Code of practice for stairs* Amendment slip no. 1: AMD 3355. Amendment slip no. 2: AMD 4450. Part 2: 1984 *Code of practice for the design of helical and spiral stairs.* Part 3: 1985 *Code of practice for the design of industrial type stairs, permanent ladders and walkways.*

BS 5588 *Fire precautions in the design and construction of buildings.* Part 6: 1991 *Code of practice for places of assembly.*

BS 6180: 1982 *Code of practice for protective barriers in and about buildings.*

BS 6399: *Loading for buildings.* Part 1: 1984 *Code of practice for dead and imposed loads* Amendment slip no. 1: AMD 4949. Amendment slip no. 2: AMD 5511. Amendment slip no. 3. AMD 6031.

Chapter 11

Approved Document L Conservation of Fuel and Power

The previous Part L contained specific U-values which had to be achieved and as such did not fit in well with the other functional requirements. The amendment to the requirement which came into force on 1 April 1990 has brought Part L into line by stating that reasonable provision shall be made for the conservation of fuel and power in buildings.

It has been argued that energy conservation is a matter which should not be included within the building regulations and should be left to market forces. There is, however, a strong commitment nationally to the conservation of energy and, with better awareness of the savings in cost which can occur through effective thermal insulation, it may be ultimately a candidate for deregulation.

The new Part L is based on the raising of overall energy efficiency standards with much more flexibility and how those standards may be achieved.

The previous requirements of L 4 – Heating systems and controls and L 5 – Insulation of heating services have been incorporated into the general requirement in L 1. There are some minor changes in the guidance in the Approved Document where these provisions are are set out in Sections 2 and 3. The requirement is:

Requirement	Limits on application
L 1. Reasonable provision shall be made for the conservation of fuel and power in buildings	This requirement applies to (*a*) dwellings, and (*b*) other buildings whose floor area exceeds 30 m²

L 1   CONSERVATION OF FUEL AND POWER

The Approved Document contains an introduction, three sections and two Appendices.
Section 1 – Limitation of heat loss through the building fabric
Section 2 – Controls for space heating and hot water supply systems
Section 3 – Insulation of hot water storage vessels, pipes and ducts
Appendix A – Calculations of U-values
Appendix B – Examples showing the use of the elemental approach and the calculation procedure.

Performance

The performance states that energy efficient measures will meet the requirement if they:
(*a*)   limit heat loss and where appropriate maximise heat gains through the fabric of the building
(*b*)   appropriately control the output of space heating and hot water systems
(*c*)   limit heat loss from hot water storage vessels, pipes and ducts.

Introduction   **0.1**   The introduction describes the ways set out in the three sections on how the requirements may be met.

Small extensions to dwellings	**0.2** If an extension to a dwelling is –

Small extensions to dwellings

0.2 If an extension to a dwelling is –
(*a*) constructed in a similar way to the existing building, and
(*b*) the floor area does not exceed 10 m²,
Part L does not apply.
NOTE This may seem surprising but the Approved Document states 'reasonable provision for the conservation of fuel and power may be considered to have been made' in these cases. There could be no small amount of heat loss from these extensions, but this can be ignored. It is probably assumed that designers will ensure that the construction of these extensions will include energy conservation measures.
It is perhaps a point of interest here that no mention is made of the methods to use when calculating heat loss when an extension greater than 10 m² is to be constructed. One such method which can be adopted is shown in the note on Appendix A.

Commercial and industrial buildings with low heating level

0.3/0.4 Because of the nature of the intended use, some commercial, industrial and storage buildings may require a low level of heating or even no heating at all, in which cases thermal insulation will be unnecessary.
In speculative developments, where the use may not be known, it will be necessary to comply with the requirements.
Low level heating is where the output from the space heating system does not exceed:
50 W/m in industrial and storage buildings
25 W/m for other non-domestic buildings

Technical risk – the effect of increased insulation

0.5/0.8 When buildings are better insulated, the technical issues not considered important for uninsulated constructions may become more significant.
Certain parts of the construction remain colder, with a greater risk of interstitial condensation. Changes to certain traditional forms of construction to improve insulation could give rise to damp penetration or frost damage to the outer leaf.
Safety margins, which were inherent in traditional construction, may be reduced with increased levels of insulation. The Approved Document states that a better understanding of the physical principles involved in construction changes the risk of the occurrence of building defects. Careful attention should be given not only to design but also to workmanship and supervision, to ensure trouble-free building. Because of the concern regarding possible risks which might arise from these further energy conservation measures the Department of the Environment commissioned the Building Research Establishment to produce a guide on the risks. The publication *Thermal Insulation: avoiding risks* is not an approved document but was made available with the Approved Document to Part L. It has a subtitle *A guide to good practice building construction* and explains the technical risks which may be associated with meeting the requirements of the Building Regulations particularly regarding roofs, walls, windows and floors.
Explanations of the more important technical issues are highlighted and these are followed by actions which could be taken to avoid the risk of failure.
There are 94 illustrations which show principles of construction and 380 recommendations giving examples of good practice detailing.
Guidance is not given on how to meet the particular U-values.
A particular point is made that although heating is not controlled through building regulations, it should be considered in conjunction with thermal insulation and ventilation in order to avoid the risk of condensation. Approved Document F also, of course, gives guidance on the provision of ventilation to reduce condensation problems.

Calculation of U-values

U-value is the thermal transmittance coefficient which is the *rate* of heat transfer in *watts* through *1 m²* of a structure when the temperature on each side of the structure differs by *1°C*.
The coefficient is expressed in watts per square metre per degree Kelvin (W/m²K).
NOTE Although Kelvin is a unit of absolute temperature, to all intents and purposes it is the same as degrees Centigrade.
Appendix A to the Approved Document shows the method by which the U-value can be calculated, calculation figures are acceptable to two decimal places. The effect of timber joists, timber framing, wall ties, thin cavity closers, mortar bedding, damp proof membranes, metal spacers and other discrete components may be ignored when calculating U-values.

Thermal conductivity

0.11   This is a measure of the rate at which heat passes through a material. It is expressed in terms of watts per square metre for one metre thickness and a temperature difference of one kelvin. This should be written $k = Wm/(m^2K)$, but in normal practice the square metre is left out and it becomes W/mK, since the one square metre is constant and the value varies only with the thickness. The lower this figure, the better the insulation value. The thicknesses of insulation given later are based on various values for this quality. These can be obtained either from the supplier of the material or Table A3.22 of the *CIBSE Guide*, extracts from which are reproduced in the Approved Document. Table A.3.1 of this *Guide* also gives values for concrete blocks, and if the claimed thermal conductivity of a product is based on a value lower than these, the claim should be supported by test certificates, as required in Appendix 4 of the *Guide*.

Windows and rooflight openings

0.12   Certain assumptions apply when considering areas of openings for windows and rooflights and these are shown in diagram [11.1].

0.12 **[11.1]** *Windows and rooflight openings.*

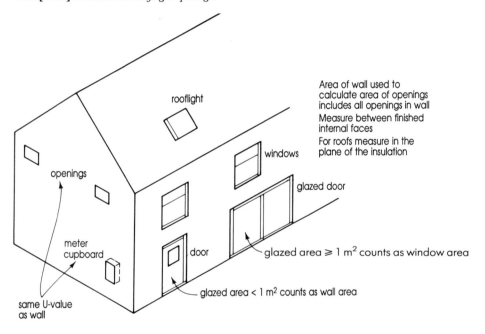

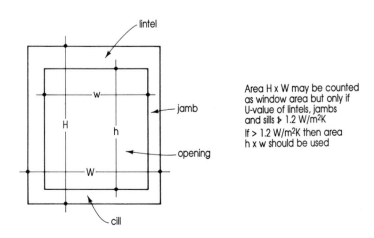

Basis for calculating areas

0.13   Measurement should be between the finished internal faces of the building and, for a roof, in the plane of the insulation.

Exposed and semi-exposed elements

0.14   For the purposes of thermal insulation an 'exposed element' is an element exposed to the outside air and a 'semi-exposed element' is an element separating a heated space from an unheated space that has exposed elements which do not meet the recommendations for the limitation of heat loss. Examples are shown in diagram [11.2].

0.14 **[11.2]** *Examples of semi-exposed elements.*

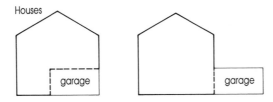

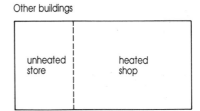

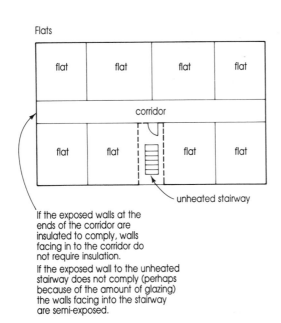

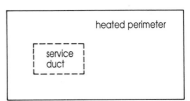

If the roof and floor to the service duct are not insulated to comply, the walls of the duct are semi-exposed

If the exposed walls at the ends of the corridor are insulated to comply, walls facing in to the corridor do not require insulation.

If the exposed wall to the unheated stairway does not comply (perhaps because of the amount of glazing) the walls facing into the stairway are semi-exposed.

Key

——— Exposed element of construction which complies with Section 1 regarding insulation

- - - - Semi-exposed element

Large complex buildings

0.15   Provisions for conservation of fuel and power in large complex buildings could advantageously be dealt with by considering separately the different parts of the building. Measures appropriate to each part could be established.

Section 1   Limitation of heat loss through the building fabric

Alternative approaches

1.1   This section shows two methods for demonstrating how loss of heat through the building fabric can be limited.
These methods are –
an *elemental* approach, or
by *calculation* procedure 1 or 2.

Elemental approach

1.2   If the U-value of relevant elements of construction does not exceed that shown in the table below, the requirement (reasonable provision) will have been met.

Table to 1.2   Maximum U-values (W/m K)

	Dwellings	All other buildings
exposed walls exposed floors ground floors	0.45	0.45
roofs	0.25*	0.45
semi-exposed walls and floors	0.6	0.6

NOTES
Any part of a roof having a pitch of 70° or more may have the same U-value as a wall.
*For loft conversions in existing dwellings it would be reasonable to have a U-value of 0.35 W/m K.

Simple alternatives

1.3   Double glazing may be used as an alternative to the levels of insulation for dwellings shown in the table above.

Walls – 0.6 W/m K
Roofs – 0.35 W/m K   – Double glaze half the total window area.
Floors – 0.45 W/m K

Walls – 0.6 W/m K
Roofs – 0.35 W/m K   – Double glaze all windows
Floors – uninsulated

1.4   A further alternative is to calculate the areas of double glazing using calculation procedure 1.

1.5
Walls – 0.45 W/m K
Roof – 0.35 W/m K   – Floor – 0.35 W/m K

1.3 **[11.3]** *Examples using simple alternatives.*

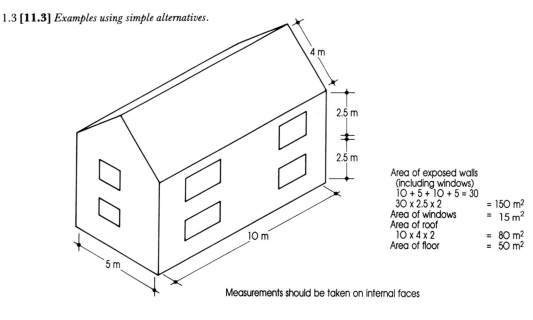

Area of exposed walls
(including windows)
10 + 5 + 10 + 5 = 30
30 x 2.5 x 2   = 150 m²
Area of windows   = 15 m²
Area of roof
10 x 4 x 2   = 80 m²
Area of floor   = 50 m²

Measurements should be taken on internal faces

Using the table				
Exposed walls	150 − 15 =	135 × 0.45	=	60.75
Windows		15 × 5.7	=	85.5
Roof		80 × 0.25	=	20
Floor		50 × 0.45	=	22.5
	Total heat loss		=	188.75 W/K

Alternatives.
1. External walls 0.6 135×0.6 = 81
   Windows – 50% single glazed 7.5×5.7 = 42.75
   – 50% double glazed 7.5×2.8 = 57
   Roof   0.35 80×0.35 = 28
   Floor 50×0.45 = 22.5

                                                Total heat loss   195.25 W/K

2. External walls 0.6 135×0.6 = 81
   Windows – all double glazed 15×2.8 = 42
   Roof   0.35 80×0.35 = 28
   Floor uninsulated $50 \times 0.82^*$ = 41

                                                Total heat loss   192 W/K

3. External walls 0.45 135×0.45 = 60.75
   Windows – single glazed 15×5.7 = 85.5
   Roof   0.35 80×0.35 = 28
   Floor   0.35 50×0.35 = 17.5

                                                Total heat loss   191.75 W/K

It will be seen that by using these simple alternatives, the rate of heat loss from the building does not significantly change.

*Taken from formula P/A. See note to 1.6 $= \dfrac{30}{50} =$ ratio of 0.6.

Ground floor insulation   **1.6**   The 1990 amendment to the Approved Document implies that the ground floors should be considered when taking into account heat loss through the fabric of a building.
If a ground floor is sufficiently large it could achieve a U-value of 0.45 without additional insulation.
The graph [11.4] shows the range of floor dimensions for which insulation is required.
It may be helpful to know what the U-value of an uninsulated floor may be and the following table shows these assumed values.

1.6 **[11.4]** *Floor dimensions for which insulation is required.*

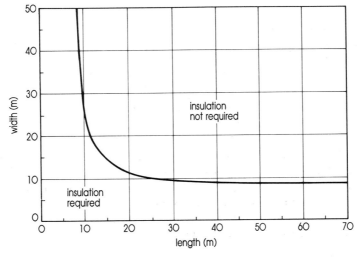

NOTE   The dimensions relate to the floor area under the whole building, e.g. for a pair of semi-detached houses the floor area would be that of both.

The value can be determined from the ratio of the perimeter (m) to area (m²). The perimeter P is measured along the finished internal faces and area A between the finished internal faces of the wall bounding the building. Linear interpolation may be used.

P/A	U-value
0.1	0.21
0.2	0.36
0.3	0.49
0.4	0.61
0.5	0.73
0.6	0.82
0.7	0.91
0.8	0.99
0.9	1.05
1.0	1.10

The table can be applied to all types of uninsulated floors next to the ground whether they are of suspended timber, suspended beam and block, slab direct on the ground or concrete raft.

Insulation thickness

1.7   To achieve the U-values shown in the elemental approach, insulation thickness can be estimated from the tables in Appendix B to the Approved Document.

Windows and rooflights

1.8   The provisions will be met if the areas of windows and of rooflights do not exceed those shown in the table.
NOTE   This table has been amended in the 1990 Approved Document but only for dwellings. The previous limit of 12 per cent has been increased to 15 per cent.

Table to 1.8   Maximum single glazed areas of windows and rooflights

Building type	Windows	Rooflights
dwellings	windows and rooflights together 15 per cent of total floor area	
other residential (including hotels and institutional)	25 per cent of exposed wall area	20 per cent of roof area
places of assembly, offices and shops	35 per cent of exposed wall area	20 per cent of roof area
industrial and storage	15 per cent of exposed wall area	20 per cent of roof area

NOTES
1 In any building, the maximum glazed area may be doubled where double glazing is used, and trebled where double glazing is, in addition, coated with a low emissivity coating (emissivity not greater than 0.2).
2 Triple glazing may be considered equivalent to double glazing with a low emissitivity coating.
3 Display windows in shops do not count towards the maximum single glazed area.
4 If double glazing is to be used to provide larger window areas as in notes 1 and 2 above, the concession for higher U-values set out in 1.3 above cannot be used at the same time. In appropriate cases a calculation procedure could be used.

NOTE   In dwellings only, the maximum single glazed areas are shown as a percentage of the total *floor* area, for all other buildings they are a percentage of the total *wall* area for windows and *roof* area for rooflights. If double or triple glazing is to be used to provide larger window areas, the simple alternatives in 1.3 cannot be used at the same time. In the example used in 1.3 the area of exposed walls was 150 m², so if triple glazing was proposed, the maximum glazed area according to the table would be 45 per cent or 67.5 m².

Using walls at 0.45	82.5 × 0.45	= 37.12
Windows triple glazed at 2.0	67.5 × 2.0	= 135.0
Roof at 0.25	80 × 0.25	= 20
Floor at 0.45	50 × 0.45	= 22.5
	Total heat loss	= 214.62 W/K

This is more than the heat loss shown in the example using the table. It will be seen why the simple alternatives cannot be used here because by using 0.6 for walls and 0.35 for roofs the heat loss would be 235 W/K. It would, however, be possible to have just over 35 per cent of window area by reducing the U-value for the floor and still be within the limit of heat loss, but this is a matter for the calculation procedures.

1.9   Diagram [11.5] shows the U-values and glazing areas for building uses.

1.10   Various examples of the elemental approach are shown in Appendix B of the Approved Document.

1.10 **[11.5]** *Elemental U-values and glazing areas.*

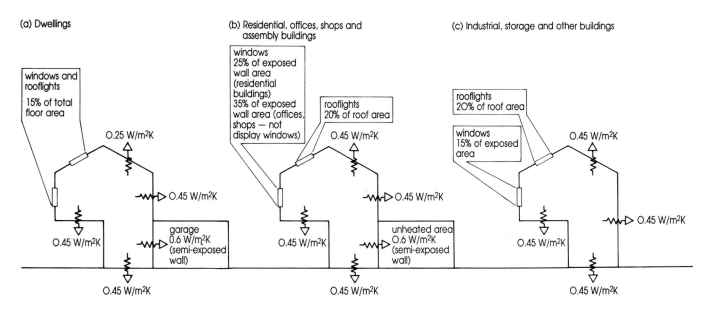

Calculation procedure 1

1.11/1.14   Calculation procedure 1 is an alternative to the elemental approach. The provisions will be met if, by calculation:

the rate of heat loss through the fabric of the building is not greater than the rate of heat loss through a notional building of the same shape and size, as the building which is designed to comply with the elemental approach.

This procedure allows larger areas of glazing than those shown in the table, but if the proposed building contains an area of glazing less than that shown in the table, this smaller area of glazing should be assumed in the notional building.

1.15   There are examples of calculation procedure 1 in Appendix B to the Approved Document.

Example of calculation procedure 1

Dwelling			Proposed U-value (W/m K)
Area of exposed walls		140 m²	0.42
Area of windows single glazed 17%		23.8 m²	5.7
Area of roof		70 m²	0.35
Area of floor		120 m²	0.35

Therefore heat loss from proposed building =

Wall	140 − 23.8 =	116.2 × 0.42	=	48.8
Windows		23.8 × 5.7	=	135.66
Roof		70 × 0.25	=	17.5
Floor		120 × 0.35	=	42

243.96 W/K

Notional building
Wall – Maximum area of glazing is 15% of floor area $= 18\,\text{m}^2$

$(140 - 18 = 122)$	122×0.45	$= 54.9$
Windows	18×5.7	$= 102.6$
Roof	70×0.25	$= 17.5$
Floor	120×0.45	$= 54$

Heat loss from notional building   229 W/K

The proposed building therefore, by calculation, has a rate of heat loss which is more than the notional building.

Calculation procedure 2

1.16/1.17   This procedure allows for a completely free design of a building by calculating an energy target.

Any valid energy conservation measure can be incorporated into the design and the requirement will be met if the calculated energy use in the proposed design is less than that of a similar building designed to comply with the elemental approach.

Solar and internal heat gains can be taken into account.

Two methods for calculating annual energy consumption are acceptable.

These are:

(*a*)   for dwellings – by BREDEM Worksheet. This is referred to in BRE Report BR 150, *1989 Building Regulations – Conservation of fuel and power – the energy target method of compliance for dwellings*, or

(*b*)   for buildings other than dwellings – in accordance with the *CIBSE Energy Guide* 1981, Part 2(a) (Worksheets 1a–1c).

NOTE   Calculation procedure 1 provides for calculations to compare with a notional building of the *same shape and size* whereas calculation procedure 2 provides for comparison with a *similar* building.

Using the calculation procedures

1.19   The use of calculations may allow U-values greater than those shown in the table but, as a general rule, they should be limited to 0.6 W/m K for exposed walls of all building types. For roofs of dwellings the limit is 0.35 W/m K and for roofs of other buildings 0.6 W/m K. Assumed U-values for glazing:

1.20   These are: single glazing   5.7 W/m K
                           double glazing   2.8 W/m K
                           double glazing with low emissivity coating not greater than 0.2   2.0 W/m K
                           triple glazing   2.0 W/m K

Certification of calculations

1.21   A 'competent person' may certify that calculation procedures have been carried out correctly and this will be acceptable to local authorities and approved inspectors. As the scheme for approved persons had not come into being when the Approved Document was issued, the question of who is a 'competent person' may arise. It is suggested that any question of competency should be settled with the building control authority prior to the submission of calculations. The local building control authority or an approved inspector remain responsible for ensuring that the requirements are met.

Section 2   Controls for space heating and hot water supply systems

There is now no separate requirement regarding these controls. The requirement is included in the general requirement of L 1 in that reasonable provision shall be made for the conservation of fuel and power in buildings. The guidance now extends to dwellings.

Performance

The acceptable performance level stated for this section is that the output of space heating and hot water systems should be controlled as appropriate and that heat loss from hot water storage vessels, pipes and ducts should be limited.

2.1   This section does not apply to control systems for commercial and industrial processes. It may also not apply to systems where heat, which is a by-product of industrial processes, is used for space heating (as is frequently the case in some large factories).

Heating controls in dwellings

2.2   The output from the heating system should be controlled by the provision of a room thermostat or thermostatic radiator valves or any form of sensing device which is equivalent.

Heating controls in other buildings

2.3   The provisions will be met in buildings other than dwellings if the following controls are provided (where applicable)

(*a*)   *Room temperature control*
Temperature sensing devices such as thermostats or thermostatic radiator valves for each part of the space heating system which is designed to be separately controlled.

(*b*)   *Weather compensating controls*
Where the space heating system uses hot water, the temperature of the water flowing in the heating circuit should be regulated by an external temperature sensing device.
Weather compensating controls are designed to adjust output in accordance with changes in outside temperature, wind speed and possibly solar radiation. They are not essential with quick response systems such as ducted air.

(*c*)   *Intermittent heating controls*
To maintain the required temperature only when the building is normally occupied, the following provision should be made;
(i)   a *clock control*, which can be manually set giving start and stop times and if the space heating has an output of 100 kW or less, and,
(ii)   *optimising control*
if the output is more than 100 kW, a control arrangement should be provided which gives start times for the system based on the rate of reaction of the building when the heating is shut off and restarted.

(*d*)   *Boiler controls*
Where two or more gas or oil fired boilers have a total output of over 100 kW, controls should be provided to start up or shut down one or more as the demand fluctuates. Boilers run most efficiently at close to maximum output, so that it is more economical to run one boiler at full capacity than two at half capacity each. The control should be able to detect variations in the need for heat in the building and cut out or modulate boilers accordingly. This is *sequence control*. Care is needed in the hydraulic design to ensure stable control. Presumably this is to avoid boilers continually being switched off and on due to small variations in the load.

Controls for hot water storage vessels

2.4   It is necessary to limit the temperature of stored hot water by:
(*a*)   a thermostat for all hot water storage vessels; and
(*b*)   a time switch which will shut off the supply of heat when there is no hot water demand.
This applies only to a hot water storage vessel with a capacity of more than 150 litres which is not heated by off-peak electricity.

Section 3   Insulation of hot water storage vessels, pipes and ducts

Commercial and industrial installations

3.1   Storage and piping systems for commercial and industrial processes are not within the scope of the Approved Document.

Insulation of hot water storage vessels

3.2   Hot water storage vessels should be insulated to limit the heat loss to 90 W/m² of the surface area of the vessel.
It is suggested that one way of achieving this would be for a storage vessel to comply with:
BS 699: 1984 *Specification for copper direct cylinders for domestic purposes*, or
BS 1566 *Copper indirect cylinders for domestic purposes*, Parts 1 and 2: 1984, or

BS 3198: 1981 *Copper hot water storage combination unis for domestic purposes*, or
BS 5615: 1985 *Specification for insulating jackets for domestic hot water storage cylinders*
The segments of insulating jackets should be taped together to provide an unbroken insulation cover for the storage vessel.

Insulation of pipes and ducts

3.3   Pipes or ducts need not be insulated if they contribute to the useful heat requirement of a room or space.

Other pipes should be insulated with material with a thermal conductivity not greater than 0.045 W/mK and the thickness should be at least equal to the outside diameter of the pipe up to a maximum of 440 mm. Alternatively pipes and ducts should meet the recommendations of BS 5422: 1977 *Specification for the use of thermal insulating materials*.

Notes on relevant British Standards

The following may be referred to:

BS 5422: 1990 Method for specifying thermal insulating materials on pipes, ductwork and equipment (in the temperature range −40°C to +700°C)

Although the Approved Document refers to BS 5422: 1977, the 1990 revisions cover domestic applications in a new Section 6.

The standard covers a much wider range than Section 3 of the Approved Document. It includes information on the types and application of insulating materials, refrigeration, chilled water and process pipework. The tables showing recommended thicknesses of insulation are based on the concept of 'economic thickness' above which the cost of extra insulation would outweigh the savings in fuel cost. This, however, depends on relative fuel costs, which fluctuate wildly.

Extracts from some of the tables relating to pipes in central heating installations and domestic hot water systems are shown in graphical form in diagrams [11.6]–[11.9].

There is also a table of thicknesses to protect against freezing and advice on fire hazard and protection against condensation when pipe surfaces are cold.

Appendix B gives a method of calculating heat losses. However the formulae are complicated, especially for cylindrical surfaces and require information additional to the thermal conductivity. They are only likely to be used by experts in large installations. The same applies to Appendix E which is a method of calculating 'economic' thickness'.

BS 699: 1984 and BS 1566: Parts 1 and 2: 1984. Copper hot water cylinders for domestic purposes

These three standards are very similar each dealing with a type of hot water storage cylinder (direct and double and single feed indirect respectively). They each make a recommendation that where factory insulated units are supplied, they should have a standing loss not exceeding 1 W/l (one watt per litre) of capacity.

BS 3198: 1981 Combination Units for domestic purposes

This deals with a range of copper hot water storage units (both rectangular and cylindrical) which combine a hot water storage vessel with cold water feed cistern. It contains the same recommendation that in factory-insulated units the standing heat loss should be limited to 1 W/l of capacity and in addition that the insulation between the hot water vessel and the cold feed cistern should be enough to prevent the cold water from rising to more than 38°C.

BS 5615: 1985. Insulating jackets for hot water cylinders

This lays down a performance standard which is based on a type 7 grade cylinder (see BS 699) which has a capacity of 120 litres. This is that the standing loss must not exceed 2.5 kW/h per 24 hours. If a jacket passes this test it is also suitable for the usual range of sizes.

NOTE   It is interesting to compare the three differing standards for standing loss from hot water vessels by bringing them all to the same basis, namely W/l using the 120 litre cylinder as the vessel being compared, thus:

* Surface area of type 7 cylinder (450 mm dia × 900 mm high)

Section 3 specifies 90 W/m² = 1.43 m²* × 90/120 = 1.07 W/l
BS 5615 specifies 2.5 kW/h per 24 hours

$$= \frac{2500}{24 \times 120} \qquad = 0.868 \text{ W/l}$$

BS 699, 1566 and 3198 all specify   1.0 W/l

The term 'standing loss' means energy consumption under steady state conditions.

3.3 [**11.6**] *Economic thickness of insulation: domestic central heating installations – heated areas.*

3.3 [**11.7**] *Economic thickness of insulation: domestic central heating installations – unheated areas.*

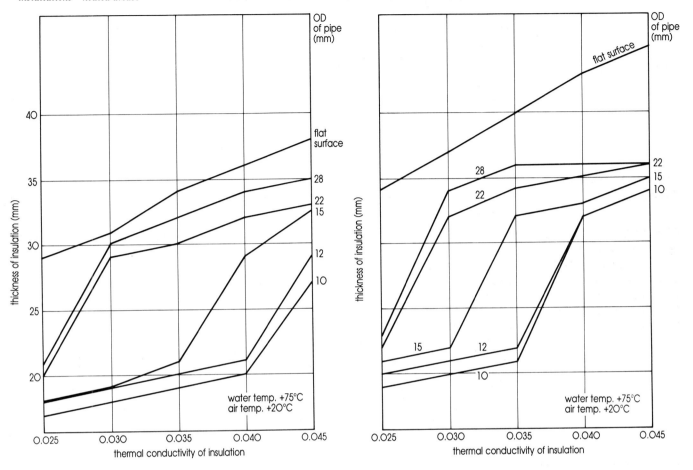

3.3 [**11.8**] *Economic thickness of insulation: domestic hot water systems – heated areas.*

3.3 [**11.9**] *Economic thickness of insulation: domestic hot water systems – unheated areas.*

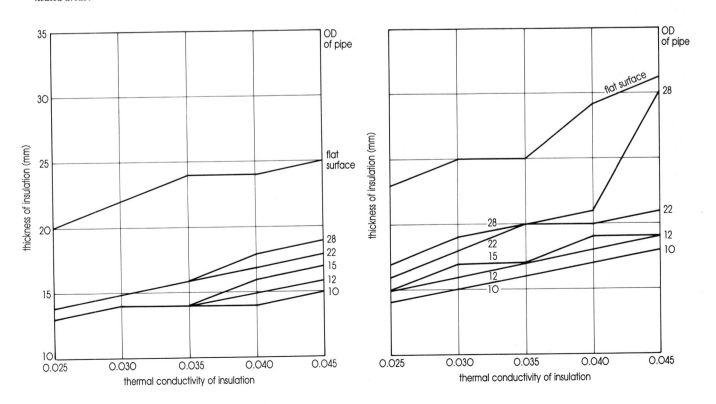

Appendix A Calculation of U-values

A1   A table giving the thermal conductivity of some common building materials has been reproduced in the Approved Document from Section A3 of the *CIBSE Guide*, 1980.

Where a manufacturer claims that the thermal conductivity of a masonry material is lower than that shown in the table, the claim should be supported by test certificates. See Appendix 4 of the *CIBSE Guide*, 1980.

Table to A1   Thermal conductivity of some common building materials

Material	Density (kg/m³)	Thermal conductivity (W/mK)
WALLS (External and internal)		
Asbestos cement sheet	700	0.35
Asbestos cement decking	1500	0.36
Brickwork (outer leaf)	1700	0.84
Brickwork (inner leaf)	1700	0.62
Cast concrete (dense)	2100	1.40
Cast concrete (lightweight)	1200	0.38
Concrete block (heavyweight)	2300	1.63
Concrete block (mediumweight)	1400	0.51
Concrete block (lightweight)	600	0.19
Fibreboard	300	0.06
Plasterboard	950	0.16
Tile hanging	1900	0.84
SURFACE FINISHES		
External rendering	1300	0.50
Plaster (dense)	1300	0.50
Plaster (lightweight)	600	0.16
ROOFS		
Aerated concrete slab	500	0.16
Asphalt	1700	0.50
Felt bitumen layers	1700	0.50
Screed	1200	0.41
Stone chippings	1800	0.96
Tile	1900	0.84
Wood woolslab	500	0.10
FLOORS		
Cast concrete	2000	1.13
Metal tray	7800	50.00
Screed	1200	0.41
Timber flooring	650	0.14
Wood blocks	650	0.14
INSULATION		
Expanded polystyrene (EPS) slab	25	0.035
Glass fibre quilt	12	0.040
Glass fibre slab	25	0.035
Mineral fibre slab	30	0.035
Phenolic foam	30	0.040
Polyurethane board	30	0.025
Urea formaldehyde (UF) foam	10	0.040

How to calculate U-values

Terms

U-value is calculated by adding together the *thermal resistances* of the component parts of the construction and by then taking the reciprocal.

Thermal resistance is obtained:

(*a*) in the case of a material by dividing the thickness of the material by its *thermal conductivity*, or

(*b*) in the case of air spaces or surfaces by using standard values for *thermal resistance*.

These standard thermal resistance values expressed in m K/W are:

Exposed walls	– outside surface	0.06
	– inside surface	0.12
	– air space (cavity)	0.18
Roofs	– outside surface	0.04
	– inside surface	0.10
	– roof space (pitched)	0.18
	– roof space (flat)	0.16
Exposed floors	– outside surface	0.04
	– inside surface	

[11.10] *Example of calculation.*

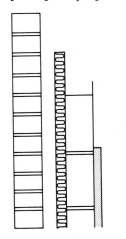

100 mm bricks, thermal conductivity 0.84 W/mK
50 mm cavity, thermal resistance 0.18 W/m K

50 mm thermal insulation,
thermal conductivity 0.035 W/mK

100 mm blocks,
thermal conductivity 0.18 W/mK

13 mm plasterboard
thermal conductivity 0.16 W/mK

Outside surface resistance 0.06 W/m K
Inside surface resistance   0.12 W/m K

The combined resistance is therefore:

Resistance			*m K/W*
Outside surface			= 0.06
Brick leaf	thickness – conductivity –	$\dfrac{0.1}{0.84}$	= 0.12
Cavity			= 0.18
Insulation material	thickness – conductivity –	$\dfrac{0.05}{0.035}$	= 1.42
Concrete block leaf	thickness – conductivity –	$\dfrac{0.1}{0.18}$	= 0.55
Plasterboard	thickness – conductivity –	$\dfrac{0.013}{0.16}$	= 0.08
Inside surface			= 0.12
Total resistance			2.53

Therefore U value $= \dfrac{1}{2.53} = 0.41$

Walls, roofs and floors

Insulation thickness to achieve U-values

Allowable reductions expressed as a percentage reduction in base insulation thickness are as follows.

Construction feature	0.25 W/m K %	0.45 W/m K %	0.6 W/m K %
Cavity		8	11
Roof space	4	8	
Brick leaf at least 100 mm thick		6	8
Concrete block leaf of thermal donductivity not more than			
0.1		49	67
0.2		25	34
0.3		16	22
0.4		12	17
0.5		9	13
Plasterboard – lining or ceiling at least 13 mm thick	2	4	5
Lightweight plaster at least 13 mm thick		4	5
Floor			
Concrete slab not less than 150 mm		6	8
Screed not less than 75 mm		9	13
Wood block floor finish not less than 10 mm thick		4	5

Appendix B Examples showing the use of the elemental approach and calculation procedure 1

Elemental approach

B1/B9 There are five tables which can be used when adopting the elemental approach. These relate to walls, roofs, solid floors in contact with the ground, suspended ground floors and exposed and semi-exposed floors. The last will be comparatively rare.

Part 1 of each table gives a base level thickness of insulation in relation to the thermal conductivity of the material. This may be used as it stands, in which case a better than minimum standard will be achieved as the construction itself will contribute to the total insulation value. If wishing to economise, the designer may take account of the construction by using Part 2 of the table, which gives a set of figures showing the deduction from the base level thickness which can be made for various elements of structure.

The tables are quite easy to use and may be the most convenient way. However, there is little point in simply reproducing them here, and so to follow one of the principles of this *Guide*, Part 1 of each table is expressed in diagrams [11.11–11.13] in graphical form and Part 2 in percentages of the base thickness level. (The graphical form also assists in using linear interpolation, which is permitted.)

Calculation procedure 1

B10 This procedure allows greater flexibility between the areas of glazing and/or the insulation levels of individual elements.

B11 No account is taken of heat gains in this procedure. Calculation procedure 2 allows these to be used.

B12 The procedure to determine whether a building will meet the requirements of the regulations is

1 Calculate the rate of heat loss for the *proposed* building.

2 Compare this with the heat loss from a notional building of the same size and shape which complies with the requirements.

Example

Two storey semi-detached house – dimensions 6 m × 5 m × 2.4 m ceiling height.

Window area 24% of floor area – double glazed.

B.1/B.9 **[11.11]** *Basic insulation thickness for roofs, walls and exposed and semi-exposed floors (mm).*

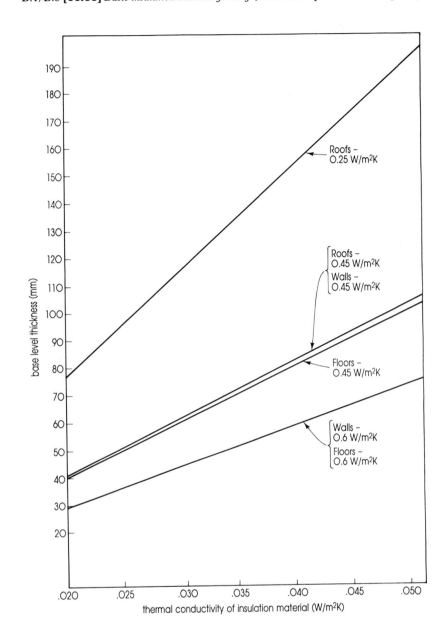

B.1/B.9 **[11.12]** *Solid floors in contact with ground: Insulation thickness to achieve 0.45 W/m²K.*

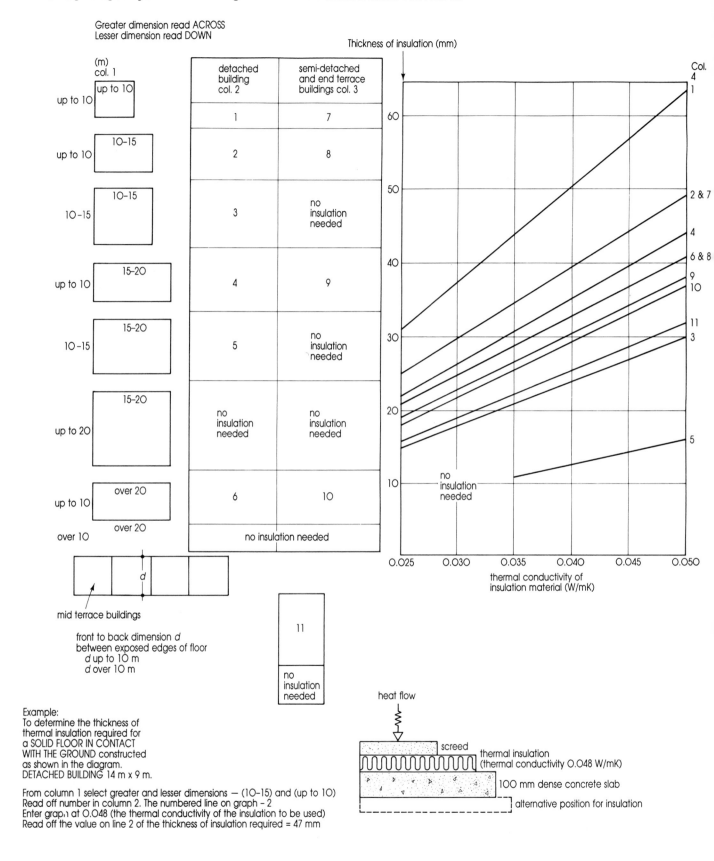

Example:
To determine the thickness of
thermal insulation required for
a SOLID FLOOR IN CONTACT
WITH THE GROUND constructed
as shown in the diagram.
DETACHED BUILDING 14 m x 9 m.

From column 1 select greater and lesser dimensions — (10–15) and (up to 10)
Read off number in column 2. The numbered line on graph – 2
Enter graph at 0.048 (the thermal conductivity of the insulation to be used)
Read off the value on line 2 of the thickness of insulation required = 47 mm

B.1/B.9 **[11.13]** *Suspended ground floors: Insulation thickness to achieve 0.45 W/m²K.*

Greater dimension (m) read ACROSS Lesser dimension (m) read DOWN col. 1	detached building col. 2	semi-detached and end terrace buildings col. 3
up to 10 — up to 10	1	7
up to 10 — 10–15	2	8
10–15 — 10–15	3	no insulation needed
up to 10 — 15–20	4	9
10–15 — 15–20	5	no insulation needed
up to 20 — 15–20	no insulation needed	no insulation needed
up to 10 — over 20	6	10
over 10 — over 20	no insulation needed	

mid terrace buildings	
d up to 10 m	11
d over 10 m	no insulation needed

front to back dimension *d* between exposed edges of floor
d up to 10 m
d over 10 m

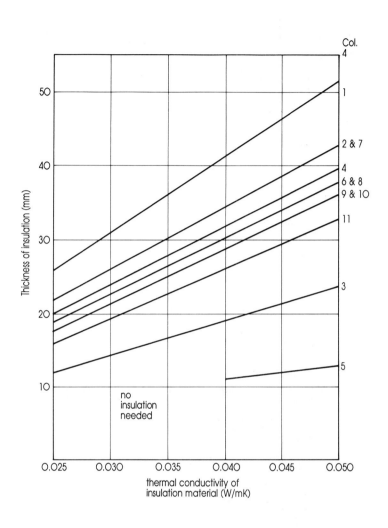

Col. 4

1
2 & 7
4
6 & 8
9 & 10
11
3
5

Thickness of insulation (mm)

no insulation needed

thermal conductivity of insulation material (W/mK)

Example:
To determine the thickness of thermal insulation required for a SUSPENDED TIMBER GROUND FLOOR constructed as shown in the diagram.
SEMI-DETACHED BUILDING 9 m × 8 m

From column 1 select greater and lesser dimensions — both up to 10.
Read off number in column 2. The numbered line on graph – 7
Enter graph at 0.042 (the thermal conductivity of the insulation to be used)
Read off the value on line 7 of the thickness of insulation required = 36 mm

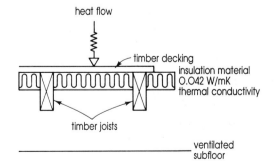

heat flow

timber decking
insulation material 0.042 W/mK thermal conductivity

timber joists

ventilated subfloor

Example 1 [11.14] *To determine the thickness of thermal insulation required for an exposed wall constructed as shown below (U-value = 0.45 W/m²K).*

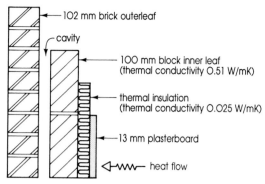

102 mm brick outerleaf

cavity

100 mm block inner leaf
(thermal conductivity 0.51 W/mK)

thermal insulation
(thermal conductivity 0.025 W/mK)

13 mm plasterboard

heat flow

From diagram (12.11) base level thickness for
thermal conductivity of 0.025   = 51 mm

To take account of construction deduct
percentages shown in table

cavity	8
brick leaf	6
concrete block leaf	9
plasterboard	4
	27%

∴ insulation to be 73% of 51   = 38 mm

Example 2 [11.15] *To determine whether an exposed wall constructed as shown below will achieve a U-value of 0.45 W/m²K.*

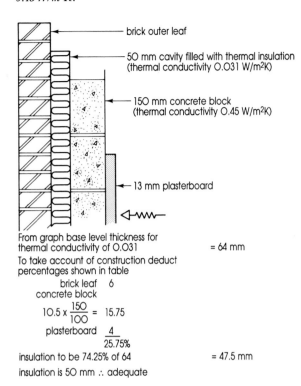

brick outer leaf

50 mm cavity filled with thermal insulation
(thermal conductivity 0.031 W/m²K)

150 mm concrete block
(thermal conductivity 0.45 W/m²K)

13 mm plasterboard

From graph base level thickness for
thermal conductivity of 0.031   = 64 mm

To take account of construction deduct
percentages shown in table

brick leaf   6

concrete block

$$10.5 \times \frac{150}{100} = 15.75$$

plasterboard   4

         25.75%

insulation to be 74.25% of 64   = 47.5 mm

insulation is 50 mm ∴ adequate

Example 3 [11.16] *To determine the thickness of thermal insulation required for a pitched roof as shown below (U-value = 0.25 W/m²K).*

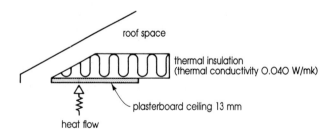

roof space

thermal insulation
(thermal conductivity 0.040 W/mk)

plasterboard ceiling 13 mm

heat flow

From graph base level thickness for
thermal conductivity of 0.040   = 154 mm

To take account of construction deduct
percentages:

roof space	4
plasterboard	2
	6

∴ insulation to be 94% of 154   = 145 mm

Example 4 [11.17] *To determine the thickness of thermal insulation for a semi-exposed floor constructed as shown below (U-value = 0.6 W/m²K).*

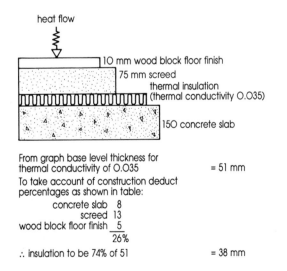

heat flow

10 mm wood block floor finish

75 mm screed

thermal insulation
(thermal conductivity 0.035)

150 concrete slab

From graph base level thickness for
thermal conductivity of 0.035   = 51 mm

To take account of construction deduct
percentages as shown in table:

concrete slab	8
screed	13
wood block floor finish	5
	26%

∴ insulation to be 74% of 51   = 38 mm

U-values proposed – Walls 0.6 W/m²K, roof 0.35 W/m²K, ground floor 0.45 W/m²K. Does this house meet the requirements of the Regulations?

1   Proposed house

(a)   Calculate the areas of each element: m²

total floor area (6 × 5 × 2 floors)	=	60
window area (24% of 60 m²)	=	14.4
area of external walling and windows (5 + 6 + 5) × 2.4 × 2	=	76.8
area of exposed walls (76.8 − 14.4)	=	62.4
area of roof. area of ground floor	=	30

Element	Area (m²)	U-value (W/m²K)	Rate of heat loss (W/K)
exposed walls	62.4	0.6	37.44
windows	14.4	2.8	40.32
roof	30	0.35	10.5
ground floor	30	0.45	13.5
total rate of heat loss − proposed construction			*101.76*

Notional house   m²

(a)   Calculate the areas of each element

total floor area	60
window area (15% of 60 m²)	9
area of external walling and windows	76.8
areas of exposed wall (76.8 − 9)	67.8
area of roof. area of ground floor	30

(b)   Using the U-values in the table and assuming single glazing, the rate of heat loss from the notional house is calculated as follows.

Element	Area (m²)	U-value (W/m²K)	Rate of heat loss (W/K)
exposed walls	67.8	0.45	30.51
windows	9	5.7	51.3
roof	30	0.25	7.5
ground floor	30	0.45	13.5
total rate of heat loss			*102.81*

The rate of heat loss from the proposed house is less than that from the notional house and therefore the requirements of the regulations are satisfied.

Example

Detached, five storey office building. Plan area – 50 m × 14 m. Height 18 m.
75% window areas all double glazed. No rooflight glazing.
Exposed walls and roof – U-value 0.6 W/m². Floor – 0.45 W/m²K.
Does this building comply?

1   Proposed building   m²

Calculate the areas of each element:

walling and windows (50 + 50 + 14 + 14) × 18	=	2304
area of windows (75% of 2304)	=	1728
area of exposed walls (2304 − 1728)	=	576
area of roof. area of floor	=	700

Element	Area (m²)	U-value (W/m²K)	Rate of heat loss (W/K)
exposed walls	576	0.6	345.6
windows	1728	2.8	4838.4
roof	700	0.6	420
ground floor	700	0.45	315
Total rate of heat loss from proposed building			5919

Notional building			*m²*
area of windows – table. 35% (of 2304)			806.4
area of exposed wall (2304 − 806.4)			1497.6
area of roof. area of floor			700

From table:

Element	Area *(m²)*	U-value *(W/m²K)*	Rate of heat loss *(W/K)*
exposed walls	1497.6	0.45	673.92
windows	806.4	5.7	4596.48
roof	700	0.45	315
ground floor	700	0.45	315
Total rate of heat loss from notional building			5900.4

The rate of heat loss from the proposed building is greater than that from the notional building therefore the requirements of the regulations are *not* satisfied.

If the window area was reduced by $9\,m^2$ the rate of heat loss would be 5899.8 W/K and the requirements of the regulations would be satisfied.

References

The AD refers to the following documents:

Chartered Institution of Building Services Engineers. CIBSE Guide Section A3. *Thermal properties of building structures.* CIBSE. 1980.

Chartered Institution of Building Services Engineers. CIBSE Building Energy Code Part 2a.

BS 699: 1984 *Specification for copper direct cylinders for domestic purposes* Amendment 1. AMD 5792.

BS 1566 *Copper indirect cylinders for domestic purposes.* Part 1: 1984 *Double feed indirect cylinders.* Amendment 1. AMD 5790. Part 2: 1984 *Specification for single feed indirect cylinders.* Amendment 1. AMD 5791.

BS 3198: 1981 *Specification for copper hot water storage combination units for domestic purposes.* Amendment 1: AMD 4372.

BS 5422: 1977 *Specification for the use of thermal insulating materials.* Amendment 1. AMD 2599. 2. AMD 5744.

BS 5615: 1985 *Specification for insulating jackets for domestic hot water storage cylinders.*

Thermal Insulation: avoiding risks HMSO.

BREDEM Worksheet.

BRE Report BR150: *Conservation of fuel and power – the energy target method of compliance for dwellings.*

Chapter 12

Approved Document M: Access and Facilities for Disabled People

Part M forms part of a phased approach which began in 1982 to give force to the relevant provisions of the Chronically Sick and Disabled Persons Act 1970, the Chronically Sick and Disabled Persons (Amendment) Act 1976 and to Section 6 of the Disabled Persons Act 1981, which added to the provisions of the Town and Country Planning Act 1971.

It has been estimated that there are more than 6 million adults in Great Britain with some form of disability. Many people have more than one disability.

For instance, it is thought that 4½ million have a problem with locomotion, 1.4 million have difficulty hearing someone talking in a normal voice in a quiet room and half a million cannot see well enough to recognise a friend across a room.

In this phase of development of Part M, the definition of disabled people has been extended to include those people who have impaired hearing or sight and the application has been extended. It now applies to:

All types of non-domestic buildings which are either newly erected, or have been substantially reconstructed; and

Extensions to non-domestic buildings which include a ground storey.

Requirement	Limits on application
Disabled people M 1. In this Part 'disabled people' means people who have – (*a*) An impairment which limits their ability to walk or which requires them to use a wheelchair for mobility; or (*b*) Impaired hearing or sight. *Access and use* M 2. Reasonable provision shall be made for disabled people to gain access to and use the building. *Sanitary conveniences* M 3. If sanitary conveniences are provided in the building, reasonable provision shall be made for disabled people. *Audience or spectator seating* M 4. If the building contains audience or spectator seating, reasonable provision shall be made to accommodate disabled people.	1. The requirements of this Part do not apply to – (*a*) An extension which does not include a ground storey; (*b*) A material alteration; (*c*) A dwelling, or the common parts of a building which are intended for the exclusive use of two or more dwellings; (*d*) Any part of a building which is used solely to enable the building or any service or fitting in the building to be inspected, maintained or repaired.

The underlying philosophy is that, as far as is reasonable, the built environment should be as accessible to disabled persons as to the able-bodied. Buildings which are so accessible are usually also more convenient for the general public.

The format of the 1992 edition of the Approved Document for Part M has been changed and it now contains a performance statement, introductory paragraphs and five Sections:

Section 1: Means of access to and into the building

Section 2: Means of access within the building

Section 3: Use of the building

Section 4: Sanitary conveniences

Section 5: Audience or spectator seating.

Each section begins with a statement of its objective, followed by design considerations and then the actual provisions.

Designers are reminded that the provisions in the Approved Documents are the ones which satisfy the requirements of 'reasonable provision'. In some instances full provision may not be reasonable and some of these cases are defined. On the other hand, developers may wish to provide for disabled people beyond the guidance given in the Approved Document and designers should perhaps encourage this approach.

Note: Relationship to other parts of the Regulations

Regulation 3(2)(b)

This stipulates that building work should not result in an altered building being less satisfactory in respect of access and facilities for disabled people than it was before.

Part B Fire safety

Reference should be made to Part B for means of escape for disabled people. The reference in B 1 – Means of escape – to disabled people is simply a note stating that management arrangements to provide escape may be all that is required. Alternatively, the recommendations of BS 5588: Part 8: 1988 *Code of Practice for means of escape for disabled people* could be considered. This introduces the concept of refuges and the use of an evacuation lift, but an effective management plan for evacuation is of vital importance.

Part K Stairs, ramps and guards

Although Part K contains guidance on stair and ramp design, the provisions of Part M are more specific regarding stairs and ramps suitable for use by disabled people.

Performance

The requirements will be met by making it reasonably safe and convenient for disabled people to gain access to and within non-domestic buildings and to use them.

The provisions for access and facilities are for the benefit of those who are either visitors to the building or who work in it.

Where the requirements apply

New buildings

0.1/0.2 The requirements apply if:

(*a*) A building is newly erected;

(*b*) A building is substantially demolished leaving only the external walls. If in reconstruction it is impracticable to:

Alter the level of the existing principal entrance or any other appropriate existing entrance, or

Provide a new entrance which is suitable to permit independent access for wheelchair users the relevant provisions for such access will not apply but the remainder of the provisions in the Approved Document are applicable.

NOTE It may sometimes be difficult and also costly to alter existing approaches to some buildings, and it is hoped that a reasonable stance will be taken by the enforcers on the word 'impracticable'.

Extensions and alterations

0.3/0.5 The application to extensions will probably be found to be somewhat confusing. When a building is extended, the *existing building* should be treated as follows:

(*a*) There is no obligation to make it more accessible than it was before;

(*b*) The extension should not adversely affect any existing Part M provision.

The *extension:*

(*a*) If it contains a ground storey should comply with Part M;

(*b*) Should be at least as accessible and usable by disabled persons as the existing building;

(*c*) If its access is through the existing building there need be no change to the existing building but a higher standard could be expected in the extension;

(*d*) If it is independently approached and entered from the boundary of the site it should be treated as a new building.

When a building is *altered* there is no obligation to improve access and facilities for disabled people. The level of provision should not be any worse after the alteration has taken place. Facilities may be moved but their suitability for use should not be reduced.

External features

0.6   Part M applies to features outside the building which are needed to give access to a building:

from the edge of the site, and

from cark parking within the site.

What requirements apply   **0.7**   If Part M applies, reasonable provision should be made for disabled people so that:

(*a*)   They can reach the principal entrance to the building and other entrances described in the Approved Document from the edge of the site curtilage and from car parking within the curtilage.

(*b*)   There are no hazards for a person with sight impairment.

(*c*)   Access within any storey and to any facilities is provided.

(*d*)   They can use the building's facilities.

(*e*)   Sanitary accommodation is provided.

(*f*)   Suitable accommodation is provided in audience or spectator seating.

(*g*)   There are aids to communication for those with impairment of sight or hearing in auditoria, meeting rooms, reception rooms etc.

Educational establishments   **0.8**   The requirements of Part M will be satisfied in schools and other educational establishments if there is compliance with: paragraphs 2.1/2/4/6, 3.1, 4.1/2/4/6 and 5.1 of Design Note 18, 1984 *Access for Disabled Persons to Educational Buildings*, published by the Secretary of State for Education and Science. To satisfy M3 some of the general design considerations may need to be incorporated.

Definitions   **0.9**   'Access' means approach or entry.

'Accessible' with respect to buildings or parts of buildings means that access is facilitated.

'Suitable' as to access and facilities means designed for use by disabled people.

'Principal entrance storey' means the storey containing the principal entrance or entrances to the building. If an alternative accessible entrance is to be provided as shown in 1.31(b) the storey containing that entrance is the principal entrance storey.

'Building' means a building or part which may comprise individual premises: a shop, an office, a factory, a warehouse, a school or other educational establishment including student residential accommodation, an institution or any premises to which the public is admitted whether or not on immediate payment, fee subscription etc.

Section 1   Means of access to and into the building

Objective   **1.1**   This is to provide a suitable means of access for disabled people:

To the building from the point of entrance to the building;

From any car parking provided within the site of the building;

Within external circulation areas between different parts of the building.

The other paragraphs under the Objective heading are really design considerations and these include:

1.2/1.6   Approach to an entrance – wheelchair users and ambulant disabled people have difficulty in negotiating changes in level.

Abrupt changes of level – people with impaired sight may not be aware of these.

Routes close to buildings – hazards on circulation routes immediately adjacent to buildings should be avoided (particular hazard to those with impaired sight).

Principal entrance for visitors/customers and entrances exclusively for staff – these should be usable by disabled persons.

Alternative means of access – the needs of disabled people vary; some ambulant disabled people may find a stair easier to negotiate than a ramp.

Level approach for the edge of the site and car parking

1.7   Where possible, a level approach should be provided.

Gradients should be as gentle as circumstances allow so as to be more convenient for wheelchair users and those with walking difficulties.

Width is important for those who use wheelchairs, sticks or crutches or who may be accompanied, and adequate space should be provided, including space for those passing in the opposite direction.

Provision

1.9/1.11   A level approach should have:

A width of at least 1.2 m

A gradient not steeper than 1 in 20

A ramped approach if site constraints mean a steeper gradient where the route crosses a carriageway, or at the top of steps

A tactile warning for people with impaired vision (see diagram [12.1]

Dropped kerbs for wheelchair users.

1.11 and 1.24 **[12.1]** *Tactile paving slabs.*

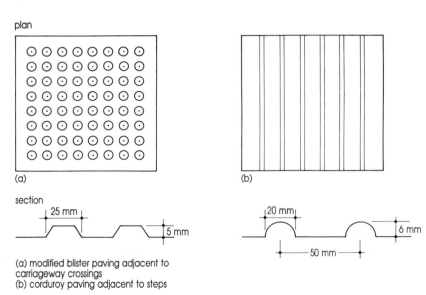

plan

(a)

(b)

section

25 mm

5 mm

20 mm

6 mm

50 mm

(a) modified blister paving adjacent to carriageway crossings
(b) corduroy paving adjacent to steps

Ramped approach

1.12/1.18   Where a ramped approach is necessary the gradient should be as gentle as possible because:

Some wheelchair users may not have the strength to propel themselves up a steep slope or may not be able to stop when descending;

Ramped approaches are not as safe for ambulant disabled people;

In adverse weather conditions the risk of slipping may increase

Disabled people or helpers may wish to stop frequently, to regain strength or breath or to ease pain.

Landings should be large enough to enable wheelchair users to stop or to open or pass through doors without reversing into circulation routes or face the risk of rolling back down the ramp.

Support on each side is required because disabled people may have a weakness on one side or another.

Kerbs or solid balustrades will help to prevent wheelchair users catching their feet beneath balustrade rails.

Easy going steps should complement ramped approaches.

Provisions

1.19   A ramped approach should have:

(*a*)   A surface which reduces the risk of slipping

(*b*)   Flights at least 1.2 m wide with an unobstructed width of at least 1 m;

(*c*)   A gradient not steeper than 1 in 15 if the length of any single flight is not more than 10.0 m; a gradient not steeper than 1 in 12 if the length of any flight is not more than 5 m;

(*d*) Top and bottom landings at least 1.2 m in length with any necessary intermediate landings at least 1.5 m in length (clear of door swing in all cases);

(*e*) A raised kerb at least 100 mm high on any open side of a flight or landing;

(*f*) A continuous handrail on each side of flights and landings if the length of the ramp is more than 2 m.

Diagram [12.2] illustrates ramped approaches.

1.19 **[12.2]** *Ramped approach with complementary steps.*

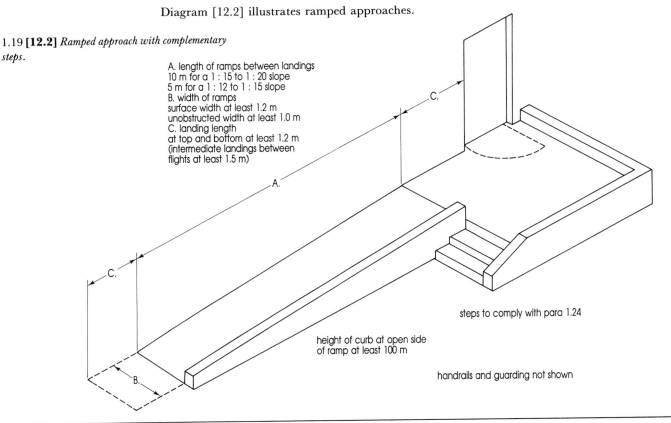

A. length of ramps between landings
10 m for a 1 : 15 to 1 : 20 slope
5 m for a 1 : 12 to 1 : 15 slope
B. width of ramps
surface width at least 1.2 m
unobstructed width at least 1.0 m
C. landing length
at top and bottom at least 1.2 m
(intermediate landings between flights at least 1.5 m)

steps to comply with para 1.24

height of curb at open side of ramp at least 100 m

handrails and guarding not shown

Stepped approach

Design considerations

1.20/1.23 When meeting sudden changes of level, especially when approaching the head of a flight of steps, people with impaired sight may trip or lose their balance. Individual steps should also be made apparent.

Tread dimensions are important so that people who wear callipers or have physical weakness or sight impairment can place their feet fully on to each tread.

Provisions

1.24 A stepped approach should have:

(*a*) A tactile surface on the top landing (see diagrams [12.1], [12.3]–[12.5]);

1.21 **[12.3]** *Tactile and visual warnings.*

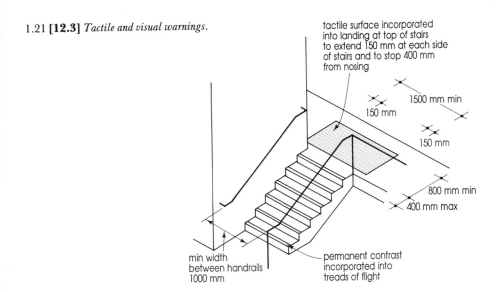

tactile surface incorporated into landing at top of stairs to extend 150 mm at each side of stairs and to stop 400 mm from nosing

1500 mm min

150 mm

150 mm

800 mm min

400 mm max

min width between handrails 1000 mm

permanent contrast incorporated into treads of flight

1.24 **[12.4]** *Stepped approach: external steps and handrails.*

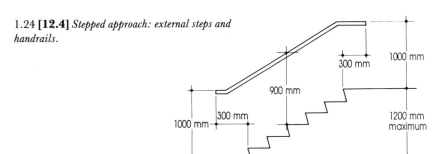

1.24 **[12.5]** *Examples of tread nosing profiles.*

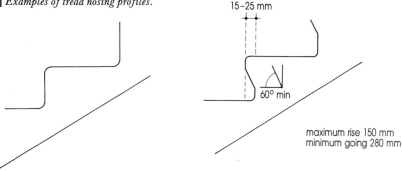

maximum rise 150 mm
minimum going 280 mm

(*b*)   All step nosings distinguishable through contrasting brightness;
(*c*)   Flights with unobstructed widths of at least 1 m;
(*d*)   In a flight between landings having a rise of not more than 1.2 m;
(*e*)   Top, bottom and any intermediate landings with a length (clear of any door swing) of not less than 1.2 m;
(*f*)   Uniform risers not deeper than 150 mm;
(*g*)   Each step with a going of at least 280 mm (the going of tapered steps should be measured at a point 170 mm from the inside of the stair);
(*h*)   No open risers;
(*j*)   A suitable continuous handrail on each side of the flight and landings if the rise of the stepped approach comprises two or more risers.

Handrails

Design considerations
1.25   Handrails should be well supported and be grippable.

Provisions
1.26   Any handrail should:
(*a*)   Be 900 mm above the pitch line of a flight of steps or the surface of a ramp or 1000 mm above the surface of a landing (measured to the top of the handrail);
(*b*)   Extend at least 300 mm beyond the top and bottom of a ramp or the top and bottom nosings of a stepped approach and terminate in a closed end which does not project into a route of travel;
(*c*)   Have a suitable profile and projection from the wall.
See diagram [12.6].

1.26 **[12.6]** *Handrail design.*

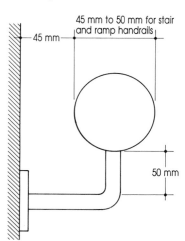

45 mm to 50 mm for stair
and ramp handrails

45 mm

50 mm

Hazards on access routes

Design considerations

1.27 Features of the building that occasionally obstruct a route adjacent to the building may be a hazard to those with sight impairment, particularly if the object is partially transparent.

Provisions

1.28/1.29 Windows or doors in general use which open outwards should not cause an obstruction on a path which runs along the face of a building (see diagram [12.7]).

1.27 **[12.7]** *External hazards.*

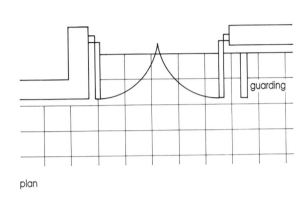

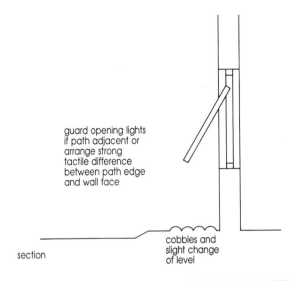

guarding

guard opening lights if path adjacent or arrange strong tactile difference between path edge and wall face

plan

section

cobbles and slight change of level

Access into the building

Design considerations

1.30 Whether disabled persons arrive at a building on foot or in a wheelchair and whether they are visitors or work in the building, convenient access should be provided.

Provisions

1.31 The principal entrance for visitors or customers and any entrance provided specifically for members of staff should be both accessible and suitable. If the space outside the principal entrance is:

Severely restricted; or

The site is on sloping ground.

An alternative entrance may be provided.

The alternative entrance intended for general use should:

Be accessible and suitable;

Provide suitable internal access from the alternative entrance to the principal entrance for all who may use the building.

Where car spaces are provided adjacent to the building but there is no suitable access from the car spaces to the principal entrance, an additional entrance intended for general use giving suitable internal access to the principal entrance would be acceptable.

Principal entrance doors

Design considerations

1.32/1.34 These should be of sufficient width for wheelchair manoeuvre with a space alongside the leading edge of the door to assist a wheelchair user. Without such a space a wheelchair footrest would normally collide with the return wall when the user tried to reach the door handle.

As people with mobility difficulties may not react quickly to avoid collisions, they should be able to see people approaching the other side of entrances and be seen themselves.

Provisions

1.35 The principal entrance door should:

(*a*) Contain a leaf which gives a minimum clear opening width of not less than 800 mm;

(*b*) Have an obstructed space on the side next to the leading edge for at least 300 mm (unless the door is opened by automatic control);

(*c*) Have a glazed panel giving a zone of visibility from a height of 900 mm to 1500 mm from the finished floor level if opening the door could constitute a hazard (see diagram [12.8]).

1.35 **[12.8]** *Entrance doorways.*

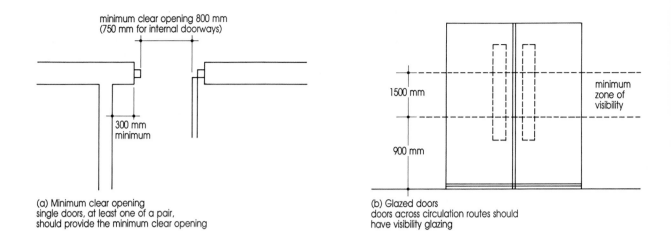

(a) Minimum clear opening
single doors, at least one of a pair,
should provide the minimum clear opening

(b) Glazed doors
doors across circulation routes should
have visibility glazing

1.41 **[12.9]** *Entrance lobbies.*

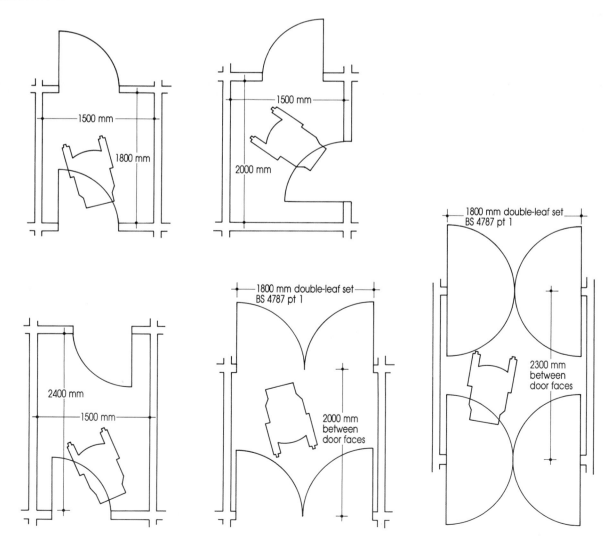

Revolving doors

Design considerations

1.36/1.37 Timing of entry and exit through small revolving doors may create difficulties for people with sight impairments or with ambulatory problems. Such doors may also provide insufficient space or little time for a wheelchair to manoeuvre.

The larger type of revolving door may be suitable but should be large enough to accommodate several people at the same time. Mechanisms should be such that they revolve slowly, can be slowed down further and stop when resistance is felt.

Provisions

1.38/1.39 Large types of revolving door may be fitted in an entrance. If the smaller type is used the entrance should also contain a door of the type described in paragraph 1.35.

Entrance lobbies

Design considerations

1.40 A wheelchair user should be able to move clear of one door before using the next one and there should also be sufficient space for a person assisting the wheelchair user and for people passing in the opposite direction.

Provisions

1.41 Diagram [12.9] gives examples of satisfactory entrance lobbies.

Section 2 Means of access within the building

Objective

2.1/2.2 The objective – the need to facilitate movement for disabled persons – is similar to that given in Section 1. Sufficient space for wheelchair manoeuvre, convenient ways of moving from one storey to another and features to help those with impaired hearing or sight to find their way are sought.

Horizontal circulation within the building

Internal doors

Design considerations

2.3 These are similar to those for principal entrance doors (paragraphs 1.32/1.34).

Provisions

Internal doors should:

(*a*) Contain a leaf which provides a minimum clear opening of 750 mm;

(*b*) Open into a space which is unobstructed on the side next to the leading edge for at least 300 mm. This may not be necessary if the door is opened by automatic control or is in a place where assistance would usually be available (for instance, when leaving a fellow-guest's hotel bedroom);

(*c*) Be provided with a glazed panel if they are across an accessible corridor or passageway. The panel should be extended from 900 mm to 1500 mm above floor level, with difference only in clear opening width (see diagram [12.8]).

NOTE Table 1 of BS 4787: Part 1 shows how clear opening widths of more than 750 mm can be achieved by using a 900 mm single-leaf doorset or one leaf of an 1800 mm double-leaf doorset.

Corridors and passageways

Design considerations

2.5 Corridors and passageways need to be wide enough for wheelchair users and for other people to pass. Narrower corridors may be acceptable in some extensions or where corridors do not give access to lifts.

Provisions

2.6 The unobstructed width of corridors and passageways should be:

(*a*) 1200 mm where there is wheelchair access;

(*b*) 1000 mm where access is only by a stairway or in an extension approached through an existing building.

Internal lobbies

Design considerations

2.7   These can be smaller than entrance lobbies but should be large enough for a wheelchair user to move clear of one door before using the next.

Provision

2.8   Examples of internal lobbies are given in diagram [12.10].

2.8 **[12.10]** *Internal lobbies.*

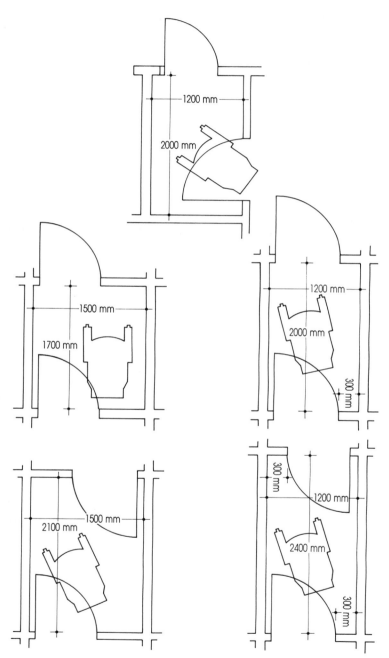

Vertical circulation within the building

Design considerations

2.9/2.11   A lift is the most suitable means of access between floors for disabled people, but it is not reasonable to require a lift in every instance.

The decision as to whether a lift should be provided should be based on the nett floor area of the storey to be reached.

If there is no lift a stair is acceptable provided it is designed for the needs of ambulant disabled people and for those who have an impairment of sight.

Passenger lifts

Design considerations

2.12   A wheelchair user needs sufficient space and time to manoeuvre into a lift and should be able to reach the controls both inside and outside the lift. It would be helpful to people with sensory impairments if they were aware of the floor the lift had reached.

Provisions

2.13   A lift should be provided where the nett floor area of the storey to be served is:

(*a*)   In a two-storey building – more than 280 m² of nett floor area;

(*b*)   In a building of more than two storeys – more than 200 m² of nett floor area; and

(*c*)   Suitable means of access is provided from the lift to the remainder of the storey.

NOTE   There were problems with the interpretation of this provision as to the correct way to measure the nett floor area, and in particular whether the area to be served was the total area or just the area of one storey.

This provision makes it clear that:

In a two-storey building – where the nett floor area exceeds 280 m²; or

In a building of three or more storeys – where the storey to be served exceeds 200 m²

a lift should be provided.

Nett floor area should be calculated in the following way.

Add together all parts of the storey which use the same entrance (include those parts which may be in another part of the same storey or used for different purposes). Deduct the area in the storey which is used for vertical circulation, sanitary accommodation and maintenance purposes.

2.14   A passenger lift should have:

(*a*)   A clear landing at least 1.5 m wide and 1.5 m long in front of its entrance;

(*b*)   A door or doors giving a clear opening width of at least 800 mm;

(*c*)   A car width at least 1.1 m wide and 1.4 m long;

(*d*)   Landing and car controls between 0.9 m and 1.2 m above the landing and the car floor, fitted at least 400 mm from the front wall;

(*e*)   Suitable tactile indication on the landing and adjacent to the lift call button to identify the particular floor;

(*f*)   Suitable tactile indication on or adjacent to internal lift buttons to confirm the floor selected;

(*g*)   Visual indication and voice indication of the floor reached, if it serves more than three storeys;

(*h*)   A signalling system giving 5 seconds' notice that the lift is answering a call and a 'dwell' time of 5 seconds before the doors begin to close after being fully open.

The system may be over-ridden by a door-reactivating device which relies on infra-red or photo-eye methods (but not a door edge pressure system), provided that the lift door remains fully open for at least 3 seconds (diagram [12.11]).

2.14 **[12.11]** *Lift dimensions.*

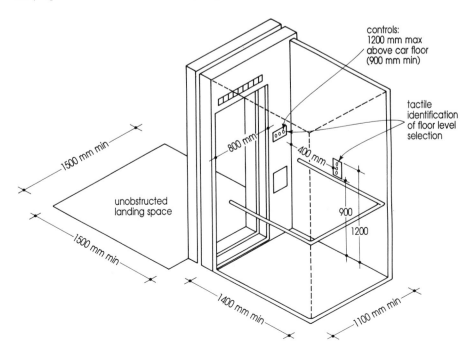

NOTE BS 5655: Parts 1, 2, 5 and 7 give details of some of these provisions and also recommend that automatic doors to lifts should have re-opening activators, operated either through an invisible beam or through contact with a person.

Wheelchair stair lifts

Design considerations
2.15   In a building where there is a unique facility such as a small library gallery, staff rest room or perhaps a training room it may be reasonable to expect access to be available for wheelchair users but impracticable to provide a passenger lift.
A wheelchair stair lift to BS 5776: 1979 could be a possible alternative.

Provisions
2.16   If a storey with a nett floor area of $100 \, m^2$, having a unique facility, is not large enough to warrant a passenger lift it should be accessible to wheelchair users.

Platform lifts

Design considerations and provisions
2.17/2.18   Ramps can provide access to changes of level within a storey but may have planning implications. A platform lift will be acceptable instead, but there should also be stair access between levels.
Guidance on platform lifts can be found in BS 6440: 1983 *Powered lifting platforms for use by disabled people.*

Internal stairs

Design considerations
2.19/2.20   Similar considerations to those for stepped approaches need to be given. However, internal stairs may need to be steeper and have less frequent landings. Soft floor coverings may make it impracticable to provide tactile warnings of changes of level, but the nosing of each stair should be clearly marked for the benefit of people with impaired vision.
A suitable stair should be provided wherever there is no lift access.

Provisions
2.21/2.22   An internal stair should have:
(*a*)   Flights with widths not less than 1000 mm;
(*b*)   Step nosings of contrasting brightness;
(*c*)   A rise between landings of not more than 1800 mm;
(*d*)   Top, bottom and, where necessary, intermediate landings each 1200 mm long clear of any door swing;
(*e*)   A uniform rise of each step, not more than 170 mm;
(*f*)   A uniform going not less than 250 mm (the measurement for tapered treads should be taken 270 mm from the 'inside' of the stair);
(*g*)   No open risers;
(*h*)   A suitable continuous handrail on each side of flights and landings if the rise of the stair consists of two or more risers.

These provisions may need to be varied in exceptional circumstances and here it would be reasonable to provide the number of risers which would satisfy requirement K 1. (See Approved Document K, Stairs, ramps and guards.) See also diagram [12.12].

Internal ramps

Design considerations and provisions
2.23/2.24   The same considerations apply as to internal ramps and an internal ramp should comply with the guidance in paragraph 1.19.

2.21 **[12.12]** *Internal stairs.*

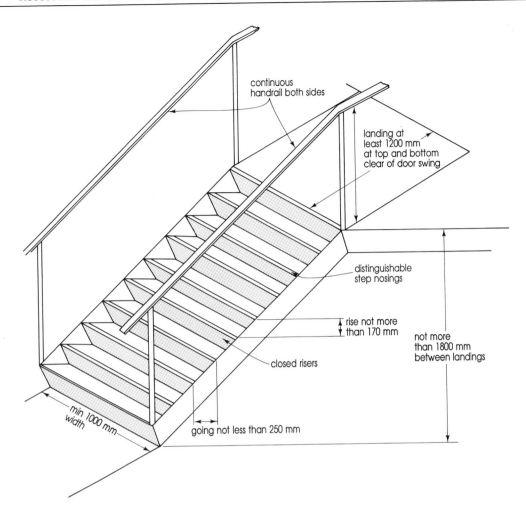

continuous
handrail both sides

landing at
least 1200 mm
at top and bottom
clear of door swing

distinguishable
step nosings

rise not more
than 170 mm

not more
than 1800 mm
between landings

closed risers

min 1000 mm
width

going not less than 250 mm

Section 3   Use of the building

Objective

3.1/3.3   Different types of building contain unique facilities and, generally, disabled people should be able to reach them all.

The objective of this section is to identify and give guidance on access which should be provided for disabled people to unique facilities such as restaurants, bars, hotel bedrooms and changing facilities.

People with hearing impairment should be able to play a full part in conferences, committee meetings etc.

Common facilities such as canteens, cloakrooms, doctors' and dentists' consulting rooms and other health amenities should be located in a storey to which wheelchair users have access.

Restaurants and bars

Design considerations

3.4/3.5   Disabled people should be able to visit restaurants and bars either accompanied or unaccompanied. Bars and self-service counters and seating areas should be accessible to them. If there is provision for waiter service and self-service, they should have access to both.

Any changes in floor level within these areas should be accessible to ambulant disabled people.

Provisions

3.6   Access should be available to:

(*a*)   The full range of services;

(*b*)   All bars and self-service counters;

(*c*)   Wheelchair users to the extent that half of any seating area provided whether the facilities are all on one floor or divided between areas or storeys is available for their use.

Hotels and motel bedrooms

Design considerations

3.7/3.8 Wheelchair users need bedrooms which are accessible and large enough to manoeuvre a wheelchair both in the bedroom and in any 'en-suite' bathroom. They may also need to gain access to bedrooms other than their own perhaps when attending conferences or on holiday with their families. It is not suggested that every hotel bedroom should be of such size as to be suitable for disabled people, but consideration should be given to the need for disabled people to be able to pass through doors to those rooms with the assumption that the other guest will open and close them.

Provisions

3.9 Guest bedrooms should:

(*a*) Be at a ratio of one per 20 or part of them, be suitable in size layout and facilities for use by a person using a wheelchair;

(*b*) If designed for use by a disabled person, have an entrance door which complies with paragraph 2.5(a) and (b);

(*c*) In any other case, have an entrance door with a clear opening width of 750 mm, with the 300 mm space at the side of the door optional.

Diagram [12.13] illustrates an example of an accessible hotel bedroom.

3.9 **[12.13]** *Example of accessible hotel bed and bathroom suite.*

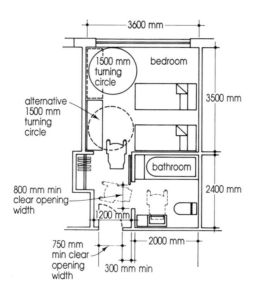

Changing facilities

Design considerations

3.10/3.11 Consideration should be given to providing in changing rooms used in connection with recreational activities:

(*a*) Manoeuvring space for a wheelchair and for transfer onto a seat;

(*b*) Suitable heights of seats, shower heads, clothes hooks and mirrors.

Provisions

Diagrams [12.14] and [12.15] show facilities which would meet the requirement.

Aids to communication

Design considerations

3.12 A person with impaired hearing needs to receive a signal some 20 dB above that received by a person with normal hearing if they are to have the full benefit of attending any public performance or taking part in discussions. Any system designed to achieve this should suppress reverberation and other extraneous noise.

Two systems are most commonly used:

1 The loop induction system takes a signal from an amplifier which directs a current through a loop around the relevant space. The magnetic field generated is then picked up by the listener's hearing aid and converted into familiar sound. Confidentiality is more difficult to achieve with this system because sound may spill beyond the boundary of the loop.

3.11 **[12.14]** *Shower compartment.*

3.11 **[12.15]** *Dressing cubicle.*

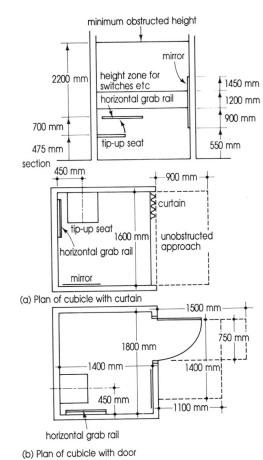

(a) Plan of cubicle with curtain

(b) Plan of cubicle with door

2   The infra-red system radiates invisible light which is picked up by a personal stethoscope receiver, demodulated and converted into familiar sound. This system can provide more confidentiality.

Provisions

3.15/3.17   Aids to communication should:

(*a*)   Be provided in booking and ticket offices where there is a glazed screen to separate customers from vendors, reception rooms, auditoria and meeting rooms more than $100\,m^2$ in floor area;

(*b*)   Be such that the sounds heard by persons using a hearing aid are of sufficient strength and not distorted through bad acoustics or other unwanted noise;

(*c*)   Be the type of system considered by the building owner to be the most suitable for the layout.

Section 4   Sanitary conveniences

Objective   **4.1**   Bearing in mind the nature and scale of the building in which provision is to be made, the aim is to provide sanitary conveniences which are no less available to disabled people than they are to the able-bodied.

Design considerations

4.2/4.4   Travel distance should reflect the fact that disabled people may need to get to a WC quickly.

The number and location of WCs will depend on the size of the building and the ease of access to them.

The design of the compartments should reflect ease of access and use.

4.5   For wheelchair users sanitary accommodation can be on a 'unisex' or 'integral' basis.

(*a*)   A unisex facility is approached separately from any other sanitary accommodation. Its advantages are that it is more easily identified, more likely to be available when needed and permits assistance by a companion of either sex. It takes up less space overall than the 'integral' provision because these would have to be provided for both sexes.

(*b*)   An 'integral' facility is contained within the traditionally separate provision for men and women. Assistance from a member of the opposite sex, by normal custom, would be precluded.

If the building is large enough to warrant several, both types could be considered.

4.6   Whether 'unisex' or 'integral', WC compartments should be similar in layout and content and should satisfy the needs to:

(*a*)   Achieve necessary wheelchair manoeuvre;

(*b*)   Allow for frontal, lateral, diagonal and backward transfer onto the WC, have facilities for hand washing and hand drying within reach from the WC prior to transfer back onto the wheelchair; and

(*c*)   Have space to allow a helper to assist in transfer.

4.7   Where sanitary accommodation is to be provided in upper or lower storeys without lift access the aim should be to make reasonable provision for people who are unsteady on their feet or who need support to stand up or sit down.

4.8   Different considerations apply to disabled people who work in a building, because someone in employment would be more likely to obtain any necessary assistance from a person of the same sex.

Visitors and customers

Provisions

4.9   Unisex compartments should be provided.

Hotel and motel guest bedrooms

4.10/4.12   Sanitary accommodation should be 'en suite' in bedrooms designed for a disabled person where that is the arrangement of the rest of the bedrooms or, where the general arrangement is not 'en suite', unisex sanitary accommodation should be provided nearby.

4.11   The facilities for hotel or motel guests are in addition to those provided for visitors and staff.

4.12   See diagram [12.16] for design of wheelchair compartment.

Staff

4.13/4.14   WC provision for disabled employees may be either 'integral' or 'unisex' and may be provided on alternate floors if:

The travel distance from a workstation to the WC is not more than 40 m; and

In a building provided with lift access the sanitary conveniences are in areas of unrestricted access.

4.15   In a building which only has stair access, suitable sanitary accommodation should be provided in the principal entrance storey unless that storey only contains the principal entrance and vertical circulation areas.

4.16/4.17   Dimensions of a suitable WC should be as shown in diagram [12.16].

Where there are two or more WC compartments for wheelchair users, they should provide for both left-hand and right-hand transfer.

Provisions for ambulant disabled people

4.18   In storeys to which the only access is by a stairway, at least one WC compartment designed for ambulant disabled people should be provided within each range of WC compartments. This is in addition to the provision included in paragraph 4.15. Diagram [12.17] illustrates a WC for ambulant disabled people.

4.12 **[12.16]** *Wheelchair WC compartment.*

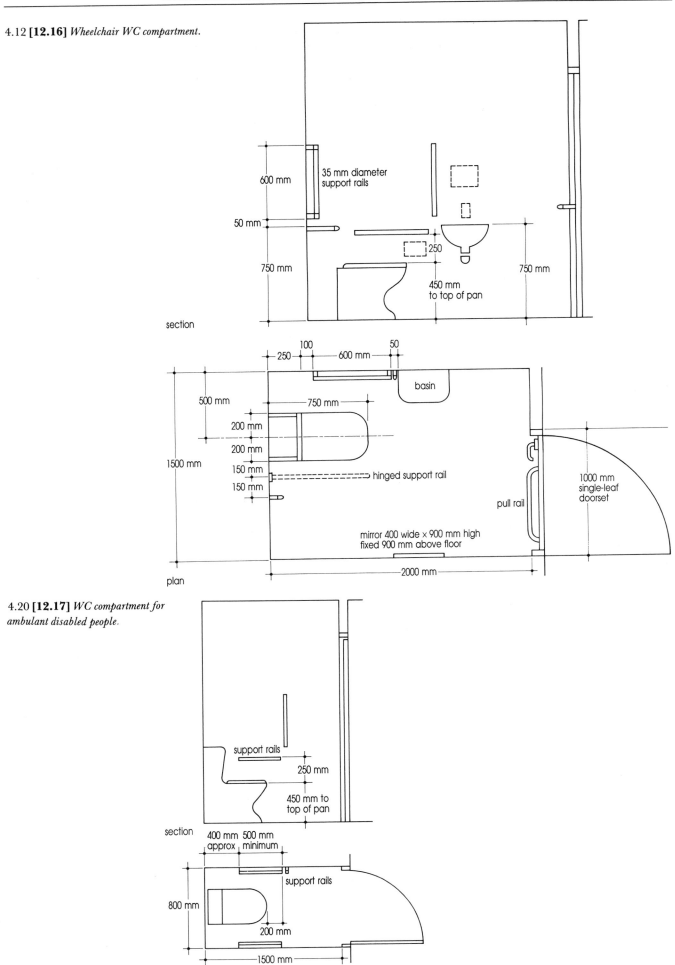

4.20 **[12.17]** *WC compartment for
ambulant disabled people.*

Section 5   Audience or spectator seating

Objective

5.1   That reasonable provisions are made for wheelchair users in theatres, cinemas, concert halls, sports stadia and similar places.

Design considerations

5.2   Wheelchair users should have the choice to sit next to disabled or able-bodied companions, have a clear view of the event and have sufficient space provided so that they can manoeuvre a wheelchair.

Provisions

5.3/5.6   The ratio of 'wheelchair spaces' to the total number of fixed audience or spectator seats available to the public should be not less than 1:100 with a minimum number of 6. The ratio could be reduced in relation to seating in a large stadium.

Diagram [12.18] shows wheelchair spaces in a theatre and diagram [12.19] shows such spaces in a stadium area.

A 'wheelchair space' is a clear space at least 900 mm wide and 1400 mm deep. The space may be kept clear or one which can readily be provided by the removal of a seat. The spaces should be dispersed among the remainder of the auditorium.

[12.18] *Notional disposition of 900 mm × 1400 mm wheelchair spaces in a theatre.*

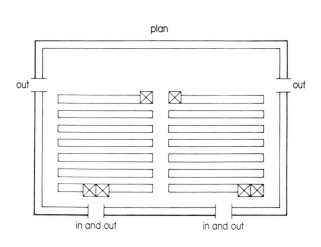

[12.19] *Typical design of viewing positions for disabled people in a stadium or arena.*

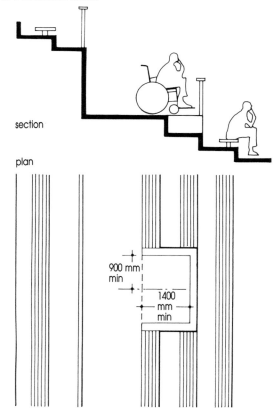

Note on DES Design Note 18 Access for the physically disabled to educational buildings

This document covers all educational buildings but is particularly directed to schools.

It includes recommendations for arrival and parking facilities in addition to those for buildings.

It also contains notes on the problem of means of escape from fire for the disabled.

Broadly speaking, its recommendations are similar to those in the AD. It concludes:

1   Recommendations for ramps are rather more extensive and include length limitations: see diagram [8].

2   Stairs: splayed risers are preferred to nosings.

3   Doors: these should have vision panels, attention should be paid to door closers and there are recommendations on door furniture.

4   An illustration of a dual access corridor divided into a ramp and a stair. This seems a doubtful advantage as there would seem to be no reason why all traffic should not use a ramp.

5   Lifts: short-rise lifts with entries on opposite sides can facilitate access to and from mezzanines.

6   Advice on surfaces: floors and lift enclosures.

7   Sanitary accommodation: There are illustrations showing the conversion of two normal WCs into one unit for disabled use (diagram [9]) and where more than one unit is provided the handing of two adjacent units to suit right or left transfer from wheelchairs.

The recommendations for escape from fire are very tentative.

References

BS 4787: *Internal and external wood doorsets, door leaves and frames.*

Part 1: 1980 (1985) *Specification for dimensional requirements.*

BS 5655: *Lifts and service lifts.*

Part 1: 1986 *Safety rules for the construction and installation of electric lifts.* Amendment 1: AMD 5840.

Part 2: 1988 *Safety rules for the construction and installation of hydraulic lifts.* Amendment 1: AMD 6220.

Part 5: 1989 *Specifications for dimensions for standard lift arrangements.*

Part 7: 1983 *Specification for manual control devices, indicators and additional fittings.* Amendment 1: AMD 4912.

BS 5776: 1979 *Specification for powered stairlifts.* Amendment 1: 4027, 2: 6523.

BS 6440: 1983 *Code of practice for powered lifting platforms for use by disabled persons.*

Draft Disability Unit Circular 1/91

The use of dropped kerbs and tactile surfaces at pedestrian crossing points. Transport and Road Research Laboratory.

Tactile markings for the guidance of visually handicapped pedestrians.

Copies of these documents are available from:

Department of Transport, Disability Unit, 2 Marsham Street, London SW1P 3EB.

Chapter 13

Approved Document N
Glazing – materials and protection

This is an additional requirement to Schedule 1 and has been introduced in an effort to reduce the number of accidents related to glass in buildings. The average annual figures are 15,000 accidents with five fatalities, and whilst these figures are low when compared with accidents and fatalities related to fire, the injuries are often very serious. There are safety recommendations in BS 6262: *Code of Practice for glazing for buildings*, but it was felt that it was necessary to bring this requirement into the regulations together with a requirement that large uninterrupted panels of glass should be readily recognised.

The requirement is as follows:

Requirement	Limits on application
N 1. Glazing with which people are likely to come into contact while in passage in or about the building, shall – (*a*) if broken on impact, break in a way which is unlikely to cause injury; or (*b*) resist impact without breaking; or (*c*) be shielded or protected from impact. N 2. Transparent glazing with which people are likely to collide while in passage in or about the building shall incorporate features which make it apparent.	Requirement N 2 does not apply to dwellings

NOTE The Approved Document points out that glazing which is installed where there was none previously as part of the erection, extension or material alteration of a building constitutes 'building work' and is thus subject to the Requirement of Part N.

Replacement glazing is not, although its supply may be subject to consumer protection legislation.

Other Approved Documents which include guidance on glazing are:

Part B: Fire safety – fire resisting glazing and the reaction of glass to fire;

Part K: Stairs, ramps and guards – glazing which forms part of the protection from falling from one level to another and to ensure containment.

See also Schedule 2 Class VII. Small conservatories and porches are only exempt if the glazing complies with Part N.

Performance

0.1/0.3   The most likely locations for impacts which cause glass to break and cause injury are in doors and door side panels, and at low level in walls and partitions. This is where children are particularly vulnerable. In doors and side panels the risk is greatest between floor and shoulder level when near to door handles etc, especially when doors stick. Initial impact may be followed by a fall through the glazing, injuring the face and body.

0.4/0.5   Glazing in critical locations would be considered reasonably safe if, upon breaking, the particles created would be relatively harmless.

Glazing should be sufficiently robust to reduce the risk of breakage, and steps should be taken to limit the risk of contact with the glazing.

0.6/0.8   The requirement N 2 will be met if as part of the design concept (permanent means of indicating the presence of large uninterrupted areas of glazing) are incorporated. These large areas represent a significant risk of injury through collision and the risk is greater between areas of a building which are essentially at the same level where persons might reasonably assume direct access.

Introduction   **0.9**   There are two sections of the Approved Document – Section 1 deals with the provisions for N 1 and Section 2 relates to N 2.

Section 1

Critical locations   **1.1**   Locations which are 'critical in terms of safety' are shown in diagram [13.1].

1.1 **[13.1]** *Critical locations in external and internal walls.*

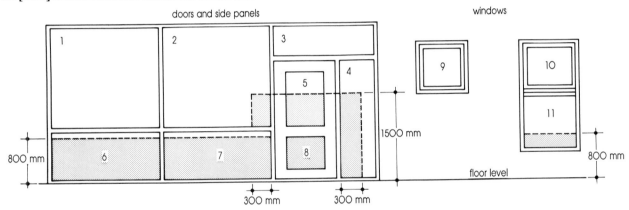

Shaded areas show critical locations to which Requirement N 1 applies
(i.e. glazing in areas 2, 4, 5, 6, 7, 8 and 11)

Reducing the risks   1.2   Glazing in critical locations should either:
(*a*)   break safely, if it breaks – see paragraph 1.3;
(*b*)   be robust or be in small panes – see paragraphs 1.4–1.6 and diagrams [13.2] and [13.3];
(*c*)   be permanently protected – see paragraph 1.7 and diagram [13.4].

1.4 **[13.2]** *Annealed glass area/thickness limits.*

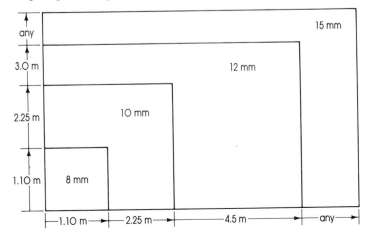

1.5 **[13.3]** *Dimensions and areas of small panes.*

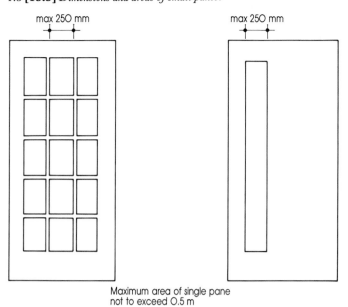

Maximum area of single pane
not to exceed 0.5 m

1.6 **[13.4]** *Permanent screen protection.*

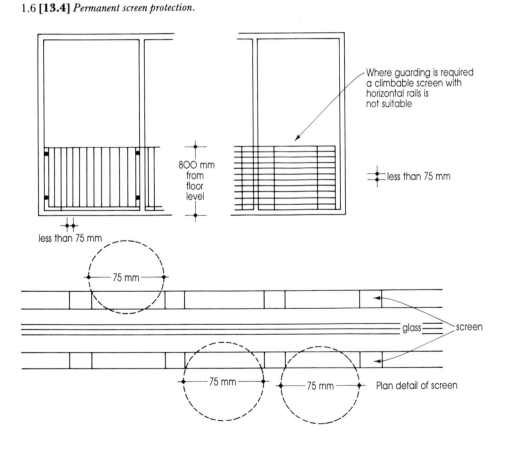

Safe breakage

1.3   This is defined in BS 6206, Clause 5.3, and is based on an impact test which requires the result of the impact to be limited to creating:

(*a*)   a small clear opening (detached particles limited in size), or

(*b*)   disintegration (small detached particles), or

(*c*)   breakage (separate pieces – no sharp points).

Robustness

1.4 Annealed glass derives strength through thickness and can be suitable for use in large areas of glass such as shop windows and fronts to showrooms, offices, factories and public buildings. The glass area/thickness limits of annealed glass are set out in diagram [13.2]. Other glazing materials such as glass blocks and polycarbonates are inherently strong.

Glazing in small panes

1.5 A 'small pane' for the purposes of this Approved Document is an isolated pane or one of a number of panes contained within glazing bars.

1.6 Small panes should be:

not wider than 250 mm

not more than 0.5 m^2 in area – measured between glazing beads

not less than 6 mm nominal thickness if of annealed glass (see diagram [13.3]).

Permanent screen protection

1.7 If glazing is installed in a critical location behind permanent screen protection, the screen should:

(*a*) prevent a sphere of 75 mm diameter from coming into contact with the glazing,

(*b*) be robust,

(*c*) be difficult to climb if it is intended to protect glazing that forms part of guarding required by Part K.

1.8 Glazing itself does not need to comply with Requirement N1 if it is protected by a permanent screen (see diagram [13.4]).

Section 2

Critical locations

2.1 Those areas where glazing should be apparent and thus termed 'critical locations' include large interrupted areas of glazing forming all or part of the internal or external walls of shops, showrooms, offices, factories or public buildings.

2.2 Where a person might reasonably have the impression that they are able to walk from one part of a building to another, clear glazing separating such parts presents the greatest risk of collision.

Permanent manifestation of glazing

2.3/2.5 Permanent indications of the existence of large uninterrupted areas of glazing may take the form of broken or solid lines, patterns or company logos which should be at appropriate heights and intervals. These indications are only necessary where people passing in or about the building may not be aware of the glazing and may collide with it. Diagram [13.5] shows the positions of these indications.

2.4 **[13.5]** *Height of manifestation of large areas of clear glazing.*

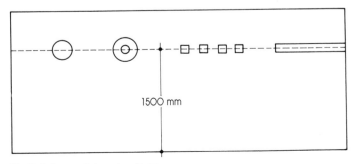

1500 mm

Manifestation can take various forms
e.g. broken or solid lines, patterns or company logos

2.5 **[13.6]** *Examples of door height glazing not warranting manifestation.*

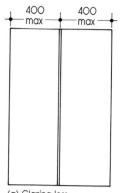

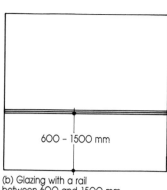

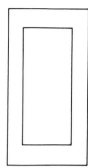

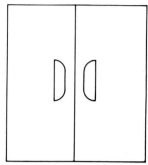

(a) Glazing less than 400 mm in width between frames

(b) Glazing with a rail between 600 and 1500 mm above the floor

(c) A single-pane glazed door with a substantial frame

(d) Glazed doors with no frame, or narrow frames, but with a large handle or push plate on each single pane

---

Alternative indications of glazing

2.6   Installations where manifestation may not be warranted are shown in diagram [13.6] and are:

(*a*)   door height clear glazing less than 400 mm in width,

(*b*)   door height clear glazing with a rail 600–1500 mm above finished ground or floor level, or

(*c*)   a single-pane clear glass door with substantial framing,

(*d*)   a single-pane clear glass door which is either not framed, or has narrow framing, but has easily seen push or pull plates or handles.

Standard referred to:

BS 6206: 1981 *Specification for impact performance requirements for flat safety glass and safety plastics for use in buildings.*

Index